D1273698

Teaching CHEMISTRY with MODELS

R. T. SANDERSON
Professor of Chemistry
University of Iowa

D. VAN NOSTRAND COMPANY INC.
Princeton, New Jersey
Toronto New York London

D. VAN NOSTRAND COMPANY, INC.
120 Alexander St., Princeton, New Jersey (*Principal office*)
24 West 40 Street, New York 18, New York

D. VAN NOSTRAND COMPANY, LTD.
358, Kensington High Street, London, W.14, England

D. VAN NOSTRAND COMPANY (Canada), LTD.
25 Hollinger Road, Toronto 16, Canada

Acknowledgments
Photography by
JAMES A. KENT

Color Separations by
CUSTOM COLOR LAB, INC.
IOWA CITY, IOWA

Published simultaneously in Canada by
D. VAN NOSTRAND COMPANY (Canada), LTD.

Printed in United States of America

PREFACE

The verb "to teach" seems so presumptuous that it is often embarrassing, for when new acquaintances discover that this is one's vocation, they immediately ask, "What do you teach?" Personally, I never know how to answer. Indeed, when grading time arrives, only the lamentable lack of an independent income and the indelible image of the hungry mouths at home deter me from plunging my class records into cleaning solution and fleeing far back into the wooded hills. What, indeed, have I taught!

Between grading periods, however, teaching is stimulating, challenging, satisfying, and real fun. Furthermore, it is educational. Whether educational for the student may be debatable, but no one who has tried to teach can deny that he has thereby learned something. If one thing that I have learned stands out above the rest, it is the importance of developing genuine understanding on the part of the students. Stuffing a student with facts he cannot understand seems quite useless. And certainly memorization, so indispensable a part of learning, can be greatly aided by understanding. Indeed, it is questionable whether memorization without understanding deserves to be called learning.

The learning of chemistry poses two great difficulties from the very beginning. The first is the unseeable nature of the fundamental particles on which the whole science depends. Students are expected to become familiar with electrons and nuclei, atoms, ions, and molecules that may remain forever invisible. The second difficulty is the inherent complexity of even the seemingly simplest phenomena, which has caused far too wide a gap between interpretative and descriptive chemistry. Indeed, explanations of many common chemical phenomena have not even been available. For these reasons students have been expected to memorize far too much without understanding.

My major research interest, therefore, from my first day of teaching thirteen years ago, has been to find reasonable, yet relatively simple explanations of common chemistry, and to devise methods of increasing student understanding through visualization. This research has led to the development of some simple concepts of chemical bonding and properties that have been easily incorporated in visual aids. Especially, colorful new atomic and molecular models have been devised which can be extremely useful in helping students to learn.

The atomic models represent the relative radius, the outer shell electronic configuration, and the electronegativity. The molecular models represent the geometric structure, the bond order and polarity, the approximate charge distribution, and the outer electrons and orbitals that are not involved directly in the bonding. The models are easily constructed from inexpensive and readily attainable materials.

Armed with but a few fundamental facts concerning the meaning of the models and the nature of matter, a student can look at any atomic model and see at once how many covalent bonds the atom can form, what their spatial arrangement will be, and whether it can then act as donor or acceptor. He can also make a reasonable guess as to the probable state of aggregation of the free element, and from this, predict its physical properties. Viewing two different such atoms, he can easily predict whether they can unite through covalence, and if so, the formula, geometric structure, and direction and approximate extent of bond polarity in the compound. He can then make reasonable predictions concerning its general physical and chemical nature.

From inspection of a molecular model, a student can not only derive an understanding of the physical and chemical properties of the compound, but also deduce what kind of atoms must have been needed in order to form such a compound.

In short, the models are an invaluable aid to understanding. My own teaching experience has made them now seem so indispensable that it is difficult to remember how I ever managed without them. Others have also found them useful, and at the time of this writing, they are being used in several hundred colleges and high schools.

This book has two purposes. One is to make the new teaching methods developed from these concepts and models more useful to teachers already somewhat familiar with them. The other is to inform other teachers of the possibilities for improved student understanding that these methods offer.

The book contains all I have learned about constructing such models. Detailed instructions for the construction of models of atoms of the elements and of about 400 individual compounds are included. Models of the more familiar types of crystal structure are also described. The 32 pages of actual photographs of over 260 such models, half in full color, should be especially useful. The general information enables a person possessing the basic structural data to calculate values and construct a model of any compound chosen. Extensive tables to facilitate calculation are provided here, for the first time anywhere. Starting with an electronegativity simply calculated, you can look up in these tables the estimated single-bond radius and the partial charge of any of the major group atoms in any of their compounds. The book also suggests, in considerable detail, some of the more effective ways in which you can use these models in lecture, laboratory, and other demonstrations.

The National Science Foundation, Course Content Improvement Section, has aided this work by contributing to the production of three filmed lecture-demonstrations of the construction and teaching applications of such models, and also by giving financial support permitting a more extensive investigation and development of such teaching aids than would otherwise have been possible. This cooperation has been greatly appreciated, as has been the help of the Graduate College of the University of Iowa, which gave financial assistance when, in the early stages of development, it was most needed and most difficult to find.

Comments and suggestions from my fellow learnhelpers will be welcomed. No small part of the inspiration for writing this book has come from the interest you have already shown.

R. T. SANDERSON

Iowa City, Iowa

CONTENTS

TABLES

CHAPTER

1

ATOMIC MODELS

The dynamic reality of an atom could never be reproduced in a visualizable model, and it would be absurd to judge a model by how closely it approximated our conception of what an atom would look like if enlarged to visibility. What, except its relative size, could you tell about an atom by looking at it? Presumably, atoms of all the elements would look very similar in other respects.

An atom does have certain qualities which, although only one would be visible if the atom were sufficiently enlarged, determine its distinguishing characteristics. These qualities cannot be reproduced, but they can be *represented* in a simple model. Such models are readily and inexpensively constructed. Their use will become indispensable once teaching methods have been adapted to take full advantage of the models as visual aids. The use of models imparts conceptive understandings not otherwise available to the student.

DESCRIPTION

The qualities which are most significant in determining the physical and chemical properties of an atom are: radius, electronegativity, and outer shell electronic configuration. The models considered here consist of painted spheres, to whose surface are fastened small balls, in appropriate number and positions. The relative covalent radius of each atom is represented by the relative size of the model. The electronegativity is represented by the color: the scale is red for low, yellow for intermediate, and blue for high. Thus a complete range from very low to very high electronegativity values is indicated by colors from red, red-orange, orange, yellow-orange, to yellow, yellow-green, green, blue-green, and blue. The outer shell electronic configuration, including only the four orbitals originating from an *s* and three *p* orbitals, is represented by four pairs of small spheres fastened to the surface of the atom. These appended spheres are painted white to represent an electron; black to represent a vacancy where an electron might be accommodated. A pair of white spheres thus represents a pair of electrons (a filled orbital), one white and one black represent an unpaired electron (a half-filled orbital), and a black pair represents an empty orbital. The electrons are distributed as in bond formation—no pairing of electrons in a single orbital until at least one electron is in each orbital.

How many atomic models are desirable for teaching? Even one is better than none, but I would recommend a very minimum of ten, representing the elements of atomic number 1-10. The next ten would also be worth making. With a set from hydrogen to calcium some very valuable lessons can be taught. Later you may at least want to complete your collection of the inert and inert-shell and 18-shell type elements. To complete the periodic table you will perhaps want models of the transition elements. In the following discussion assume that a set of models of the first twenty elements is available. What is said about these will also be applicable to others.

The complete directions for constructing these models begin on page 17. In order to visualize these models better here, the following verbal description is given for the first ten elements. See also Figures C-1 and C-2.*

1) *Hydrogen:* On a scale of 3 inches per Ångstrom, this model painted a pale yellow-green, is a sphere about 2.5 inches in diameter. Attached to it, about half an inch apart, are two spheres an inch in diameter, one white and one black.

2) *Helium:* This sphere is about 6 inches in diameter, painted black, and has two 1-inch diameter white spheres attached to it as in the hydrogen model.

3) *Lithium:* This sphere is about 8 inches in diameter, bright red, and has four pairs of 1-inch diameter spheres, seven of which are black and one white. The spheres are attached at the corners of an imaginary tetrahedron circumscribed by the lithium sphere.

4) *Beryllium:* This red-orange sphere is about 6 inches in diameter, with two half-filled orbitals (black and white pairs) attached at opposite sides of the sphere. Two empty orbitals (black pairs) are placed to form a square around the atom with the first two orbitals. (The placement of the empty orbitals is of course arbitrary, symmetry in the model being the only consideration.)

5) *Boron:* This yellow-orange sphere is about 5 inches in diameter, and holds three half-filled orbitals (black and white pairs) at the corners of an equilateral triangle centered on the boron. A fourth, empty orbital (black pair) is attached at a 90° angle from the plane of the triangle.

* A special photo section near the center of this book consists of 16 pages of color, Figs. C-1 to C-16, and 16 pages of black and white, Figs. B-1 to B-16. References will be to figure numbers.

6) *Carbon:* This model about 4.5 inches in diameter, is a yellow-green sphere, only faintly greener than the hydrogen. To it four half-filled orbitals (black and white pairs) are attached at the corners of a regular tetrahedron.

7) *Nitrogen:* This model is green, slightly bluish, only slightly smaller than the carbon, and has four orbitals also attached at the corners of a regular tetrahedron. Three are half-filled, the fourth filled.

8) *Oxygen:* This greenish-blue model is nearly equal in size to the nitrogen model, and has two half-filled and two filled orbitals at the corners of a tetrahedron.

9) *Fluorine:* This model, practically the same as oxygen in size, is blue, again with four tetrahedrally placed orbitals, but with only one vacancy.

10) *Neon:* The model is a black sphere 8 inches in diameter, with four pairs of white spheres attached at the tetrahedral corners.

USES IN TEACHING

Some of the most effective teaching applications of atomic models are in conjunction with molecular models, and will be described later. The following discussion emphasizes the uses of the atomic models alone.

Relative Sizes of Atoms and of Their Ions

You will find it desirable to stress to your students that the electronic cloud which comprises the exterior of an atom is both nebulous and deformable. Consequently, no definite "skin" or outer boundary of an atom exists, the electronic cloud only gradually diminishing to nothingness as its distance from the nucleus increases. The most definitive indication of the outer limit of an atom is its closeness of approach to another atom, which can be measured experimentally as the distance between their nuclei. Two kinds of internuclear distance are observed, depending on whether or not a bond is formed. A covalent bond permits—indeed, requires—closer approach than is ordinarily possible if no bond exists. Half the internuclear distance between adjacent like atoms is taken as the atomic radius. The radius in the direction of the bond is the "covalent radius." The larger, non-bonding radius is the "van der Waals radius."

The atomic models are constructed to represent the *covalent radius.* This means that your students must imagine the electronic cloud to extend outward from the model in an elastic, invisible barrier to other nonbonding atoms, but correctly to represent the closeness of approach necessary for bond formation.

The scale of 1.5 inches per Ångstrom recommended for the "medium" size models is equivalent to a linear magnification of 381 millions to one. A table tennis ball, enlarged to this extent, would be a little larger than the earth. A comparison such as this can help your students appreciate the relative sizes of atoms and the models in their proper perspective.

The hydrogen atom is, of course, smallest of all the elements, and its model represents one extreme. Cesium atoms, with the probable exception of those of francium, are largest. Your students will easily realize from comparing these two that all atoms are, within a factor of ten, alike in diameter.

For example, if you have models of the ions as well as the atoms of sodium and chlorine, you can show very clearly that increasing the number of electrons causes a large amount of expansion in the electronic cloud of an atom. Decreasing the number of electrons causes a correspondingly large contraction.

Electronic Configuration and Valence

Only the outermost shell electrons are shown by the models, but these are by far the most important. If your students have not been introduced to atomic structure in detail, you may decide to present electronic configurations in either of two ways, depending on the level of understanding sought.

The simplest way is merely to give the total numbers of electrons in each principal quantum shell. Thus, for the first twenty elements, you might present a table such as that shown on page 5.

If you choose to present the substructures of the principal shells, you may want to describe the four quantum numbers. You may at least wish to point out that by consideration of these numbers and applying the Pauli Exclusion Principle (no two electrons in the same atom may have the same set of quantum numbers) the numbers of electrons in each principal quantum shell n are limited to $2n^2$. Thus, the capacity is $2 \times 1^2 = 2$ for the first shell, $2 \times 2^2 = 8$ for the second, $2 \times 3^2 = 18$ for the third, and $2 \times 4^2 = 32$ for the fourth. You may wish to explain that different kinds of regions may be occupied by electrons within a principal quantum shell and that the number of different kinds, up through four, is the same as the principal quantum number of shell number, n. Thus, the first shell can have only one kind of energy region to be occupied by electrons, called an s orbital; the second shell can have s and p orbitals; the third, s, p, and d orbitals; and the fourth, s, p, d, and f. Furthermore, the number of orbitals of each kind in a given shell is odd: one s, three p, five d, and seven f. Each region or orbital can hold only 2 electrons.

The limiting capacity of 2 electrons in the first shell thus follows from the fact that only one orbital (s) can be there. In the second shell one

DISTRIBUTION OF ELECTRONS

Element	Atomic No.	First Shell	Second Shell	Third Shell	Fourth Shell
H	1	1			
He	2	2			
Li	3	2	1		
Be	4	2	2		
B	5	2	3		
C	6	2	4		
N	7	2	5		
O	8	2	6		
F	9	2	7		
Ne	10	2	8		
Na	11	2	8	1	
Mg	12	2	8	2	
Al	13	2	8	3	
Si	14	2	8	4	
P	15	2	8	5	
S	16	2	8	6	
Cl	17	2	8	7	
Ar	18	2	8	8	
K	19	2	8	8	1
Ca	20	2	8	8	2

s orbital and three *p* orbitals make a total of four, with a total capacity of 8 electrons. Similarly, the third shell can hold 18 electrons because, in addition to 8 *s* and *p* electrons, there can be 10 *d* electrons. All these plus 14 *f* electrons make the capacity of the fourth shell 32, and no shell beyond this ever contains more than 32.

The shells, in the building up of atoms, do not fill up in smooth succession, because they overlap in energy, and electrons tend to fill in the most stable positions first. One result of this overlapping is that more than 8 electrons are never found in the *outermost* shell. A ninth electron always starts a new shell before a shell of 8 can begin to fill up to 18 or whatever its capacity may be. Consequently, no atom has more than 8 outermost electrons, and the models are quite adequate for most purposes in showing only four outermost orbitals. A very useful device for helping students visualize the different energy levels and their electron capacities is a series of shelves[1] to represent the energy levels, and glass beakers to represent the orbitals. Each beaker can hold two "electrons" (two-inch diameter styrofoam balls serve well) and each shelf can hold only the correct number of beakers (orbitals). One can start with empty

[1] R. T. Sanderson, *J. Chem. Educ.*, 37, 262 (1960).

shelves, first placing the orbitals in position as the atomic number increases, and then filling them with electrons as the electronic cloud increases. In this way one can explain and describe the electronic configurations of all the elements by building them up one by one in order of increasing atomic number.

Most stably, as in the "ground state," within a given principal quantum level, the electrons always fill the *s* orbital before starting the *p*, *p* before *d*, and *d* before *f*. However, for chemical bond formation the arrangement is always the one leading to the greatest number of stable bonds. Therefore *s* electrons never, for practical purposes, remain paired while a *p* orbital in the same shell is vacant. One of the *s* pair always advances to an otherwise empty *p* orbital. The models are constructed with bonding in mind, and therefore show the bonding or "valence structure" instead of the "ground state" or paired *s* structure, whenever the two would be different. This applies only to the elements of Groups II, III, and IV. In carbon, for example, the model shows one electron in each of four tetrahedral orbitals rather than two in one *s* orbital and one in each of two *p* orbitals with the third *p* orbital vacant.

Ordinary covalent bonds require that each atom provide one unpaired electron *and* one vacancy—in other words, one half-filled orbital—for each bond. The two electrons, one from each atom, are thus jointly held in the two orbitals, one from each atom (or their coalesced equivalent), by the nuclear attractions. By merely counting the number of electron-plus-vacancy combinations, the number of covalent bonds that each atom can form is easily seen from the model.

Hybridization. Different kinds of orbitals should have different bonding characteristics, but no evidence for any differences is found experimentally when the same atom uses both *s* and *p* orbitals in the bonding. It is concluded that the actual bonding orbitals become averaged and equalized. The "new" orbitals are called "hybrid." When only two covalent bonds can be formed, using one *s* and one *p* orbital, the bonding orbitals appear identical and are called "*sp* hybrids." Similarly, there are sp^2 hybrids and sp^3 hybrids, as well as others not pertinent here.

Directional Nature of Covalence

The orientation of orbitals with respect to one another is customarily described as a characteristic of the kind of orbital, or type of hybridization. However, a simple consideration of electrostatics leads to essentially the same results. Outer electron pairs, whether involved in bonding or not, repel one another and therefore tend to become located as far from one another as possible. Where only two bonds are formed and the other two orbitals are empty, the latter can have no effect and the two bonds are as far apart as possible. This, of course, is at opposite sides of the atomic sphere, making an angle of 180° between the bonds. The only other possibility for two single bonds is when the number is limited by the number of available vacancies—in other words, when the other two orbitals are filled. Here, with only two bonds but with two extra pairs of electrons, the mutual repulsion among the four pairs leads also to their moving as far apart as possible. The greatest separation of four positions on the surface of a sphere is at the corners of a regular tetrahedron, bond angles thus being 109°28′.

Similarly, two kinds of outer shell configuration can lead to three single bonds per atom. One involves only three outer electrons which, when engaged in covalence, form three electron pairs. The fourth orbital, being empty, has no influence. The farthest apart three positions can be on the surface of a sphere is at the corners of an equilateral triangle, the center of which coincides with the sphere center. The bond angles are therefore 120°. The other possibility for trivalence occurs when the vacancies limit the bonding—when there are five outer electrons but only three vacancies. The fourth orbital here is filled, and influences the positions of the three bonds such that tetrahedral arrangement, with angles close to 109°, again results.

When four electrons and four vacancies occur in the outer shell, naturally four single bonds can be formed, and the bond angles resulting from the tetrahedral configuration are 109°28′.

This logical rule of thumb may also be applied to atoms forming multiple bonds, as will be discussed in a later section.

The electronic configurations of the outermost shells of atoms are clearly shown in the models, which represent the valence state, with no pairing until each orbital first has one electron. The directional properties of the bonding are shown by the positioning of the orbitals—pairs of electrons, vacancies, or electron-plus-vacancy—on the surface of the atomic sphere. Your students can see with their own eyes how many covalent bonds each atom can form, and *why*. They can see the reason for the bond angles that will result. They can see how the atomic radius changes as the number of outermost electrons changes and as the principal quantum level of the outermost electrons increases.

Coordinate Covalence

Ordinarily, covalent bonds involve the sharing of two electrons, one from each atom, and the utilization of two orbitals, one from each atom. Another possibility is where one atom provides a pair of electrons and the other, a vacant orbital. Such a bond is called a "coordinate covalent" or "coordination" bond. It is similar to an ordinary covalent bond, in that both kinds involve sharing of a pair of electrons by two atoms, with each supplying one orbital. Coordinate bonds do not appear to form, however, until after all possible ordinary covalent bonds are formed. In other words, they tend to be bonds between molecules or between ions that are capable of stable separate existence.

The outer shell representation of the atomic models shows the capacity of the atoms to form coordinate as well as ordinary covalent bonds. For example, boron with its three half-filled orbitals can form three single covalent bonds, which are directed toward the corners of an equilateral triangle. This gives a planar structure, on which the remaining empty orbital has no effect. But students can see the fourth orbital, and recognize the possibility that it could be used in a fourth bond if an electron donor atom were available. What they may not realize is the effect this fourth bond would have on structure. Increasing the number of electron pairs from three to four does not change the rule that these pairs locate as far apart as possible, but this means a change in structure from planar to tetrahedral. This change cannot be shown by the atomic model, but may be inferred from it. An electron donor, on the other hand, will function without substantial change in structure because its electron pairs affect the structure whether or not they are involved in bonding. The atomic models do show the expected structure, as well as indicating the possibility of coordinate covalence. You may wish to use the models of nitrogen, oxygen, and fluorine to point out that although after all ordinary covalent bonds have formed, nitrogen atoms have one extra electron pair, oxygen two, and fluorine three, only one pair is usually employed in coordinate covalence. On the other hand, vacant orbitals frequently become fully occupied in coordination, and the number of stable vacant orbitals is usually the same as the number of coordination bonds that can be formed.

Electronegativity

What your students can see most vividly of all in the models is the electronegativity, and its relation to the size of the atom and the number of outermost electrons. They will observe that as the number of outermost electrons increases, the size of the atomic sphere decreases and the electronegativity increases. You may wish to point out that crowding of electrons together, as occurs with increasing number of outermost electrons, increases their repulsion, and if an atom holds its own electrons close despite this repulsion, this may be taken as a clue to its possible behavior toward outside electrons. If there exists a vacancy to accommodate an outside electron, this atom will attract electrons strongly. In other words, its electronegativity is high. In fact, the relative electronegativities of the elements can be evaluated in terms of the relative compactness of the electronic spheres of their atoms.[2]

The significance of electronegativity lies mainly in the electronegativity differences among the various chemical elements. The greater this difference between two atoms, the more polar the bond between them. From the models students can easily see which combinations will give ionic compounds, which nonpolar, and *why*.

Indeed, such atomic models can be extremely helpful to students by demonstrating that chemistry makes sense. Why, for example, should one be satisfied to tell students the composition, structure, and properties of water when this information is so easily reasoned from the models of the atoms? Even if a person has no idea what element is represented by the hydrogen model, he can see at once, if he is familiar with the scheme of representation, that this atom has the capacity to form one ordinary covalent bond and no more, and that it is only slightly above medium in electronegativity. Examination of the oxygen model will show that this element is divalent and very high in electronegativity. It becomes almost immediately evident that two of the first kind of atom would unite with one of the second kind, that the bond angle would be close to 109°, and that the bonds would be appreciably polar with the second kind of atom taking more than half share of the electrons, thus becoming partially negative and leaving the other atoms partially positive.

If a student could see a model of the water molecule, which will be discussed later, he would find its composition, structure, and bond polarity exactly as he predicted from the examination of models of its atoms before reaction.

Introduction to Metals and Nonmetals

The atomic models will serve well to set the stage for the later development of the physical and chemical differences between metals and nonmetals, and their distinguishing characteristics. Your students will be able to see that, although most of the elements range from yellow through oranges to red, which indicates relatively low electronegativities, some range from greenish yellow to blue. The latter are all nonmetals; the former, mostly metals. They will also note that the elements of higher electronegativity invariably have more outermost electrons than vacancies, whereas the reverse is true of the elements of lowest electronegativity. Again this is a fundamental distinction between nonmetals and metals. Recognizing the gradual nature of the change in qualities of the

[2] R. T. Sanderson, *Chemical Periodicity,* Reinhold Publishing Corporation, New York, 1960; page 26.

atoms, your students will then be prepared to understand that no abrupt and definite demarcation separating metals from nonmetals exists, but rather the change is gradual and a number of elements are borderline in their qualities.

Teaching Periodicity

Atomic models of the first twenty elements or more are almost ideally suited to the exposition of chemical periodicity. What the founders of the Periodic Table did was to consider the elements in order of increasing atomic weight, in an effort to see whether any consistent trends in either physical or chemical properties could be observed. You can, if you wish, repeat this procedure in your classroom, in a way that will emphasize vividly to your students the fundamental causes of the Periodic Law. For this purpose it is useful to equip the atomic models with connectors, such as hooks and eyes, by which they can be strung or hung together. The collapsible tripods from two inexpensive music stands can be combined with a 6- or 7-foot piece of aluminum tubing, 1 inch in diameter, to make a simple display stand for lecture bench or floor.

It is suggested that you place models of the first twenty elements on the lecture bench in random positions. You may then suggest to the class that, since John Newlands, Lothar Meyer, and Dmitri Mendeleev began to investigate the relationships among the chemical elements by first lining them up in order of increasing atomic weight, you will do likewise. However, you may point out that, although at the time of the early development of the periodic table the existence of electrons may have been suspected and there was ample reason to believe in the importance of electricity in the composition of matter, actually no one knew of protons or neutrons. The concept of the nuclear atom was yet forty years or more ahead. We know now that the atomic number, then unknown, is of greater significance in chemistry than the atomic weight. Fortunately, when the pioneers of the Periodic Table were aligning the elements in order of increasing atomic weight, they were unknowingly aligning them also in order of increasing atomic number, with but few and minor exceptions. In the modern concept of periodicity it is atomic number that is important, and you may then proceed to align the models in order of increasing atomic number. Starting with hydrogen, you connect the models together one by one, attaching the hydrogen end to the right-hand side of the supporting framework. In a few minutes, by naming each element and giving its atomic number as you attach it to the chain of models, you will have assembled the entire twenty elements and can attach the far side of the calcium model to the left-hand side of the frame. Thus suspended before your students, these models present a vivid display in which certain trends are spectacularly obvious. (See Fig. C-1.)

If you remind the students that the earlier workers knew nothing of atomic radius, nothing of electronic configurations, and relatively little about electronegativity except in a very general way, you will help them to appreciate that the discovery of the Periodic Law was quite startling and hard to believe. The difference between then and now will be the more striking, because the exhibit which you have just displayed before them shows up the periodicity of the elements so obviously and so clearly that no one could easily fail to observe it! They will see at once that the size of the atoms does not increase continuously with increasing atomic number, but rather goes through cycles, or periods—it changes *periodically*. They will see just as clearly that the electronegativity likewise does not change continuously or at random with increasing atomic number, but also is *periodic*. Then, if they examine the models more closely to count the electrons and vacancies shown in the outer shell, they will observe that the number of electrons also varies periodically, going from 1 to 8, one electron at a time, and then to one again.

Now, if they compare these three qualities shown by the models, with respect to their periodicity, they will observe that they all change in periods of the same length. That is, while the number of electrons is changing from 1 to 8, the electronegativity is changing from very low to highest and then zero, and the radius is changing from high to low and then upward.

"Nonpolar Covalent" Radii of the Inert Elements. One question that seems inevitably to arise concerns the "nonpolar covalent radii" of the inert elements. Why are they represented as larger than those of the halogens? If the radius diminishes as electrons are filling the outer octet from 1 to 7, why does addition of the eighth electron cause a sudden increase in radius? This is a good place to emphasize to your students that much remains to be learned about chemistry, and until we know it all, we must make certain assumptions. These assumptions are necessary because they are frequently much more fruitful than merely accepting our ignorance. Since the inert elements are so-called because they cannot form chemical bonds, the term "nonpolar covalent radius" is of no practical meaning when applied to them. We shall never be able to measure experimentally the radius of an atom in the direction of its covalent bond to another atom when it steadfastly refuses to form any covalent bonds. If we wish to know what would be the covalent radius of an inert atom *if* it had a covalent radius, we must guess. Nothing is to be gained by a wild, random guess, but for "educated" guesses, made with caution and acceptable only tentatively and never with reckless abandon, much is to be said in favor. Indeed, the progress of science would be greatly impeded if all scientists were too cautious to speculate, too unimaginative to try to picture what they cannot see. In this instance the covalent radii of the

inert atoms were taken as intermediate between those of the halogens and those of the alkali metals, mainly for the reason that the radii of the neutral atoms with inert atomic number would seem logically to be intermediate between those of unipositive ions with inert atomic number and those of uninegative ions with inert atomic number. For example, the sodium ion holds 10 electrons with a nuclear charge of 11; the fluoride ion holds 10 electrons with a nuclear charge of 9. The neon atom, which holds 10 electrons with a nuclear charge of 10, would reasonably be expected to be intermediate in size. Furthermore, the van der Waals radii of the inert elements, as well as those of the alkali metals and the halogens, are known experimentally. The inert elements are intermediate here, and although van der Waals radii (nonbonding radii) are larger than covalent radii, they should be consistently so. The implication from this evidence also is that the covalent radii of the inert elements should be intermediate, between alkali metal and halogen, as selected.

Students may note that although the radius does diminish as the outer shell is being filled up to 7 electrons, the decrease is most rapid at the beginning and tapers off so much that from carbon through nitrogen, oxygen, and fluorine the reduction is very small. The trend toward smaller radius has practically stopped when it reaches oxygen, and might as logically begin to rise again with neon as to remain nearly the same.

In summary, if you would rather believe that covalent radii of the inert elements should be smaller than those of the adjacent halogens, no law compels you to accept the idea that they are larger. Whatever your personal opinion, your students deserve to know that the selection of "nonpolar covalent" radii for the inert elements has been somewhat arbitrary, and indeed could never be otherwise.

Constructing the Periodic Table

When confronted with a periodic system such as presented by the chain display of atomic models, one cannot necessarily find a firm basis for deciding at what point a period ends and a new period begins. Your students will probably not object, however, to the somewhat arbitrary procedure of choosing the inert element as the end of a period, as long as they understand that it is arbitrary but nevertheless very useful, and actually more logical than any other choice would be. For the inert atom marks the completion, at least temporarily, of one principal quantum shell, and the following alkali metal begins the filling of the next higher shell. Thus the inert atom may be regarded as the terminus of a specific process, the point where any further change involves beginning a new cycle. If a period is therefore defined as the series of elements of consecutive atomic number beginning with an alkali metal (1 electron in the outermost shell) and ending with an inert element (8 electrons in the outermost shell, except 2 in helium), students can profitably begin to compare the periods.

They can see that the first period is very short, consisting of only two elements, hydrogen and helium. The peculiar position of hydrogen, not even approximately duplicated by that of any other element, arises from the fact that although it has but a single electron in the outermost shell, it also is but one electron away from the next higher inert element. It begins a new shell and at the same time nearly ends it. Instead, therefore, of being closely comparable to other elements which begin periods, or with other elements that nearly end the periods, hydrogen is intermediate between these two kinds. This intermediate nature is clearly shown by the yellow-green color, which indicates an intermediate electronegativity. The first period, therefore, is not closely related to subsequent periods.

Beginning with lithium, students can see that the trend from a large atom of low number of outermost electrons and low electronegativity to a smaller atom of high number of outermost electrons and high electronegativity, and then to an inert element, is very similar to the trend from sodium to chlorine and then argon. Furthermore, the last two atoms of the twenty, potassium and calcium, appear to be beginning a trend very similar to those set by lithium, beryllium, and sodium, magnesium. It should not be difficult, therefore, for them to visualize the advantages of rearranging the models so that not only the horizontal trends would be clearly shown, but also the different periods could be compared more directly. In other words, it would be very convenient if the elements were arranged to show both differences and similarities.

You can suggest, or ask the students to suggest, how the models might be rearranged to show the interrelationships of all the elements more effectively. The most obvious answer, of course, is to place the third period under the second and the fourth period under the third so that the beginning atoms are all next to one another, and likewise across the period until the inert atoms are also grouped together. At this point you can perform this rearrangement literally by disconnecting the atomic models and reconnecting them. For this purpose you will need a hook for each group of the periodic table with which you can suspend the group from its proper position on the horizontal bar support. First, you may suspend the helium model from the side of the support at your left. The hydrogen you may disregard for the time being. Then you may suspend the lithium atom at the right-hand end of the support, and beneath it the sodium, then the potassium. Next come the beryllium suspended to your left of the lithium, and beneath it the magnesium. Next to the left from the main bar is suspended the boron model, and below it the aluminum. Then the carbon; below it the silicon atom. Nitrogen with phosphorus follows, and to their left (right hand from the student viewpoint) oxygen and sulfur, and then fluorine and chlorine, then neon and argon. (See Fig. C-2.)

At the conclusion of this reassembling of the models, you have reproduced before the very eyes of the students the exact beginnings of the periodic table, in much the same manner as was developed by Lothar Meyer and Mendeleev. Your students will have a great advantage over these earlier scientists, however, for they can visualize not only the periodic chart but also at the same time its reasons for being and its fundamental significance. They can see that periodicity results from the successive filling of electron shells. They can see that elements in the same group of the periodic table have fundamental similarities, in relative size, number of outermost electrons and therefore ability to form bonds, and electronegativity and therefore tendency for similar polarity in their compounds. They can note, in the downward change from period two to period three and period four, that elements in the same group tend to have larger atoms and, in the examples of the first twenty elements, lower electronegativity. The fact that electronegativity increases from left to right across a period and decreases down a group will help clarify the "diagonal relationships," which indicate similarities between lithium and magnesium, beryllium and aluminum, boron and silicon. These relationships are especially clearly displayed by the models in this arrangement, because of the similar colors of the elements of these diagonal pairs.

The position of hydrogen must be arbitrarily selected in this arrangement of the periodic table. My own preference is to place it above and slightly to the left of carbon. In a negative sense, this emphasizes the fact that hydrogen does not properly belong with either the alkali metals or the halogens, despite its electronic similarity to both. In a more positive sense, this placement emphasizes the fact that hydrogen resembles carbon in two important ways: (1) both are, at least in effect, midway in their periods; the outer shell is exactly half-filled in each; (2) both of these elements, and none of the other elements, have completely utilized all outer electrons and vacancies in their ordinary covalence (silicon and other IVA elements can use outer *d* orbitals in their bonding, not present in carbon). The importance of hydrogen-carbon chemistry is better understood when this relationship of hydrogen to carbon is recognized. Their similarity in electronegativity appears to make a very significant contribution to the stability of hydrocarbons.

You can hardly, of course, stop here in your exposition of the periodic table. If you have atomic models of all the other elements, you can build a much more elaborate display. In any event, difficulty is encountered in representing the transition elements by atomic models. How does one show the *d* orbitals and electrons? The simplest idea that has occurred to me thus far is to show the outer four orbitals exactly as for the other models, and in addition, to paint on the atomic surface a large, easily legible number corresponding to the number of *d* electrons present. If this is done, students can see at least that transition elements are not like the other elements, and this is important for them to know. They can also infer from the number what the distribution of electrons in the five *d* orbitals is most likely to be by following the rule that electrons do not begin to pair until each available orbital has at least one. If the special stability of a set of orbitals each half-filled (or each filled) is pointed out, then it will be clear why the model of chromium shows only one outermost electron instead of two, why the copper model does likewise, and why an important oxidation state of iron is three.

(Currently under development, at the time of galley proof checking for this book, is an atomic model that may prove useful in the teaching of the chemistry of the transition metals. It consists of a styrofoam sphere like the others, but with representation of the five *d* orbitals, and their electron content, as well as the outer *s* and *p* orbitals. The *d* orbitals each tend to have a boundary surface resembling a square cross, made of four lobes extending from the nucleus toward the corners of a square. If we consider the nucleus to be the origin for a set of orthogonal coordinates with *X*, *Y*, and Z axes, we can then imagine placing three such orbitals symmetrically between these axes, so that the point of intersection of each cross, and for all three crosses, is at the nucleus of the atom. For example, one cross would lie in the X-Y plane but at a 45° angle from the axes. These three orbitals are named d_{xy}, d_{xz}, and d_{yz}. We can then place a fourth orbital, identical in shape to the first three, so that its lobes are directed along the *X* and *Y* axes. This is called the $d_{x^2-y^2}$ orbital. It fits snugly among the first three. If we now were to try to fit a fifth orbital similarly, along the *X* and Z axes, or along the *Y* and Z axes, it would interfere with the fourth. The fifth orbital is therefore a hybrid of these latter two possibilities, which extends only along the Z axis, with a relatively small, doughnut-shaped portion around the nucleus in the *X*-*Y* plane. This fifth orbital is called the d_{z^2} orbital.

At the surface of the atomic sphere, we now have a very symmetrical arrangement of 18 lobes, 4 from each of the first four *d* orbitals and 2 from the fifth. The location of these is represented on the model by circles, painted a different color for each *d* orbital. Any one of the first four *d* orbitals appears, therefore, as four circles of the same color on the surface of the atomic sphere, located at the corners of a square circumscribed by a great circle of the sphere. For the fifth *d* orbital, there are two circles of like color, directly opposite one another. The sites for octahedral coordination are the six circles representing the four lobes of the $d_{x^2-y^2}$ orbital and the two lobes of the d_{z^2} orbital.

In constructing the atomic model, these orbitals can be located by drawing circles in tangential contact around a great circle of the sphere, 8 in number, so that each has a diameter one-eighth of the sphere circumference. Perpendicular to this ring of 8 circles is drawn a second ring of 8 circles, which will have 2 circles in common with the first ring, at the points of intersection. Then perpendicular to both these rings, a third ring of 8 circles is drawn. This ring will share 4 of its circles in common (2 each) with the other two rings, thus adding only four new circles. The total number of circles is thus 8 plus 6 plus 4, or 18. The 6 sites for octahedral coordination mentioned above are the six circles at the 6 points of intersection of the three rings.

The portions of the atomic model not covered by the *d* orbital circles can be painted a color representing the electronegativity of the element. To these portions can be attached small black spheres and white spheres to represent the usual outer shell orbitals, *s* and *p*, with the *s* orbital filled and the three *p* orbitals empty in the usual ground state of most of the transition metals. The distribution of electrons in the *d* orbitals can be represented, although not ideally, by placing electrons and vacancies only in one of the four (or two for the d_{z^2} orbital) exposed lobes of each orbital. For easy visibility, these can be any five circles of different color that are in a group closest together. The *d* electrons and vacancies can be differentiated from the outer shell by representing them by smaller size. For ordinary teaching purposes, the *d* electrons may be permanently attached, following the rule of no pairing of electrons in one orbital until each of the five has at least one electron. For more sophisticated discussions, such as explaining ligand field theory, it may be helpful to fasten small pieces of sheet iron to the bottoms of the "electrons" and "vacancies," and small bar magnets to the *d* orbitals on the surface of the atomic sphere. It will then be possible to demonstrate how the change in relative energies of the initially equivalent *d* orbitals, brought about by the approach of ligands, may influence the distribution of electrons and thus the structure and properties of transition metal compounds.

Time has not yet permitted thorough testing of models of the above type in the classroom, and improvements may well suggest themselves to anyone who experiments with them.)

The electronegativities of transition elements are known with less certainty, as also are their covalent radii. However, they appear to be quite similar to one another in both these properties, and an approximate representation in the models can serve at least to show how, as a group, the transition elements differ from the other elements, even though differences among the transition elements themselves will not be apparent except in terms of the number of *d* electrons.

To explain the complete periodic table in its various common forms requires a more detailed presentation of electronic configurations, but on an elementary level one can at least indicate that potassium and calcium, for example, contain electrons in the fourth shell only because the *d* orbitals do not become sufficiently stable until the nuclear charge has increased to at least 21. From here on, they are stable and electrons fill them by preference until the shell of 18 is complete, whereupon the filling of the outermost shell is resumed. It is very important to point out here that the 18-shell elements are a distinct class of elements and resemble the inert-shell elements only in the kind of orbitals primarily used for valence—outermost *s* and *p*. This similarity is sufficient to justify grouping 18-shell elements with inert-shell elements in the periodic table, but students must not lose sight of the fact that beyond major Group IIA the elements of a periodic group are not electronically similar and therefore cannot be expected to display as uniform or consistent trends as would be shown if they were electronically similar. Thus the trend begun by boron and aluminum is not continued necessarily by gallium, indium, and thallium, and the trend begun by carbon and silicon is not necessarily continued by germanium, tin, and lead. The models show this by their color which indicates an increase in electronegativity in the change from inert-shell to 18-shell type within a group, greatest in IIIA and diminishing until no longer present in VIIA. This alternation in electronegativity down the periodic group is quite consistent with observed alternations or differences in properties.

A CONCLUDING JUSTIFICATION OF THE ATOMIC MODELS

You will find models of the individual atoms of the elements to be indispensably useful in your explanations of chemistry if you wish your students to acquire a fundamental understanding rather than a mere familiarity with descriptive facts. Yet there are those, and especially those having above-average facility in mathematics and intimate knowledge of theoretical chemistry, who will believe it useless and wrong to hold "false images" before students. They will believe that more harm than good can come of efforts to simplify what in fact is not simple. They will be of such conviction that electrons cannot be represented as stationary spheres, that wave characteristics and probability considerations are so fundamental to the structure and behavior of atoms that they will be unable to imagine any utility in the simple models described herein.

It is obvious that I do not agree. In teaching chemistry, except at the most advanced levels, one does not have a choice between "the most accurate" representation of atoms (as conceived by experts in chemical theory, many of whom are actively engaged in trying to change this representation by their own researches), and some other method of representation. The "most accurate" representation is simply out of reach of most students (and most professional chemists as well). The choice is between some other method and none. A difficult concept can be explained only to the limits of a student's experience. If it can be made clear by resorting to simple models which, although they cannot depict the true complexities of reality, do no actual violence to reality and do help the student to detect some reasonableness in natural law, then what valid objection can be raised to using them? If a student can look at a simple painted assemblage of styrofoam identified as an atom of an element, and from it know correctly that the atom has a certain relative size compared to other atoms, that it has the capacity to form a specific number of covalent bonds and *why* it has that capacity, that these bonds have specific directional characteristics and *why,* that it can act as electron donor or acceptor or neither, and *why,* that it has a certain relative attraction for valence electrons that will result in bond polarity in combination with different atoms, of a direction and approximate extent that could immediately be determined by inspection of a similar model of the other atom—and in addition to all this, if he can with the help of a little supplementary information predict accurately from these models many of the physical and chemical properties of the compounds or other aggregates formed by these atoms, as will be described in later sections of this book, then why not use such models? Indeed, what excuse is there for not using them?

An instructor has always the responsibility to emphasize to his students the limitations as well as the extent of human knowledge. In presenting these models of atoms you will, of course, wish to be certain that your students understand clearly that real atoms are not believed to bear close physical resemblance to the models, except to the relative extent to which they occupy space. As long as you make it very clear that atoms are dynamic systems and that electrons are in effect more cloudlike, not stationary particles, and that your justification for using the models lies in the clarity with which important real qualities of the atoms may be represented rather than in the fidelity with which they reproduce the true physical picture, students are unlikely to become hampered by the absorption of false concepts.

CHAPTER

2

MOLECULAR, IONIC, AND CRYSTAL MODELS

Models of molecules and crystal models are certainly not new, for both kinds have long been used in teaching and research. Sets of connectable atomic models from which all manner of molecular models can be assembled or disassembled at will have been indispensable in organic chemistry. Similar models for inorganic compounds, with the exception of portions of organic model sets and of certain complex ions, have not been generally available.

The models to be described herein were developed for two reasons. First, the steadily increasing emphasis on structure in the teaching of general and inorganic chemistry made models increasingly desirable as visual aids. The second reason was the belief that an atom does not remain unaffected by chemical combination, but varies in condition depending on its environment. If this is true, then models assembled from a standard set of atoms must be deficient in making no distinction among different conditions. For most hydrocarbon derivatives, the differences are probably not large enough to justify the loss in convenience if the atoms of the models were not interchangeable. For most inorganic compounds, on the other hand, some indication of differences in condition of atoms in different combinations seems not only desirable, but essential. For example, the chlorine atoms in phosphorus trichloride are certainly not in the same condition as in magnesium chloride, and to be adequately useful, models should show the differences.

The first problem, then, was to learn what changes that might be visualized in a model are undergone by combining atoms. If the atoms combine only with like atoms, no important changes in the models would seem to be required, except as needed to show any bond multiplicity that may occur. But if the atoms combine with unlike atoms, the electronegativities of the two or more elements are unlikely to be equal, and if unequal, uneven sharing of bonding electrons results. If shared electrons spend more than half time more closely associated with one atom than with the other, the effect must be that of a partial negative charge on the one with a partial positive charge remaining on the other. Some of the ways in which such unevenness of charge distribution may influence both physical and chemical properties of compounds will be discussed in detail in following chapters. Some means of making possible the visualization of charge distribution in molecules would certainly be helpful in models.

Another effect of charge that might usefully be shown in models is its probable effect on radius. Experimental measurements have established beyond reasonable doubt a predictable relationship between atomic and ionic radius. A positive ion is always smaller and a negative ion larger than the neutral atom. In an "isoelectronic series" (having the same number of electrons) the higher the positive charge, the smaller the ion. Radius diminishes in the order: F^-, Na^+, Mg^{++}, Al^{+++}. Then what of an atom that becomes only partially negative or positive? Should not the electronic sphere tend to expand as it acquires part of an additional electron, with its repulsive effect on the other electrons uncompensated for by any corresponding increase in the nuclear charge? Should not the sphere contract as the repulsion among its electrons is decreased by the withdrawal of part of an electron without corresponding reduction in the nuclear charge?

In fact, the electronic spheres about atoms are so nebulous and so easily distorted that it is impossible to describe their shape or volume exactly. However, experimental measurements do lead to accurate determination of the internuclear distance between the two bonded atoms, and it is from such distances, called "bond lengths," that covalent radii are inferred. Abundant evidence has been accumulated to show that bonds are shorter the more polar. If one accepts the postulate that an atom with partial negative charge has a larger covalent radius and an atom with partial positive charge has a smaller covalent radius, an explanation for this shortening is provided, for in practically all cases the contraction of the atom that loses part of an electron exceeds the expansion of the atom that gains. The sum of the two radii, which should give the bond length, is therefore smaller than the sum of the two nonpolar covalent radii.

Futhermore, this adjustment in atomic size with charge is quite consistent with the charge adjustment, as will be discussed in the following section. Therefore one might find it desirable to show such variations in radius in the models of molecules.

The models under discussion are constructed to show the radii of the individual atoms as they are believed to be in the molecules. If the charge is not great, these radii do not differ very significantly from the radii of the atoms in nonpolar bonds. Larger charges show deviations that are quite perceptible in the models, and of course the difference between total charge (ionic radii) and nonpolarity (nonpolar covalent radii) is very evident.

Covalent versus van der Waals Radii. As mentioned in the discussion of atomic models, two principal kinds of internuclear distance between adjacent atoms have been observed. These kinds are well illustrated by the iodine crystal, in which each atom has one neighbor at 2.67Å and the next closest neighbor is 4.30Å away. The crystal consists of I_2 molecules. The shorter distance is the length of the I—I single covalent bond. The longer distance is the nonbonded interatomic distance. The covalent radius is the effective atomic radius in the direction of the bond, and is taken as half the bond length in I_2, or 1.33Å. Half the nonbonding distance is 2.15Å, which is called the van der Waals radius.

Most models, such as the Fisher-Hirschfelder type, try to show both radii, to represent as well as possible both the bond length and the space-filling qualities. Also, most artist sketches of molecules attempt to depict van der Waals radii. Consequently, models in which the atoms are represented only by covalent radii may appear rather strange, and some will not approve of them.

The models described here are of the latter type, and I believe some justification or rationalization would be appropriate here. My personal preference is for covalent radii, for these reasons:

1) Covalent radii are easily estimated from bond lengths and easily corrected for polarity effects, whereas van der Waals radii are vague and uncertain and depend on conditions not easily evaluated. For example, in solid CCl_4 two chlorine atoms of different molecules appear to approach no closer than twice the generally accepted van der Waals radius, but two chlorine atoms in the same molecule, which hardly seem bonded directly to one another, are much closer together than twice the van der Waals radius.

2) Model construction using van der Waals radii is much more difficult, requiring careful cutting of highly special shapes instead of the use of readily available spheres.

3) One would not easily be able to distinguish between single and double bonds if van der Waals radii were used, because even single bonds would require much closer than tangential contact.

4) In more complex models interior visibility might be easily possible with covalent radii but blocked out completely if van der Waals radii were used.

5) Although van der Waals radii show approximately the closest dis-

tance of nonbonding approach and therefore allow prediction of steric interference, chemical reaction presumably requires closer approach, and covalent radii should show this more realistically.

In summary, neither type can be altogether right or altogether wrong, but all things considered, my vote is for covalent radii. If you use these radii, you will wish to emphasize to your students that the molecular models must be regarded as being surrounded by an invisible, elastic electronic barrier extending into space perhaps half a diameter beyond each atomic sphere surface. In most teaching applications, this is not even very important. However, it does become significant in crystal models, if you use covalent instead of ionic radii. Here the anions may not appear to be in contact, whereas they actually would be if van der Waals radii were used. But if you used the latter, your students would be unable to see inside the crystal in many models without cutting them apart.

If, after studying the above invincible arguments, you still wish to use van der Waals radii, go right ahead. Your models can be just as useful as mine except for the disadvantages (3) and (4) above. They will be superior to mine in showing somewhat more realistically the approximate extension of the electron clouds out into space. I have not included a table of van der Waals radii here to guide you, however, because of the uncertainty as to what their values should be.

Partial Charge Representation. Partial charge is shown in the models by a color scale similar to that used in the atomic models to represent electronegativity. An attempt is made to make these two uses of the same colors reasonably consistent, in the following way. Elements of low electronegativity, whose atomic models would therefore be red, are the elements most likely to become most positive in chemical combination. Red is chosen in the charge-color scale to represent high positive charge. Similarly, elements of high electronegativity, whose atomic models would therefore be blue-green or blue, are most likely to become most negative in chemical combination. Blue is chosen in the charge-color scale to represent high negative charge. Yellow is taken to indicate zero charge, or neutrality. A charge range from high positive through neutral to high negative is thus shown by a color range from red through red-orange, orange, yellow-orange, yellow, yellow-green, green, blue-green, to blue.

The molecules, ions, or crystals are assembled by fastening together atomic spheres of appropriate size and color to represent accurately the geometric structure of the aggregate. Specific directions for the construction of several hundred different models are given in Chapter 10. The general directions are given here for you to see at once that no unreasonable expenditure of time or money and no unreasonable requirement of skill is involved.

The basic material is styrofoam, a foamed polystyrene plastic available at relatively low cost from a number of small manufacturers, often of Christmas ornaments, in the form of spheres ranging in diameter from less than 1 inch to as much as 8 or 10 inches, and priced from a few cents each to perhaps a few dollars each for the largest. If one uses a scale of 1.5 inches per Ångstom unit, models large enough for the average classroom are obtained, hydrogen atoms averaging about 1 inch in diameter and carbon, oxygen, and nitrogen atoms about 2½ inches in diameter, and chloride ions less than 6 inches in diameter. For use in very large lecture rooms, twice this scale is advantageous, although this is not necessary and perhaps is most desirable for those few compounds, such as water, which are under most frequent discussion. For display purposes you may wish to have models on a much smaller scale; these need not necessarily be made of polystyrene but any of several other materials will do, as suggested below or as you may devise. Examples of other materials especially suited to smaller models are asbestos, bakelite, wood, clay, etc. Some of these are discussed in Chapter 10.

The atoms for these models are first painted and then glued together, using wooden connectors to strengthen the joints when styrofoam is the sphere material. Tangential contact represents single bonds, and multiple bonds are shown by closer than tangential contact, attained by first slicing segments from the spheres to be joined.

You may wish to indicate unshared outer shell electron pairs on the atoms of molecular models. Such supplementary representation may be especially useful for molecules like ammonia, in which the availability of an electron pair on the nitrogen permits it to act as donor and thus makes a very significant contribution to the chemistry of the compound. In this model the electron pair is also useful in explaining the physical properties of ammonia, such as its "anomalously" high melting and boiling points that reflect protonic bridging among molecules.

Likewise, in molecules such as the boron halides, representation of the outer shell unoccupied orbital(s) can be useful in explaining the action of "Lewis acids" with their electron acceptor function.

Indeed, the representation of outer vacancies and outer electrons in all molecular models may have advantages although it is not always necessary and, as will be discussed later (page 65), cannot always be done unambiguously. As a general principle of chemical combination, combination tends to proceed until all external vacancies are utilized or at least shielded from access to electrons of other atoms. In the boron halides the outer vacant orbital seems either partly used in the bonding as possibly occurs in BF_3, or sterically prevented from stably coordinating electrons from another molecule of the same kind, in which the outer pairs may not be relatively easily available. With these as perhaps the only exception, all simple molecules having external unshared electron pairs on one atom and unoccupied outer orbitals on another atom tend to unite further, usually to form an "ionic" or polymeric crystal lattice in which single molecules are no longer distinguishable. Occasionally, as in Al_2Br_6 and Al_2I_6, dimerization seems to complete this process, leaving the molecules whole, although associated, in the solid state.

For this reason representation of the outer orbitals in the molecular models has the general value of permitting reliable predictions of the state of aggregation, or at the very least, reasonable guesses. When, in contrast to the above situation, atoms of a molecular model have only filled outer orbitals, the compound is almost certain to be relatively volatile and to condense in molecular crystalline form. There exist also, of course, "giant molecule" structures like SiO_2 in which single molecules cannot exist.

As in the atomic models, these outer electrons and vacancies can be represented by small white and black balls fastened to the atomic sphere surface at the correct locations.

When you have constructed such models, what do you have? What can your students learn from them? In the first place, as will be detailed later, they can use the atomic models to predict the characteristics of the molecular model in many instances, before they have even seen it. Then, examining the molecular model, they can see at a glance how the component atoms are joined together, what is the general geometric shape of the molecule, what is the approximate polarity of each bond, as well as the multiplicity of bonding. The representation of charge distribution and bond polarity is unique in these models, never having been attempted before. It is a feature that enhances the utility of models enormously, making much simpler the instructor's job of explaining and the student's job of understanding chemistry.

CALCULATION OF CHARGE AND RADIUS

Fundamentals

The complete details of the fundamental principles and postulates involved in the assignment of partial charge to individual combined atoms are presented in my book, *Chemical Periodicity* (Reinhold, New York, 1960). Here will be given only the most essential features of the methods of estimation.

First, as suggested in the preceding chapter, electronegativity appears to be related to the compactness of the electronic spheres of atoms. The model of fluorine shows its atoms to be much smaller than those of lithium, for example, although they contain three times as many electrons. This means that in fluorine the electrons must be packed more tightly together than in lithium. If an atom can hold its own electrons close together despite their mutual repulsion, this signifies that the nuclear attraction is especially effective and suggests that if low-energy vacancies capable of accommodating outside electrons are present, they too can be strongly attracted by the nucleus. On the other hand, if an atom cannot hold its own electrons close together, there is no reasonable expectation that it will be able to exert a very significant attraction on an outside electron, whether or not orbital vacancies may be available. Thus a logical relationship between atomic compactness and electronegativity appears.

A measure of the atomic compactness is the average "electronic density," which is simply the ratio of the atomic number to the volume of the atom expressed as number of electrons per Ångstrom³:

$$D = Z/4.19r^3$$

In this expression, D is the electronic density, Z the atomic number, 4.19 is $\frac{4}{3}$ pi, and r is the nonpolar covalent radius. D then gives the average number of electrons per cubic Ångstrom.

When electronic density is determined for many of the elements, and compared with electronegativity values obtained by other means, a remarkably close relationship is apparent, but it is not in all cases consistent with chemical fact. By assigning to the inert elements "nonpolar covalent radii" as previously discussed, one can calculate D values for these. Some variation is found—and this kind of variation is clearly not associated with electronegativity differences since the atoms are not electronegative. Evidently some change in compactness is associated with the filling of successive principal quantum shells and independent of any electronegativity change. Therefore it seemed desirable to correct the average electronic densities of the elements for changes resulting solely from change in atomic number. The correction was accomplished by dividing the electronic density of each element by the electronic density of a hypothetical inert element having the same number of electrons per atom. This latter value is obtained by linear interpolation on a plot of D versus Z for the inert elements. This value is designated as D_i. The ratio, D/D_i, is then taken as a correct representation of the relative electronegativity, S:

$$S = D/D_i$$

The question now arises, what happens to the electronegativity when atoms combine? A change in radius, and therefore in volume, with the acquisition of charge has already been discussed. The relationship between this change and the question under discussion may be simply interpreted. If two atoms initially different in electronegativity combine through a sharing of electrons (covalent bond), do they remain different in electronegativity in the combination, or compound? Can a pair of electrons remain equally shared between two atoms if one attracts them more than the other? Or, if one atom attracts the electrons more than the other, why do not the electrons move all the way to this atom, forming ions?

Let us imagine the electron pair initially evenly shared, but gradually, so that we can observe what happens, beginning to spend more and more of their time more closely associated with one atom than with the other. This will introduce on this atom the effect of partial negative charge, and through increased repulsion without corresponding increase in attraction cause expansion of the electronic sphere. In the expanded state the electrons are no longer as closely associated with the nucleus as they were before, and this includes the valence electrons forming the bond. In other words, as the atom succeeds in acquiring more than half share of the bonding electrons, its attraction for them diminishes. Similarly, consider the state of the initially less electronegative atom. As an electron is withdrawn from its complete control, spending more than half time with another atom, the average number of electrons in the cloud of this atom decreases, and therefore their repulsion decreases, but without any loss of charge on the nucleus. Consequently, the remaining cloud is pulled more closely to the nucleus—as the atom acquires partial positive charge, the electron cloud contracts. This means that for the time the bonding electrons are within the zone of influence of this atom, they are more tightly held than they were when they were equally shared by both atoms. In other words, the electronegativity of this atom has increased as it acquired positive charge.

Such adjustment, which of course must occur practically instantaneously, causes the electronegativities of the two atoms, initially different, to approach one another. This adjustment must cease at the most stable arrangement, and the most logical point for cessation seems to be the point or situation in which both electrons are attracted equally by the two nuclei.

The physical picture sketched above may be vastly oversimplified, but the essential validity of the argument seems quite acceptable. Surely an atom must become less electronegative as it succeeds in acquiring negative charge—fluorine is extremely electronegative but a fluoride ion is not at all. Surely, too, an atom must become more electronegative as it loses control of its electrons—metal atoms are never oxidizing agents but their cations attract electrons, some of them being strong oxidizing agents. And finally, atoms are certainly not rigid, inflexible objects but must adjust to the electrical stresses placed upon them by the proximity of other atoms, through a mobility of their electrons. On the basis of such reasoning, one can generalize to systems containing more than two atoms, by assuming that in such chemical combinations, adjustments occur with electrons becoming distributed throughout the system according to the relative attractions exerted by the several nuclei.

These ideas can be stated as the **Principle of Electronegativity Equalization:** *When two or more atoms initially different in electronegativity combine chemically, they become adjusted to the same intermediate electronegativity in the compound.*

The next question is, what intermediate electronegativity is reached? Here, unfortunately, only a certain amount of circumstantial evidence is available to suggest the right answer. From a comprehensive study of bond lengths, as will be discussed briefly a little later, it was concluded that a satisfactory intermediate value of the electronegativity in a compound is given by the geometric mean of the electronegativities of all the atoms before combination. To calculate the electronegativity in a molecule, then, one obtains the logarithms of the electronegativity of each of the component atoms (whether of the same or different elements), adds them, and divides the total by the number of atoms in the molecule. The antilog of this value is the molecular electronegativity.

For example, what is the electronegativity in H_2SO_4? The values for the separate elements are: H 3.55, S 4.11, and O 5.21. The geometric mean of these, $S_{H_2SO_4}$, is the electronegativity of H_2SO_4 and also of each atom in it. The geometric mean is the root of the product:

$$S_{H_2SO_4} = \sqrt[7]{3.55^2 \times 4.11 \times 5.21^4}$$

Logarithms are ideally suited to this calculation.

$$\begin{aligned} \log 3.55 &= 0.5502; \times 2 = 1.1004 \\ \log 4.11 &= 0.6138; \times 1 = 0.6138 \\ \log 5.21 &= 0.7168; \times 4 = 2.8672 \\ \hline & \text{sum} = 4.5814 \end{aligned}$$

$$4.5814/7 = 0.6545 = \log S$$
$$\text{antilog} = 4.513 = S_{H_2SO_4}$$

The calculation of the electronegativity of ions requires knowledge of the partial charges, as will be described below.

Estimation of Partial Charge

Neutral Molecules. The method of estimating partial charge on a combined atom involves comparing the change in electronegativity undergone when the atom combined, to the change which it would have undergone had it acquired unit charge. Two assumptions are needed. One is an assumption as to the way in which electronegativity changes with charge. It is assumed that the change is linear. The other assumption requires a reasonable guess of the ionic character of the covalent bond in any specific diatomic molecule. Unfortunately, a guess is necessary because no experimental or theoretical method of obtaining such information reliably is known. For the purpose of estimating charge, the bond in an isolated molecule of NaF was guessed to be 75 per cent ionic. In other words, the unevenness of sharing of the electron pair forming the bond is taken to produce a partial charge of 0.75 electron on the sodium atom and −0.75 on the fluorine. To make such a guess may seem an extraordinarily arbitrary procedure, but as will be recognized later, by far the most useful application of partial charges is as a means of comparison where the absolute value need not be accurate as long as the relative order is correct. Furthermore, a substantial body of indirect evidence suggests that the values obtained, based on 75 per cent ionic character of gaseous sodium fluoride, are close to the correct order of magnitude.

Having made these assumptions, one can proceed easily to the estimation of the electronegativity change that should accompany the acquisition of unit charge. The electronegativity of sodium is 0.70. That of fluorine is 5.75. The geometric mean for NaF is 2.007. This means that in combining with fluorine sodium has gained in electronegativity by the amount, $2.007 - 0.70 = 1.307$. But this is only 75 per cent of the amount which it would have gained had it lost an electron completely. Therefore, $1.307/0.75 = 1.743$, the change in electronegativity of sodium that would correspond to acquisition of unit charge (complete loss of one electron). Similarly, in combining with sodium fluorine has lost electronegativity by the amount, $5.75 - 2.007 = 3.743$. But, if fluorine had acquired an electron completely, becoming a fluoride ion, it would have lost $3.743/0.75 = 4.988$. Thus for any compound of sodium we can calculate the electronegativity of the compound and subtract the electronegativity of sodium, 0.70, from it to find how much electronegativity the sodium gained in forming the compound. The ratio of this amount to the amount it would have gained in becoming sodium ion (1.743) is taken as the partial charge on sodium in the compound. Suppose this compound were sodium chloride. Then the partial charge on sodium as thus calculated would be equal to, but of opposite charge from, that on chlorine. From this one could easily calculate how much the electronegativity of chlorine should have changed, had the chlorine become chloride ion. In a similar manner, one can compute the changes in electronegativity for most of the elements that would correspond to acquisition of unit charge. The partial charge on any element in a compound, then, is calculated as the ratio of the change in electronegativity in forming the compound to the change in electronegativity that would correspond to unit charge.

The necessary data for calculating molecular electronegativity and partial charge are given in Table 2-1; see also Table 10-2, page 136.*

Complex Ions. The calculation of partial charge on atoms in complex ions presents the problem of estimating the electronegativities of these ions. The method is the following:

First calculate the electronegativity of the ion as though it were a neutral molecule. Then calculate the electronegativity of an appropriate salt containing this ion. From the change in electronegativity undergone by the other component (conveniently silver or fluorine), the ionicity of the "salt" is determined. The change in S from neutral radical to salt is then corrected to integral charge, and thus the electronegativity of the complex ion can be calculated.

Example: To determine the electronegativity of acetate ion, $C_2H_3O_2^-$, the S value for $C_2H_3O_2$ is first computed. This comes out to be 4.036.

Next, the S value of silver acetate is computed. It is 3.762. Thus, in forming the silver salt, the $C_2H_3O_2$ group has lost electronegativity, from 4.036 to 3.762, a difference of 0.274.

But the silver has gained, from 2.300 for free silver to 3.762, an increase of 1.462. From Table 2-1, you can see that if silver had lost an electron completely, forming Ag^+, the gain in S would have been 3.155. According to this, the silver in silver acetate must have a partial charge of 1.462/3.155, which is the ionicity of silver acetate.

Therefore the S change that would have been undergone by $C_2H_3O_2$, if it had become $C_2H_3O_2^-$ ion, is given by the actual change divided by the ionicity:

$$0.274 \times 3.155/1.462 = 0.591.$$

Negative charge means lower S. Hence 4.036 – 0.591 or 3.445 is the electronegativity of acetate ion.

If this is now used to calculate the partial charges on the component atoms in the described manner, their sum will equal, not zero as for a neutral molecule, but −1 for the net charge on the ion.

* All tables are located at the end of the book, beginning on page 131.

Estimation of Radius-in-Combination

The electronegativity S is defined as a ratio of the average electronic density D to that, D_i, of a hypothetical isoelectronic inert element. But each such density is the ratio of atomic number, Z, to the volume: $Z/4.19r^3$ where 4.19 is ⅘ pi. Therefore

$$S = D/D_i = Z/4.19r^3 \times 4.19r_i^3/Z = r_i^3/r^3$$

Thus in a molecule or ion the radius of each atom as it is in the combination can be computed:

$$r = \sqrt[3]{r_i^3/S_m}$$

where S_m is the molecular electronegativity.

Table 2-2 gives the r_i^3 values for each atomic number for use in such calculations. All the radii of Chapter 10 were calculated in this way. (See also Table 10-2, page 136.) These values, especially as applied to compounds conventionally considered "ionic," may be considered somewhat controversial, but the controversy is seldom serious. The most important point in model construction is that the *internuclear distances* be correct to scale. In the absence of experimental data the radii calculated as above will, when the spheres are in tangential contact, give reasonably reliable single bond lengths. The use of these values in calculating lengths of multiple bonds will be discussed in Chapter 10.

CHAPTER

3

PHYSICAL STATES AND PHYSICAL PROPERTIES OF THE ELEMENTS

The models of the atoms of the elements will prove very valuable in helping students to understand the nature of the aggregates of atoms which make up the elements in their "free" state. This is necessary as a preliminary to an explanation of the physical properties of the elements, because all those properties possessed by an element in bulk result directly from the state of aggregation and only indirectly from the atomic structure. It is important that your students recognize that a single atom does not have such properties as electrical conductivity, thermal conductivity, melting point, boiling point, density—these are properties of aggregates of atoms and very dependent on the structure of the aggregate.

THE METALLIC STATE

Most of the elements are metals, and no treatment of their physical properties can be complete without first a presentation of the nature of the metallic state. You may wish to point out to your students that covalent bonds are only formed when at least one of the combining atoms has as many outermost electrons as vacancies, or more. Unless this is true, covalent bonds are not formed. Instead, the atoms join together in a much more closely packed arrangement in which each atom has far more neighbors (most commonly 12) than could possibly be held by conventional covalent bonds. Nevertheless, the stability of such aggregates is well recognized. In many elements it is astonishingly high. The bonding under these conditions is called "metallic bonding." It seems to involve a nonlocalization of bonding electrons, as opposed to a localization in covalent bonding where two electrons can be assigned to a specific pair of atoms. In metals the bonding electrons appear to be shared jointly by all the atoms. One can picture a metal as consisting of a collection of cations imbedded in and held together by an electrostatic glue of mobile electrons.

According to the rule just stated, atoms from Group IVA through VIIA must constitute at least half the pair of atoms being joined together, or a covalent bond cannot form. All other combinations will involve metallic bonding. In addition, as the principal quantum level of the valence shell increases, outer *d* orbitals tend to become increasingly available. If one assumes that these *d* orbitals may, to some extent, count among the available vacancies, then elements having the outer octet half filled or more than half filled may also satisfy the requirement of an excess of vacancies over outer electrons in order to have metallic bonding. Thus germanium, tin, lead, antimony, and bismuth are accounted for as metals, and other borderline elements may thus also derive their known metallic qualities.

The atomic models will be found very helpful in suggesting whether the free element will be metallic. Very simply, if no more than three electrons occupy the outer four orbitals, the element is sure to be metallic, with the single exception of boron, which is intermediate in nature. Models with 4 and 5 outer electrons will show elements tending toward metallic properties as their size (principal quantum number of valence shell) increases.

Three crystal models are especially desirable for showing metallic lattices. These should be the "body-centered cubic, BCC"; the "face-centered cubic, FCC"; also called "cubic close packed, CCP"; and the "hexagonal close packed, HCP." They are the most common types of metallic lattice. In the first, each interior atom is surrounded by eight closest neighbors at the corners of a cube, and six more about 15 per cent farther distant, at the centers of the six adjacent cubes. It is bonded then to either 8 or 14 other atoms, depending on the interpretation. This is not the closest possible packing of spheres, for if uniform spheres are packed together, each interior sphere will have 12 closest neighbors, each in direct contact with it. The face-centered cubic and hexagonal forms are two variations possible. Each may be represented, at the start, as a planar hexagonal ring of atoms with one at the center. In fact, you may wish to demonstrate with unattached balls of like size that a ring of six fits very neatly around one on a level surface. Then each solid hexagon has a triangle of atoms above, and another below, all six atoms of these also being in direct contact with the central atom. The difference lies in the orientation of the two triangles with respect to one another. If the triangles point in the same direction, the structure is hexagonal. If one triangle is the reverse of the other, the structure is face-centered cubic. You may wish to construct but one model to represent both. If one triangle and the hexagon are connected to the central atom, then the other triangle may be constructed separately. Held in place, this triangle will then serve to show either structure. When you are holding the model to represent face-centered cubic packing, by rotating the model slightly you will be able to see that it forms a face of a cube, together with the centers of the eight faces that begin with the edges of the first face.

Metals having these structures are listed in Tables 3-1, 3-2, and 3-3. Unfortunately, no obvious relationship between atomic structure and crystal structure of metals can be observed. For photos of models, see Figs. B-4, B-5, B-6, and B-7.

STATES OF AGGREGATION OF INDIVIDUAL ELEMENTS

If the atomic radius chosen for the body-centered cubic model is that of lithium, and for the hexagonal model that of beryllium, a beginning can be made toward showing models of all elements in Period 2, in their normal state of aggregation. The next would be boron, of which at least one crystalline form features icosahedral (20-faced) clusters of twelve atoms. (See Fig. B-6.) Each of the twelve has five close neighbors in the cluster and is attached to one boron outside the cluster, making six neighbors in all. The number of bonds is twice the three that are permitted by the three outer electrons if ordinary covalent bonds are to be formed, yet the solid does not have metallic properties either. Boron is probably best presented to your students as intermediate between metal and nonmetal, but your ingenuity may be taxed if someone asks *how* it is intermediate.

To show carbon, you will need two models, one of graphite and one of diamond. A study of the atomic model of carbon will show your students how logical and predictable is the diamond. The atomic model shows clearly how and why a carbon atom can form four covalent bonds, directed toward the corners of a regular tetrahedron. The diamond is nothing more than a crystalline form that results when many carbon atoms join to one another by single bonds, each interior atom having four close neighbors at the corners of a regular tetrahedron. At this point it would probably only be confusing to point out that another structure for carbon seems theoretically possible, although apparently never observed—but later on, you may wish to consider the question of the wurtzite structure and the zinc blende structure, and why carbon assumes the latter but not the former. See Fig. B-2 for a photo of a model of diamond.

An explanation of graphite, and especially an explanation of its slightly greater stability under ordinary conditions, is not so simple. However, if your students study the diamond structure carefully, they will observe that it contains nonplanar layers of condensed six membered rings, joined to one of the next layers by bonds from three alternate atoms of each ring, and to the other of the adjacent layers by bonds from the other three atoms of each ring. If these bonds joining the condensed ring layers could be severed, the liberated bonding electrons, six to a ring, could establish bond multiplicity in the rings which then would become planar, with shorter bonds, since all outer electrons would now be used in three bonds per carbon instead of four. The structure would thus consist of planar layers of condensed rings, held together loosely by relatively weak interaction of the layers. This is the structure of graphite. One can see how by forcing the layers much closer together, the planar layers might be caused to change to the diamond structure. Indeed, this has recently been accomplished by using very high pressures.

You may wish to point out that an alternative form of graphite may exist in which the layers are arranged a little differently; it seems hardly worth while to prepare a separate model to show this. A model of graphite is pictured in Fig. B-2.

The nitrogen atomic model of course shows clearly the capacity of a nitrogen atom to form three single covalent bonds. From this one might predict that three-dimensional aggregates of nitrogen atoms joined through single bonds might be the natural state of the free element. However, a tendency for bond multiplicity in these period 2 elements, as already shown by carbon in its graphite structures, appears to result from the fact, not shown by the models, that as these atoms grow more compact with increasing nuclear charge, when they form one single bond, other available orbitals begin to overlap. This favors bond multiplicity, and in nitrogen results in triple bonds that are very strong, leading to diatomic molecules N_2 (Fig. B-1). The presence of a shell of only 2 electrons underlying the valence shell, instead of the more common 8, allows closer contact of two atoms than would otherwise be possible.

Some bright student may point out another possibility, or more, for both carbon and nitrogen. Why, he may ask, do not carbon atoms unite by alternate triple and single bonds or by chains of double bonds? Why do not nitrogen atoms unite by alternate double and single bonds? For carbon, you may answer that perhaps carbon atoms do form such chains; the exact nature of soot, for example, or other forms of "amorphous" carbon, is not always known. The nitrogen question might make a good class discussion, but no simple explanation seems obvious.

Oxygen atoms, as you can show by an atomic model, can each form two single or one double bond. One would therefore expect oxygen to consist either of indefinitely long chains of singly bonded atoms, or rings of singly bonded atoms, or diatomic molecules held together by double bonding. The chains would be zigzag, as shown by the atomic model.

Here the possibility of overlapping of other orbitals is important, for the other orbitals in oxygen would already be full. Repulsion would result, tending to weaken the bonding and allow such a chain to be easily disrupted. Formation of a double bond would thus appear to be favored, and O_2 molecules would thus seem explained. Unfortunately, however, the situation is not quite that simple, for such a molecule would have only paired electrons. Magnetic properties, which are possessed by oxygen, depend on unpaired electrons. By molecular orbital theory a structure involving double bonding but two unpaired electrons is shown to be more stable than with the same electrons paired. No simple picture, however, seems available, and for most purposes an oxygen molecular model is quite satisfactory if it shows the closeness of ordinary double bond approach. (See Fig. B-1.)

The fluorine atomic model shows that only one kind of aggregate is possible, for each atom can form but one single covalent bond. Diatomic molecules are evidently the only possibility, and this is how elementary fluorine exists, as clearly shown by the F_2 model, Fig. B-1.

The neon model shows no bonding possibilities, the external octet of electrons leaving no gap in the effective screening of the nucleus from electrons outside the atom. The existence of the element only as monatomic molecules is thus easily understood.

Sodium, magnesium, and aluminum are all clearly metallic, as your students can readily perceive from the structure shown by the atomic models. The exact crystalline form may be demonstrated by use of a BCC model for sodium, an HCP model for magnesium, and a CCP model for aluminum.

Silicon is easily seen from the atomic model to resemble carbon in its outer electronic structure. The diamond form of silicon is thus easily explained. The nonexistence of any multiple bond structure, for example, analogous to graphite, needs to be explained. Probably this is a consequence of the underlying shell containing 8 instead of only 2 electrons. Repulsions of inner shells may help to prevent the closeness of interaction necessary for multiple bonds. Also, the overlapping of orbitals beyond that of single bond formation may be much weaker with higher principal quantum level.

An atomic model of phosphorus will show it to resemble nitrogen, but the greatly diminished ability of atoms having underlying electron octets to form multiple bonds is exhibited here as in silicon. If single bonds are to form, the simplest possible structure is a tetrahedron of phosphorus atoms. In such a structure each atom would be joined by a single bond to each of the other three. A model of the P_4 molecule (Fig. B-3) will show clearly the "cramping" of the bond angles necessary for such a structure, angles of 60° being observed. A tendency to avoid this distortion of bond angles would be expected, and P_4 molecules—typical of white phosphorus—tend to rearrange to less strained structures such as those of red and black phosphorus.

Sulfur, like oxygen, has two outer vacancies, as shown by the atomic model, but the relative inability to form multiple bonds with itself persists. Two single bonds result, in the joining together of sulfur atoms. It is not easy to explain exactly why, but somehow greatest stability appears to lie in 8-member staggered rings, for a description of which a molecular model is almost indispensable. (See photo, Fig. B-3.)

An atomic model of chlorine, like one of fluorine, shows clearly that the only possibility is for two atoms to join by a single covalent bond, forming a diatomic molecule whose model can be shown (Fig. B-1).

PHYSICAL PROPERTIES

Many of the common physical properties of the elements, such as density, melting and boiling temperatures, electrical and thermal conductance, and mechanical properties such as tensile strength, elasticity, hardness, and malleability, are not properties of single atoms. They are therefore, as previously pointed out, not direct consequences of atomic structure, but rather of the way in which the atoms are connected together. This is why it is so important for your students to understand at least the reasonableness of the states of aggregation, as a consequence of the nature of the atoms. If, then, they can be shown the relationship between properties and state of aggregation, they will be able to appreciate *why* the individual elements possess the physical properties that characterize them.

A brief discussion of the general origin of properties may be useful here. Density is perhaps the easiest to understand. It depends simply on how many atoms are packed within a given unit of volume and how much each atom weighs. Mechanical properties, melting and boiling points, and volatility all depend on the nature and strength of the attractive forces that hold matter together. When a substance is struck with a hammer, for instance, does it splash, does it merely dent, does it spread out (flatten) without apparent rupture, or does it break into fragments? Breaking into fragments requires overcoming forces that held it together—if they are weak, it breaks easily, but if they are strong, it may be very hard. If the relative position of the component particles can be changed without breaking bonds, as in most metals, the substance may be malleable and ductile. If the relative position of the component particles cannot be changed without breaking bonds, the substance will be brittle.

Electrical and thermal properties arise mainly from the outermost electrons. If these are relatively mobile—free to move among the atoms instead of localized between pairs of atoms—the electrical and thermal conductivity is relatively high. If the outermost electrons are localized between specific pairs of atoms, however, the substance is more likely to be thermally and electrically insulating. Finally, if melting or boiling require that large forces be overcome, then the temperatures required are usually high, but if only small forces need be overcome, melting and boiling points are low. Specific examples will be given in the following paragraphs.

Unfortunately, the crystal structure alone does not suffice to explain all physical properties of metals. For example, some of the densest, toughest metals of all have the same type of metallic lattice as that of the soft, weak, alkali metals. Within the general group of metals, one must look to the number of valence electrons and the number and type of bonding orbitals for explanations of most physical properties. However, it is worth demonstrating with models of hexagonal and cubic closest packing that more planes can be passed through the latter without dislodging atoms. Malleability and ductility can be understood from the general nature of metals with their nonlocalized bonding, for the relative positions of atoms can easily be changed without changing their environment significantly, and, more important, without breaking bonds. The existence of more "glide planes" in cubic close packing than in hexagonal close packing means, therefore, greater malleability and ductility in the former.

Aside from this difference, one may observe a tendency for metal structures to be denser, stronger, higher melting and boiling, the more compact the atoms and the more valence electrons are available. Furthermore, *d* orbitals and electrons seem to contribute more than *s* and *p* orbitals and electrons to these qualities.

The alkali metals, whose atoms are relatively large and have only one electron for valence, are very low in density, melting and boiling temperatures. In contrast, some of the heavier transition elements, whose atoms are relatively small, being very compact, and whose *d* orbitals are about half filled, are highest of all the elements in density, melting and boiling points.

Although models of the metallic elements in their normal states of aggregation thus cannot be very helpful in suggesting physical properties, models of the aggregates of the nonmetals show very clearly why they possess the physical properties that characterize them.

The first nonmetallic element of course is hydrogen. The diatomic molecules (Fig. B-1) with their two electrons largely localized between the two nuclei, have very low interaction except repulsion among one another. Furthermore, van der Waals forces cannot be large, with the result that hydrogen has extremely low melting and boiling points, being gaseous under most conditions. The next nonmetal is helium. Here the inability of the atoms to form covalent bonds is consistent with their general symmetry and resistance to outside influence. Consequently, helium is a monatomic gas and not only has the lowest of all boiling points, but also cannot even become solidified except under pressure, at extremely low temperature.

The exact nature of the bonding of boron is not yet understood, but it appears to be intermediate between metallic and covalent, and whatever it is, it seems that strong bonds hold the boron atoms together in the aggregate. These bonds, at least some of them, must be broken before the crystal can break down. This makes boron very hard and more brittle than malleable, and requires high melting and boiling temperatures. In both major forms of carbon, covalent bonds must be broken in order to produce liquefaction or vaporization. These are strong bonds and therefore carbon is nearly highest among the elements in melting and boiling temperatures. Carbon forms give a very good example of how the identical atoms can result in entirely different properties when joined together in different ways. You can show your students that in graphite the space between layers is so great that fewer carbon atoms can be within a given volume than in diamond. Consequently, the density of diamond is considerably greater than that of graphite. Furthermore, diamond is hardest of the elements because it cannot be broken without rupturing very strong carbon—carbon bonds. Graphite, on the other hand, consists of layers between which the forces of attraction are much weaker, and graphite is relatively soft and flaky. Diamond grinds; graphite lubricates. However, the lubricity of graphite seems to result at least partly from sorption of moisture and other substances between the layers. In a crystal of diamond are no free electrons, and carbon in this form is a nonconductor of electricity. In graphite, however, each carbon forms only three bonds, and its fourth electron, although involved in the bonding, is more mobile and can assist in the conduction of electricity.

Your models of nitrogen, oxygen, and fluorine molecules will show very clearly (Fig. B-1) why these elements are normally gaseous, for there can be but weak van der Waals forces among molecules here and only intermolecular forces, no bonds, need be broken for melting and boiling. Consequently their melting and boiling points are all very low and similar to one another. The model of the neon atom, with its 8 outermost electrons, will explain the gaseous nature of neon, and the larger number of electrons than in helium will also help to explain why although neon has very low melting and boiling points, these temperatures are substantially higher than for helium.

The physical properties of silicon to some extent resemble those of diamond, and you can also show the diamond model as representing the state of aggregation of silicon. A model of white phosphorus, P_4 (Fig. B-3), will be very instructive, for your students can see that if phosphorus consists of these molecules, the attractions among them must be quite weak, and low melting point and relatively high volatility are predictable. They can also note the strained bond angles in P_4, and recognize that such a molecule should be much more easily reactive with other substances than any form of phosphorus such as the red or black modifications in which the bond angles are normal. Sulfur has also relatively low melting and low boiling points; with the help of an S_8 model (Fig. B-3), you can explain that no bonds need to be broken for these changes, only the relatively weak forces between S_8 molecules.

Models of the diatomic molecules of chlorine, bromine, and iodine will lead your students to expect low melting and easy volatility here. With fluorine they can serve very well to illustrate how with increasing atomic radius, increasing number of electrons, and increasing polarizability the melting point and boiling points increase because of higher van der Waals forces among the molecules. The same point can then be made about the inert elements themselves, whose monatomic gases have very significantly higher melting and higher boiling points with increasing atomic number.

Much remains to be learned about physical properties of the elements from the viewpoint of understanding exactly why. The models can create no miracle, therefore, in the minds of your students. They can, however, when thoughtfully applied in lecture demonstration, do much to impress your students with the dependence of state of aggregation on atomic structure, and with the dependence of physical properties on state of aggregation. Even though the picture cannot be complete, it is certainly superior to a mere collection of descriptive facts that bear no obvious relationship to one another.

CHAPTER

4

GENERAL APPLICATIONS OF MOLECULAR, IONIC, AND CRYSTAL MODELS

MOLECULAR GEOMETRY

The directional nature of covalence has already been discussed in terms of their representation by atomic models. With molecular models in addition, the picture can be completed.

For example, atoms capable of forming only two covalent bonds are chiefly of two types, exemplified by beryllium and oxygen. A model of a gas molecule of $BeCl_2$ or BeF_2 (Fig. C-11) or any similar compound will show the linear nature of the bonding that results when all outer electrons are used in forming two bonds. Models of CO_2, acetylene, and similar compounds are useful in showing how this principle includes multiple bonding. The effect of two unshared electron pairs is shown well by models of H_2O, H_2S, SCl_2, Cl_2O, OF_2, $(CH_3)_2S$, and many other compounds. Extension to multiple bonding is demonstrated by models of ozone, SO_2, SeO_2, and others; in SO_2 there is only one unshared electron pair, so the bond angle is 120° (Fig. C-7).

When all outermost electrons are involved in only three bonds, the planar triangular structure predictable from the atomic models of boron and aluminum and gallium results. Models of BF_3, BCl_3 (Fig. C-11), and $B(CH_3)_3$ are helpful in illustrating this. Inclusion of multiple bonding adds models of nitric acid, NO_3^-, ethylene or other olefins, formate or any other carboxylate ion, SO_3, benzene, borazene, carbonate ion, $COCl_2$, and many others.

To demonstrate the pyramidal structure predictable from atomic models of VA elements, where an unshared electron pair must be taken into account, models of NH_3, NCl_3, NF_3, PCl_3, PBr_3, PH_3, PF_3 (Fig. C-11), and others, are suggested. Inclusion of multiple bonding adds to this list models of such compounds or ions as ClO_3^-, $SO_3^=$, and $SOCl_2$.

The tetrahedral structure indicated by atomic models of carbon and silicon is shown in models (Fig. C-14) of CH_4, SiH_4, CH_3OH, CCl_4, CF_4, SiF_4, $SiCl_4$, diamond, CH_3F, SiH_3Cl, and any of hundreds more. The inclusion of multiple bonding adds such models as those of H_2SO_4, $SO_4^=$, $HClO_4$, ClO_4, POF_3, $POCl_3$, and many more. The increase from two or three to four bonds, brought about by coordination, is shown by models of $BF_3 \cdot O(CH_3)_2$ (Fig. C-11), $BF_3 \cdot NH_3$, $Be(H_2O)_4^{++}$, $Zn(NH_3)_4^{++}$, Al_2Cl_6, BH_4^-, AlH_4^-, BF_4^-, and others, which are also tetrahedral.

(You will wish to point out that certain transition metals form four bonds at the corners of a planar square around the central atom, but unshared pairs influence such structures.)

When all outer electrons are involved in five bonds, the structure is more likely to be triangular bipyramidal, as shown by a model of PCl_5, $Fe(CO)_5$, or AsF_5. But if there are six bonds, many models can be used to illustrate the structure. Examples are SF_6, $Al(H_2O)_6^{+++}$, $SiF_6^=$, PF_6^-, $Co(NH_3)_6^{+++}$, and others (Figs. C-11, C-13).

In all these demonstrations, a careful consideration of models of the component atoms, followed by study of the molecular models, should serve to help your students understand clearly that molecular geometry has a relatively simple and logical basis in the structure of the individual atoms.

POLARITY AND PHYSICAL PROPERTIES OF COMPOUNDS

The general principles explaining physical properties of elements were discussed in the preceding chapter. In compounds electronegativity differences add their influence. To the extent of these differences, they make the bonds polar. If oppositely charged atoms of a molecule are both exposed to possible outside contact, then electrostatic attraction between molecules is possible, as the molecules align themselves so that oppositely charged atoms of separate molecules are adjacent. This may result in ionic crystals or in polar covalent solids, but in any case it increases the intermolecular attractions far above any ordinary van der Waals interactions. Consequently, higher crystal energy, higher melting and boiling temperatures, and lower volatility result. Models of individual molecules such as NaCl or $MgCl_2$ will help to illustrate this, especially when shown together with the models of their crystals.

When the bonds are less polar, the molecules may be attracted to one another, but not to the extent of losing their identity as in a NaCl crystal. As a result, the crystal energy is usually much lower, as are the melting and boiling temperatures, and the volatility is higher. Examples are represented by models of such molecules as PCl_3 (Fig. C-11), F_2O (Fig. C-7), SO_2 (Fig. C-7), AsF_3, and ICl.

If the molecules are symmetrical, on the other hand, so that the positively charged atoms are completely, or nearly, protected from outside contact, then the degree of polarity can exert little influence. Indeed, it may even result in reduced intermolecular attractions if the outermost atoms are all of relatively high negative charge. Examples can be shown by models such as of CF_4 (Fig. C-11), SiF_4, CCl_4 (Fig. C-11), and SF_6 (Fig. C-11).

For many purposes a representation of the outer unshared electron pairs and outer vacant orbitals of a molecule is unnecessary. One valuable application of such representation, however, often justifies the extra labor in the construction of the models. This application is to the prediction of the state of aggregation of the compound. An important general principle of chemical combination is that *exterior orbital vacancies tend to become filled,* or at least to become shielded so that they are no longer accessible to outside electrons. *If a model shows both unshared outer electron pairs and unoccupied outer orbitals, the compound may be predicted to condense under ordinary conditions to a crystalline solid.* The only known exceptions are the boron halides, wherein the fourth boron orbital, which would remain unoccupied if boron forms three single covalent bonds to halogen, appears either to participate in the bonding or otherwise to be unable to assist in condensation to larger aggregates.

Conversely, any model in which no exterior vacancies occur represents a molecule which can only unite with other molecules through van der Waals interaction, and the crystals are molecular, much lower melting and more volatile.

In addition, relatively stable and nonvolatile "giant molecules" may result when the formation of all possible single covalent bonds leads, as in SiO_2, to a 3-dimensional network. Such stability may be enhanced by multiple bonding involving electron pairs on oxygen and outer *d* orbitals on silicon.

VISUALIZATION OF CHEMICAL EQUATIONS

Models can be of great help to students learning about chemical equations for the first time. If they can visualize the molecules involved in a chemical reaction, they will understand much more readily why, for example, the formulas for the common gaseous elements must be written H_2, O_2, N_2, Cl_2 (Fig. B-1), instead of H, O, N, and Cl. They will see what is meant by "balancing an equation," for once they understand that atoms can neither be created nor destroyed in any chemical reaction (excepting nuclear reactions), they will see the necessity of representing the same number of atoms of each element on each side of the equation. They will also understand the logic of reducing such an equation to its simplest terms, numerically.

The burning of hydrogen is a good reaction for which to illustrate the equation by models. You can exhibit one H_2 model, pointing out that hydrogen gas occurs in this form, and since the molecule contains two atoms, no fewer than two atoms can be involved in the reaction. You can exhibit one O_2 model, and point out that here also two atoms are the minimum number that can be involved. Then you can explain that when hydrogen burns in air, the hydrogen combines with oxygen to form water, illustrated by a model of H_2O. If you set these models on the lecture bench in the proper order to represent a chemical equation and write the corresponding equation on the board behind them in its incomplete form, the students can begin to see at once the requirements for the complete reaction. With your guidance they can see first that if the minimum number of oxygen atoms that can be involved is two, because a single oxygen molecule contains two atoms, then at least two H_2O molecules must result. You can then supply a second H_2O model, placing it next to the first one on the bench. Your students can then see that it would be impossible to have two H_2O molecules if four hydrogen atoms were not available, and a single H_2 molecule supplies only two. Therefore two hydrogen molecules are needed, and a second H_2 model can be placed with the reactants on the bench. Now your class can see that the number of hydrogen atoms and of oxygen atoms is the same in reactants as in products. No atoms have been lost or created. The equation is therefore complete, or, as is often said, "balanced." Literally, an equation implies an equality, and if inequality exists there is no equation. For this reason it seems preferable to speak of "completing" rather than of "balancing" chemical equations.

In a similar manner, you can illustrate by models any chemical reactions for which you have models available. The following are by way of suggestion:

1) $H_2 + O_2 \rightarrow H_2O$
2) $H_2 + Cl_2 \rightarrow HCl$
3) $NaOH\ (Na^+ + OH^-) + CH_3COOH \rightarrow H_2O + CH_3COONa$ $(CH_3COO^- + Na^+)$
4) $H_2O \rightarrow H_3O^+ + OH^-$
5) $CH_4 + Cl_2 \rightarrow CCl_4 + HCl$
6) $CH_4 + O_2 \rightarrow CO_2 + H_2O$
7) $NH_4^+ + OH^- \rightarrow NH_3 + H_2O$
8) $NH_4^+ + H_2O \rightarrow NH_3 + H_3O^+$
9) $HCl + H_2O \rightarrow H_3O^+ + Cl^-$
10) $NH_3 + HCl \rightarrow NH_4Cl\ (NH_4^+ + Cl^-)$

You will, of course, wish to point out the convention of using the simplest formula of substances existing as nonmolecular solids, such as Fe for iron and NaCl for sodium chloride. Also you may wish to point out the inconsistencies of choice of formula for molecular solids, sulfur and white phosphorus normally being indicated merely as S and P although they occur as S_8 and P_4, but iodine being indicated as I_2, its actual molecular formula. You can reassure your students that these exceptions or inconsistencies are not numerous and, in general, the true molecular formula is used for all compounds that are liquids or gaseous under ordinary conditions.

OXIDATION-REDUCTION

The concept of "oxidation state" and "oxidation number" has limited usefulness, but it also has serious defects. Molecular models are much needed to show more nearly the true state of affairs. For example, electrons are withdrawn to a greater extent from phosphorus in PF_3 than in PCl_5, yet convention dictates that the oxidation state of phosphorus in the former is only 3 but 5 in the latter. Partial charge representations in models show better the actual condition of the individual combined atoms. The formal oxidation state can ordinarily be deduced from the model by noting the number of electrons involved in the bonding and the direction of the polarity.

In general, electronegativity serves as an active force in chemical reaction, in that the higher the electronegativity, the more strongly the atom attracts electrons of other atoms and therefore the stronger an oxidizing agent it is. Now, even though a highly electronegative atom has formed as many bonds as it is capable of, unless it has acquired substantial negative charge in the process, it has not lost its potential oxidizing power. The compound, or the electronegative atom in the compound, is therefore an oxidizing agent. It is a general principle that *a highly electronegative atom will tend to leave its combination with other atoms from which it has not acquired much charge, in order to join with other atoms that can give up electrons to it more easily*. This point, which accounts for most displacement and double decomposition (metathetical) reactions, will be illustrated in detail in later chapters, but here it should be noted that any model in which an initially highly electronegative atom is only yellow-green to green is at least potentially an oxidizing agent, and will tend to oxidize any element from which it can acquire higher negative charge. As the negative charge on the combined electronegative atom increases, the potential oxidizing power of the compound decreases, to the point that with color blue-green or blue, for the initially highly electronegative atom, oxidizing power no longer characterizes the compound. At the extreme, a negative ion cannot act as oxidizer.

Similarly, the capacity of any atom to act as a reducing agent improves as its negative charge is higher. Consequently, the ease of oxidation of a compound tends to be higher if its initially more electronegative atoms are more negative. At the extreme, a negative ion is a better reducing agent than the same atom with any lesser degree of negative charge.

DONOR-ACCEPTOR ACTION

Donor-acceptor, or more general base-acid reactions, are closely related to reducing-oxidizing ("redox") reactions. In general, no atom can act as an electron donor unless unshared electron pairs are available to donate and for a given element this availability tends to improve with increasing positive charge. Other factors contribute and may even dominate, but a good rule of thumb is that if other factors are equal or negligible, a given element will be a better donor the higher its partial negative charge. With positive charge, as on the nitrogen in NF_3, donor ability is nearly or completely lost.

Similarly, acceptor activity always requires available orbitals, but orbitals tend to become more available with higher positive charge. This apparently holds not merely for obviously available *s* and *p* orbitals, but also for outer *d* orbitals.

Examples of models illustrating these principles will be discussed in detail in later chapters.

THERMAL STABILITY

Several factors determine the forces bonding atoms together. In general, thermal stability, or bond strength, appears to increase with increasing bond polarity. One can therefore predict from the models, in a very approximate manner, which compounds are likely to be most stable thermally and which to decompose easily when heated. Heats of formation are of course closely related to thermal stability, being generally higher per equivalent, the more polar the bond and the greater the thermal stability. In any series of binary compounds of the same two elements, in which one exhibits different oxidation states, the heat of formation per equivalent is always higher for the lower positive oxidation state and diminishes with increasing positive oxidation state of the central atom. In a series of chlorides of the same element, for example, the models will show more yellow in the blue, the higher the oxidation state of the other element, corresponding to lower polarity and lower bond energy.

One can also observe a relationship between bond strength and relative sizes of the atoms, or principal quantum levels of the valence shells. Two trends are evident: (1) small atoms form stronger bonds with one another than do larger atoms; (2) atoms similar in size form stronger bonds with one another than atoms not similar in size. Here the models are helpful also in predicting the relative stabilities of different bonds.

Further, multiple bonds are stronger than single bonds, and since multiple bonds can easily be distinguished in the models, here is another factor to be considered in estimating the probable stability of a compound.

CHAPTER

5

WATER AND ITS IONS

Perhaps no more important examples of the wide usefulness of the new molecular and ionic models can be discussed than those of water and its ions (Fig. C-3).

PREDICTING WATER FROM ATOMIC MODELS

You may usefully begin with atomic models of oxygen and hydrogen. Your students will be able to predict the interaction of hydrogen and oxygen atoms very easily and accurately from these models. They will see at once that each hydrogen atom can form but one covalent bond, and that each oxygen atom can form two. The combination of hydrogen with oxygen in a 2:1 atomic ratio to form molecules of H_2O is thus instantly predictable. (Your more alert students will also predict hydrogen peroxide and speculate about long oxygen chains terminated at both ends by hydrogen.)

From the oxygen model your students will also see that the two single bonds will be separated by an angle approximating 109°. Unshared outer electron pairs, as on the oxygen, appear to repel one another more strongly than they do bonding pairs or than bonding pairs repel one another. This would result in some tendency for the two bonding pairs to be forced closer together, although no way of calculating the exact observed angle of 104.5° in water is yet known. The important point is that the dissymmetry of a water molecule is readily predictable from the oxygen model.

In addition, the yellow-green color of the hydrogen model and the blue-green color of the oxygen model show the latter to be substantially more electronegative. From this your students can predict at once that the bonds must be polar, with oxygen becoming partially negative at the expense of the hydrogens. This combination of bond polarity with structural dissymmetry of the molecule should lead, it should be observed, to a net polarity of the molecule, giving it a dipole moment, or tendency to become oriented by an electrical field. The loss of electronic control by the hydrogen, corresponding to partial positive charge, should result in some contraction of the remaining electronic sphere. Similarly, the acquisition of partial negative charge by the oxygen should cause some expansion of its sphere. In the water molecule, then, one could predict that the hydrogen would be a little smaller, and the oxygen a little larger, than in the atomic models.

Students can also note that two pairs of unshared electrons on each oxygen, together with the partial negative charge, should help the water molecule to act as an electron donor. They can infer from the predicted partial positive charge on hydrogen that water might lose a proton relatively easily. And, if they know anything about protonic bridging (hydrogen bonding), they can even recognize the possibility that such bridging might occur between water molecules.

All this, and even more, just from the atomic models!

After you have succeeded in extracting most of these predictions from your students, you can then proceed with great effectiveness to produce for the first time a model of a water molecule. Their predictions are verified in startling detail and accuracy. The molecule contains two hydrogen atoms attached to an oxygen atom just as they said, with a bond angle close to that they predicted. The predicted negative charge on the oxygen is shown by the green color and by the slightly larger radius. Similarly, the slight contraction of the hydrogen atoms together with their orange color confirm their partial positive charge. Inclusion of the two unshared electron pairs on the oxygen in the water model ensures that the students will not overlook its potential ability as donor or ligand.

Such a demonstration is the more remarkable when you realize that your students could easily have predicted a molecule exactly like a water molecule even if the atomic models had not been identified! For example, they would not have needed to be distracted by thoughts such as, "This is hydrogen—what can I remember about how hydrogen is supposed to react?" Instead, they could concentrate on the qualities of the atom as represented by the model. It is not necessary to identify the atom as hydrogen to recognize that it can form one and only one covalent bond, and no coordinate covalent bonds, and that its electronegativity is intermediate. And, similarly for the oxygen model.

Such an example is only one of thousands that might have been chosen. The power of atomic models as a teaching aid must be keenly felt when one realizes that seeing only two anonymous atomic models, any student having a simple knowledge of their meaning could specify accurately a reasonable formula *and* molecular structure *and* bond polarity of a chemical compound to be formed from these two unidentified elements. As will be demonstrated later, with knowledge of a few more principles, your students solely from inspection of the atomic models could also make reasonable guesses regarding the physical state and properties of the compound and predict its chemical behavior. This, I think you will agree, is coming pretty close to achieving an *understanding* of chemistry.

PHYSICAL PROPERTIES OF WATER

Protonic Bridging

Let us now consider the water model. It shows at once why water molecules are polar. It shows also the possibilities of "protonic bridging" —as I believe most "hydrogen bonding" should be termed. The association of water molecules is therefore easily understood, and with it, the relatively high melting and boiling points. Here a model of ice is useful (Fig. C-4). If your students know that protonic bridges are linear, then the ice structure can easily be predicted, for each water molecule can form four protonic bridges at the corners of a regular tetrahedron around the oxygen. And, although the models show covalent rather than the larger van der Waals radii, one can see from the ice model that the regularity of its structure prevents closest possible packing of the molecules. Here, then, is a clear and reasonable explanation of the highly important fact that when water crystallizes at 0° and one atmosphere, it expands. There is obviously more empty space within the ice lattice than would be likely in a more random although still quite structured body of liquid water.

The disruption of this orderly protonic bridging in ice does not require breaking all bridges, of course, for many persist, or are broken and remade continuously, up to the boiling temperature. Nevertheless, it does require breaking enough bridges that a relatively large amount of energy must be absorbed. The heat of fusion of ice, as well as its melting point, is therefore relatively high. Much intermolecular attraction remains in the liquid state, giving to water its viscosity and high surface tension. The process of vaporization requires not just the breaking down of some of the structure, but the separation of the individual molecules one from another. This requires still more energy, and whereas the heat of fusion of ice is about 79 calories per gram, the heat of vaporization at the boiling temperature is 540 calories per gram. The boiling point, 100°, is thus also relatively high.

Self-Ionization

The model of the water molecule should show the two pairs of outermost electrons on the oxygen atom that are not involved in the bonding to hydrogen. The presence of these pairs, together with the fact that the oxygen bears a partial negative charge, make it easy to understand why water through oxygen can act as an electron donor. To a limited extent, you can point out water is so acting when it forms protonic bridges, for it is these extra pairs of electrons on oxygen that attract the positively charged hydrogen atoms of other water molecules. But normally the positively charged hydrogen cannot actually accept a pair of electrons from the oxygen of a second water molecule because its one and only orbital is already involved in the bond to its own oxygen. However, you can demonstrate by holding up two models of water molecules that they can be joined by a protonic bridge. Then you can point out that although these stationary models represent the correct relative internuclear distances for the average positions of the atoms, in reality these atoms are oscillating about these positions and two bonded atoms are now closer together, now farther apart. You can also point out that the kinetic activity of the molecules in liquid water causes the protonic bridges to be continuously broken and remade, the individual molecules constantly changing partners. Most commonly, when a protonic bridge breaks, the bridging proton remains with its original oxygen, because it is normally closer to that oxygen and held much more strongly by it. However, every now and then, owing to special combinations of circumstances which we can only imagine, the protonic bridge breaks in such a way that the proton remains on the wrong oxygen atom—one which already has two hydrogens of its own. When this happens, the water molecule gaining the extra proton becomes a hydrated proton, or "hydronium ion," H_3O^+, and the water molecule that lost this proton is left as a hydroxide ion, OH^-. Here it is helpful to produce models of both these ions and illustrate with all the models the following equation:

$$H_2O + H_2O \rightleftharpoons H_3O^+ + OH^-$$

You will want to explain that this is undoubtedly a simplified version of what really happens because within the liquid water protonic bridges are constantly forming, breaking, and reforming, and all the species represented by the models are in a dynamic sort of way attached to other water molecules.

The students should be impressed with the great changes that occur in the hydrogen and oxygen atoms, as represented by the models, when this formation of ions takes place. The proton that leaves a water molecule leaves behind it the electron that it once had when it was a hydrogen atom. If we make the reasonable assumption that this electron becomes distributed between the remaining oxygen and hydrogen atoms in proportion to their relative electronegativities, the oxygen must become quite negative, much more so than in water, and therefore expand, and become a much superior electron donor. Even the hydrogen atom benefits by this extra electron, acquiring partial negative charge itself. The model of the hydroxide ion therefore shows the atoms both to be larger than in the atomic models, with the oxygen now blue and the hydrogen blue-green. These are very significant changes, but hardly imaginable from the stark formulas as usually written on the blackboard or on the printed page. Similarly, the proton that joins a new water molecule, forming the hydronium ion, has a high attraction for electrons, and pulls charge from the oxygen, which in turn takes more than it previously had, from the other hydrogens. If, again, we make the reasonable assumption that the valence electrons distribute themselves over the four atoms in proportion to their relative electronegativities, we find that all three hydrogens are now alike, smaller, and much more positive than they were in water, before the extra proton was acquired. Likewise, the oxygen atom is smaller and much less negative than it was.

These changes must certainly affect the properties of the combined atoms. In general, there will be many occasions to observe that an atom that is initially very electronegative is an oxidizing agent and loses oxidizing power only to the extent that it is successful in withdrawing electrons from other atoms in the compound. But when it has succeeded in becoming quite negative, then its residual oxidizing power is negligible. If it holds extra pairs of electrons, these in general become more available to other atoms as the negative charge on the donor atom increases. Applying these principles to the hydronium ion, we may observe that it must no longer be an effective electron donor, as is water, but will be mainly an oxidizing agent, since the oxygen in it has not succeeded in acquiring much charge. We may of course also observe that the hydrogen, being much more positive, might more easily separate as a proton if some other electron donor should make available to it a pair of electrons. Looking at the hydroxide ion model, we can observe that here the oxygen must be an excellent electron donor, much better than water, and not an oxidizing agent at all. Furthermore, the hydrogen, no longer being positive, can no longer form protonic bridges or be tempted, figuratively speaking, to seek an electron pair elsewhere.

Now, if these are the properties of the hydronium and hydroxide ions, what must occur when they come together? Immediately the hydroxide oxygen must donate a pair of electrons to one of the protons from the hydronium ion. What happens? Two water molecules are formed:

$$H_3O^+ + OH^- \rightleftharpoons H_2O + H_2O$$

For when a hydronium ion comes in contact with a hydroxide ion, one may helpfully picture the competition between two electron donors for a proton. One donor is a water molecule. The other is a hydroxide ion. The fact that the water molecule already has possession of this proton makes no difference; when contact has been made, the competition is even. Now, if at this point you direct the attention of your students to the oxygen atoms involved, they will see that the oxygen on water cannot be nearly as good an electron donor as the oxygen on hydroxide ion, simply because it does not have nearly as high a negative charge. Consequently, when both species, the water molecule and the hydroxide ion, are given equal opportunity to take on a proton, the outcome is unquestionable—the hyroxide ion wins. Therefore it readily removes the extra proton from the water molecule, destroying the hydronium ion, liberating that water molecule and forming another water molecule.

Then how is it possible to build up, within a body of water, appreciable concentrations of hydronium and hydroxide ions? Why, immediately after the accidental rupture of the protonic bridge on the wrong side, do not the two ions thus formed react with one another to reform the original two molecules of water? Again, we can only imagine, but it is easy to picture ways in which these ions could become separated from one another at almost the instant of their formation, thus preventing reaction until they chanced to meet later. One way, of course, is by molecular collision. If either ion should be struck by a moving water molecule just at the moment of formation, it might be knocked out of reach of the other ion. Another way, as effective or more so, would be through protonic bridging with the other molecules. Consider first the hydroxide ion. Among water molecules a hydroxide ion is really among other hydroxide ions, which, however, happen already to have acquired an extra proton each. A proton is no more stable on one water molecule than on another, and thus easy transfer can be imagined. Thus, at almost the same instant that a hydroxide ion is formed by loss of a proton to a neighbor, it may acquire, on the other side, a proton from another water molecule that happens to be bridged to it at the time of ion formation. In turn, this new hydroxide ion may acquire a proton from still another water molecule. In effect, through a swapping of protons, the hydroxide ion is moving rapidly away from the scene of its formation, even though the same oxygen which lost the proton is still right there in the immediate vicinity of the hydronium ion.

We may imagine a similar situation around the hydronium ion. A hydronium ion is simply a water molecule which happens to have an extra proton. An extra proton is just as stably held by one water molecule as by another, so if at the moment of formation of a hydronium ion, another water molecule happens to be bridged at the far side, it may take on a proton, leaving the hydronium ion originally formed almost immediately converted to water again. The proton may thus jump from one water molecule to another throughout the liquid, and in effect this is exactly the same as if the original hydronium ion were doing the travelling, which it is not. In summary, even though hydroxide ions and hydronium ions react instantly on contact, such contact may easily be postponed by migration, real or in effect, of either or both ions from the scene of their formation.

Within a relatively large volume of liquid water, one lone hydronium ion and one lone hydroxide ion might travel around at random for a long time before they happened to collide with one another. Before this occurs, other hydronium ions and hydroxide ions might be formed in a similar way. Then, as the concentration of these ions increases within the liquid, the probability of their meeting one of opposite sign increases. Soon a concentration is reached such that the rate of meeting exactly equals the rate of formation. Meeting always results in destruction of the ions, but if they are being formed at the same rate, the net result is a constant concentration. This equilibrium concentration, at room temperature, is in pure water about 10^{-7} mole per liter, for each ion, since one of each is formed simultaneously. The product of these concentrations, called the "ion product" of water, is 10^{-14}. For each pair of ions, then, there are about 550 million undissociated water molecules.

AQUEOUS ACIDS AND BASES

The concept of aqueous acids and bases can now be explained readily, with the help of models of water and its ions. An acidic solution is simply a solution in which the concentration of hydronium ion is greater than in pure water. A basic solution is one in which the concentration of hydroxide ion is greater than in pure water.

You may explain the importance of the constancy of the water ion-product by discussing the effect of dissolving a substance in water that increases the hydronium or hydroxide concentration. Hydrogen chloride exemplifies the former. A molecular model of it shows a polar covalent molecule. The reaction of hydrogen chloride with water can be demonstrated by models:

$$HCl + H_2O \rightleftharpoons H_3O^+ + Cl^-$$

If hydrogen chloride is dissolved in water, a competition is set up between chloride ions and water molecules as electron donors to the protons. The fact that the protons are initially already attached to the chloride ions in the HCl molecules makes little difference. The great numerical excess of H_2O molecules ensures that the reaction will go mainly to the right, the water stealing protons from the chloride ions. As this excess of water is diminished, then the chloride ions more readily recover the protons and molecular HCl, as from a solution of concentrated hydrochloric acid, is evolved.

Dissolution of hydrogen chloride in water thus leads to a concentration of H_3O^+ ions higher than 10^{-7} mole per liter. What effect can this have on the hydroxide ion concentration? Certainly, the probability of encounters between H_3O^+ ions and OH^- ions is greatly enhanced by increasing the concentration of H_3O^+ ions. Therefore the rate of recombination must be increased. If the concentration of OH^- ions originally was partly the result of the rate at which these ions are formed, and if this rate remains constant, then the concentration of hydroxide ions must be reduced by addition of hydronium ions because they are now destroyed *faster* than they are formed. However, the rate of destruction must diminish as hydroxide ions become increasingly more dilute, because the probability of encounters with hydronium ion is diminished. Hence, a new equilibrium is reached where the rate of recombination of hydronium and hydroxide ions still equals the rate of their formation but the concentration of hydroxide ions at which this is true is much smaller. In fact, the probability of opposite ion encounter is the same whether $H_3O^+ = OH^-$, or H_3O^+ is 10^{-2} and OH^- is 10^{-12}, or H_3O^+ is 10^{-12} and OH^- is 10^{-2}. Hence the condition for the rates of dissociation and reforming of water must be that the ion product *constant* is 10^{-14}.

Similarly, if NaOH is added to water, its ions become separated and the concentration of hydroxide ions therefore becomes higher than 10^{-7} mole per liter. This enhances the probability that an encounter between the hydronium ion and the hydroxide ion will occur, but thus reduces quickly the concentration of hydronium ion to a value much lower than 10^{-7}. Again a new equilibrium is reached, at which the ion-product is 10^{-14}.

Obviously any attempt to increase the concentration of both hydronium and hydroxide ions in an aqueous solution must result in combination of these ions to form water until the ion product is again 10^{-14}. This is *neutralization.* It is the fundamental reaction when any aqueous acid and aqueous base react.. The common definition of neutralization as a reaction between acid and base to form a salt plus water is correct in water only because the cation from the base and the anion from the acid are left in solution after neutralization has occurred, and evaporation of the solution could result in combination of these oppositely charged ions to form a salt.

Acid and Base Strength

When your students understand the ionization of acids and bases as actually being competitive chemical rather than physical reactions, they will then come to understand the differences in acid and base strength. The ionization of acids, you can point out, involves competition between water and an anion as electron donors for protons. This has already been illustrated by the HCl-H_2O reaction described above. Other examples are:

$$H_2SO_4 + H_2O \rightleftharpoons H_3O^+ + HSO_4^-$$
$$HClO_4 + H_2O \rightleftharpoons H_3O^+ + ClO_4^-$$
$$HCN + H_2O \rightleftharpoons H_3O^+ + CN^-$$
$$HAc + H_2O \rightleftharpoons H_3O^+ + Ac^-$$
$$HNO_3 + H_2O \rightleftharpoons H_3O^+ + NO_3^-$$
$$H_2CO_3 + H_2O \rightleftharpoons H_3O^+ + HCO_3^-$$
$$HCO_3^- + H_2O \rightleftharpoons H_3O^+ + CO_3^=$$
$$HPO_4^= + H_2O \rightleftharpoons H_3O^+ + PO_4^\equiv$$
$$HI + H_2O \rightleftharpoons H_3O^+ + I^-$$

If, under the prevailing conditions, which nearly always include a large numerical excess of water molecules, water is completely successful in removing protons from the anions, the acid is strong. Incomplete removal means that the anions are more nearly competitive with water as electron donors to the proton. The acids are then weaker, and the better their anions function as electron donors to protons.

Unfortunately, no general and simple explanation can be given as to *why* certain anions are better donors than others. For example, one might not easily predict that an iodide ion would be so much poorer an electron donor to a proton than is a cyanide ion, although, of course, the experimental facts are that HI is a strong acid and HCN a very weak one. In such instances, models can suggest little of help. One can, however, point out that with increasing size of the donor atom, concentration of an electron pair so as to be easily available to a proton becomes, evidently, increasingly difficult. This may, indeed, help to explain why bonds between very small and very large atoms tend to be weak. Unless an electron pair can be concentrated within the sphere of influence of a proton, a proton can be acquired only weakly. The hydrogen halides as a group appear to illustrate this, in that HF is a weak acid, and HCl, HBr, and HI, although all strong, increase in strength in that order, corresponding to larger anions and weaker electron donation to protons.

Among oxyanions, however, the controlling factors are not quite as diverse. In a rough, qualitative way one can recognize the applicability of the principle that the higher the negative charge on an atom, the better donor it can be. Thus in all oxyanions the donor is oxygen, and the partial charge on oxygen roughly is inversely related to the acid strength. You can demonstrate this very well with oxyanion models, for example, of nitrate, perchlorate, carbonate, and phosphate ions. In the first two, the green color of the oxygen shows it to be negative but not more so than in water. In the second two, the oxygen is blue-green or blue, showing much higher negative charge. HCO_3^- ion and $HPO_4^=$ ion are extremely weak acids consequently, whereas HNO_3 and $HClO_4$, especially the latter, are very strong acids.

Hydroxides not only vary from strongly to weakly basic, but even to strong acids, for even perchloric acid, $HOClO_3$, is a hydroxy compound. The question of why this range in properties occurs can find partial answer in models. One can make models of hypothetical molecules of such compounds as $Ca(OH)_2$ and $Zn(OH)_2$, even though such molecules have no individual existence. A comparison of these models with one of H_2SO_4 (actually, $O_2S(OH)_2$) (Fig. C-5) provides a fair basis for explaining the differences in terms of bond polarity. In the $Ca(OH)_2$ model, the Ca—O bonds are seen to be highly polar, and one can imagine a separation of hydroxide ions to occur readily. On the other hand, the H—O bond is not very polar, and the hydrogen is even partially negative. No reasonable likelihood of proton separation is apparent. The basic, nonacidic properties are thus visualizable and logical.

In the model of $Zn(OH)_2$, the Zn—O bonds are seen to be quite polar but not nearly as polar as in $Ca(OH)_2$. Separation of hydroxide ions therefore cannot occur so readily, although it can to some extent. Here, the hydrogen is no longer negative, but bears substantial positive charge. One can visualize a proton separation as being possible, although not too readily. Thus the amphoteric nature of the compound is shown, even though the mode of action is oversimplified.

The model of H_2SO_4 shows the polarity of S—OH bonds to be so low that separation of hydroxide ions would seem highly unlikely. On the other hand, the O—H bonds are here seen to be very polar, and separation of protons, or acid ionization, seems logical and understandable. Sulfuric acid is a strong acid and has no basic properties.

Hydrolysis of Salts

You may wish to point out, that not only can the balance of ions in pure water be upset by addition of hydronium or hydroxide ions or hydrogen compounds or hydroxyl compounds that furnish these ions, but also the concentration of one or the other of the ions already present in pure water can be reduced by reaction with some added substance that does not directly contribute either hydronium or hydroxide ions. In other words, hydrolysis of neutral compounds can produce acidic or basic solutions.

The preceding discussion suggests how basic solutions can result from oxyanions. For example, a model of the carbonate ion was suggested to illustrate the strong donor properties of its oxygen which cause bicarbonate ion to be a very weak acid. If a carbonate ion can compete successfully against water for a proton, perhaps it can remove protons from hydronium ions already present in water, or even from water itself:

$$CO_3^{=} + H_3O^+ \rightleftharpoons HCO_3^- + H_2O$$
$$CO_3^{=} + H_2O \rightleftharpoons HCO_3^- + OH^-$$

Since the hydronium ion of the first equation came from the water itself, its destruction must leave an excess of hydroxide ions in the solution. Thus, by either or both reactions, the solution is made alkaline.

Even if the anion is not an oxyanion, if it is the anion of a weak acid, it will hydrolyze in water producing an excess of hydroxide ions:

$$CN^- + H_2O \rightleftharpoons HCN + OH^-$$

In a similar manner, any cation that when combined with hydroxide ion gives a weak base will tend to combine with hydroxide ions from water, thus leaving an excess of hydronium ions:

$$Zn^{++} + 2\ H_2O \rightleftharpoons Zn(OH)^+ + H_3O^+$$
$$NH_4^+ + 2\ H_2O \rightleftharpoons (NH_4OH) + H_3O^+$$

The acidity of certain metal ion solutions can be explained with the help of a model of a hydrated zinc or aluminum ion, $[Zn(H_2O)_4]^{++}$ or $[Al(H_2O)_6]^{+++}$. If equalization of electronegativity throughout these ions is assumed, then these models show the hydrogen in the coordinated water to be more positive than in free water and the oxygen to be less negative. Some transfer of protons to the free water is therefore expected, since we know that it occurs even from free water to free water:

$$[Al(H_2O)_6]^{+++} + H_2O \rightleftharpoons H_3O^+ + [Al(H_2O)_5OH]^{++}$$

You may point out that aiding this reaction is the fact that oxygen in hydroxide ion is a much better donor than oxygen in water and would coordinate more stably to the aluminum.

In conjunction with considering the hydrolysis of ammonium ion, you may wish to expand on the subject of ammonia. You can point out on a model of ammonia the presence of an unshared pair of electrons on the nitrogen. The fact that ammonia is in general a better donor than water is not apparent in the molecular models. The atomic models, however, show nitrogen to be less electronegative than oxygen. Other factors, such as negative charge, being nearly equal, combined nitrogen would be expected to be, therefore, a better donor than combined oxygen. Once this is established, it explains the fact that in water ammonia is basic:

$$NH_3 + H_2O \rightleftharpoons NH_4^+ + OH^-$$

The fact that the reverse reaction occurs to an appreciable extent accounts for two phenomena. One is the hydrolysis of ammonium ion to yield slightly acidic solutions. The other is the destruction of ammonium ion by hydroxide ion, with liberation of ammonia. Showing the model of hydroxide ion, you can point out that it is a far stronger donor than ammonia and thus easily takes protons away from ammonium ions.

WATER AS AN ELECTRON DONOR: HYDRATES

The ability of water to act as donor to a proton is also applicable to any acceptor, of which the most numerous and important are cations. A model of an inert-type cation, with its four outer orbitals vacant, can be helpful here along with a water molecule model. You can point out that in principle all cations will attract the negative end of the water dipole and have vacant orbitals that might accommodate an electron pair of the water oxygen. The attraction is expected to be least strong where the cations are alkali metal, for these have least electronegativity, but even here, as will be discussed below, loose hydration occurs in solution. With cations of higher charge or higher electronegativity, definite hydrates may form, the water becoming coordinated in a sphere of usually either four or six molecules around the cation. Again, models of the hydrated zinc and aluminum ions (Fig. C-13) will suggest the nature of such hydrates.

WATER AS A SOLVENT

Models of at least three types of compounds, besides water, should be helpful in explaining something about solubility. Unfortunately, full explanations are not yet known. I would suggest a nonpolar compound such as carbon tetrachloride or a hydrocarbon, a hydroxy compound such as ethyl alcohol or sucrose, and a salt such as sodium chloride.

In order for two liquids and/or solids to mix molecularly (to form a solution), the component particles of each must become separated to make room for particles of the other. The fact that they exist initially as solid or liquid proves that substantial forces must be overcome to separate these component particles. Consequently, no separation and thus no solution can result unless some new force compensates for the old.

For example, water molecules are held together in the liquid by protonic bridging. Very little of other substances can penetrate unless they have the means to compensate for the resulting reduction in bridging. A hydrocarbon, or carbon tetrachloride, is held together by weaker van der Waals forces and can be penetrated relatively easily. However, if water and the hydrocarbon are placed in contact, water molecules cannot separate from the water layer to penetrate among the hydrocarbon molecules because the latter have very little attraction for them and the protonic bridging would need breaking. Hydrocarbon molecules, for their part, might be able to break loose from one another relatively easily, but they have no attraction for water molecules, comparable to protonic bridging. They could not penetrate the water layer without breaking this bridging. The two liquids therefore are immiscible.

Two ways of joining water to another compound exist. One is through protonic bridging, the other, by coordination bond formation and/or dipole-ion attraction. A model of sucrose (Fig. C-15) admirably illustrates the first. In it the hydroxyl groups closely resemble those in water. The molecules of the sugar crystal are probably held together by protonic bridging, but they could evidently form bridges to water molecules just as easily. Likewise, water molecules could as easily become bridged to sugar molecules as to one another. Naturally, water and sugar molecules mix easily with one another, and sugar is very soluble.

A crystal model of NaCl (Fig. C-12) is better, but models of the individual ions would be better than none, to illustrate the dissolving of an ionic compound. The cations will attract the oxygen end of the water dipole and the anions, the hydrogen end. The energy of solvation of these ions is enough to break down the crystal lattice, and the salt becomes dispersed, to a certain limit, through the water in the form of its ions. By holding the water model properly oriented to the ions of the crystal, you can help the class visualize the nature of occurrences that result in solution when the salt and solvent come in contact.

Other properties of water, such as the hydrolytic decomposition of certain hydrides and halides, will be discussed in later chapters.

CHAPTER

6

OXIDES

The full significance of water chemistry cannot be found in brief treatments such as that of the preceding chapter, but only when the proper place of water among all the oxides in the periodic table is understood. For hydrogen is just a little above the median in electronegativity, and oxygen highest of all but fluorine. Thus, hydrogen oxide (water) must stand near the middle of the oxides when they are grouped in order of increasing electronegativity of the second element.

PHYSICAL STATES AND PROPERTIES

You may find it useful to introduce this subject by first considering carefully the nature of the oxygen atom with respect to atoms of the other elements. This will give your students additional practice in reasoning from cause to effect and additional insight into the reasonableness of properties as a consequence of structure.

The water model has been discussed in detail in the preceding chapter. Similar treatment of other binary compounds of oxygen can also be useful.

Beginning with lithium oxide, if you show the lithium atomic model and the oxygen atomic model, your students will be struck at once by the great contrast in appearance. The large lithium atom, with only three electrons, is remarkably larger than the much more compact oxygen atom with eight electrons. As previously pointed out, this difference in compactness is closely associated with the difference in the ability of these two atoms to attract electrons. The very low electronegativity of lithium is represented by the red color and the high electronegativity of oxygen by its greenish-blue color. From the outer electronic configurations of the two, your students can see that one oxygen atom can unite with two lithium atoms, establishing the formula as Li_2O. The high polarity which would be predicted from the models suggests that this substance should not exist as separate molecules, but must be highly condensed in crystalline form. You may not wish to try to provide crystal models of all the solid oxides, but you will find it helpful to have type models and also "atom-pair" models. The latter consist simply of two atomic spheres, in this case, one of lithium and one of oxygen (Fig. C-7), showing by relative size and color the calculated covalent radii and partial charge in Li_2O. These spheres are attached not in contact but through a bar of some kind—a wooden stick for the larger models, a piece of pipe cleaner for the smallest scale—indicating that this pair is intended to show only the individual atoms of the compound and not the state of aggregation. It is helpful to represent outer electrons and vacancies on these spheres, in the amount that would be left uninvolved in simple covalence. In the lithium oxide the lithium sphere would have three pairs of black balls appended to the surface to represent three vacant orbitals. The oxygen sphere would have two pairs of white balls attached to represent two electron pairs left over after normal covalence. The presence of both vacant orbitals and otherwise unshared electrons thus serves as a basis for predicting a crystalline aggregate of a highly polar nature, since individual molecules would condense rapidly when possessed of these qualities.

The exact nature of this crystalline aggregate can be described with the help of a model (Fig. B-13) of fluorite, CaF_2. Li_2O has the fluorite structure in reverse—sometimes called the "antifluorite" structure—in which the lithium atoms occupy the positions of the fluorine and the oxygen atoms occupy the positions of the calcium.

The atomic model of beryllium shows that beryllium atoms can form two bonds, and since the oxygen model shows that oxygen also can form two bonds, an empirical formula of BeO can be predicted. The red-orange color of the beryllium shows it to have higher electronegativity than lithium but still relatively low, especially compared with the greenish-blue of oxygen. A highly polar type of bonding is therefore easily predictable. An "atom-pair" model of BeO will serve to verify these predictions, and, by showing two empty orbitals on the beryllium and two pairs of otherwise unshared electrons on the oxygen, suggests very strongly that the state of aggregation will be that of a crystalline solid. A model (Fig. B-11) of wurtzite (ZnS) will serve to illustrate the structure of beryllium oxide crystal, in which each beryllium is surrounded tetrahedrally by four oxygen atoms, and each oxygen by four berylliums. Evidently all four orbitals of the beryllium and all outer electrons of the oxygen are effectively occupied in the crystal bonding.

Boron atoms, as shown by the model, have three outermost electrons and can form three covalent bonds. The formula B_2O_3 is therefore predictable. The state of aggregation is not so evident; however, the presence of a fourth unoccupied orbital on the boron after three single bonds are formed suggests that this orbital might assist in any condensation which might occur. Actually boric oxide appears to consist of a boron-oxygen network, or giant molecule type of crystal. Certainly one could predict considerable polarity in the individual bonds, from the contrast between the yellow-orange of the boron and the greenish-blue of the oxygen (Fig. C-7).

Molecular oxides begin with the next element, carbon. Here the atomic models would suggest that carbon might unite with oxygen to form a giant molecule network of single bonds, each moderately polar, judging from the initial electronegativities. Instead, greater stability appears to result when two double bonds per carbon atom are formed. Carbon dioxide molecules appear to have bonds of essentially this nature. If all the carbon valence electrons are used in the bonding, and only two bonds are formed, then, as previously generalized, these two bonds must be as far apart from one another as possible. This prediction is borne out by the model of carbon dioxide molecule, which is linear, and shows the predicted polarity of bonds and the bond multiplicity (Figs. C-7, C-4).

From the atomic model of nitrogen and that of oxygen, the only directly predictable formula would be N_2O_3. Actually this compound is quite unstable, decomposing to NO and NO_2 very easily. The latter two are not directly predictable from the atomic models, and neither is N_2O, or, for that matter, N_2O_5. The last named seems to exist in the crystalline state as nitronium nitrate, $NO_2^+NO_3^-$, but its easy volatility suggests that the ionic lattice energy must be very low. Your students can, however, predict that in none of these compounds would bond polarity be very great, because nitrogen is too near oxygen in electronegativity. In all, some partial positive charge must be assignable to nitrogen. Models of all the oxides of nitrogen should be instructive, and especially the model of N_2O_5 for comparison with other models in considering the periodic changes in the chemistry of oxygen as described in a later section. The structure of a gaseous molecule of this oxide should be predictable, for if your students assume, probably correctly, that all outermost electrons of each nitrogen are used in the bonding, then the three bonds formed by each nitrogen atom must be in the same plane with the nitrogen nucleus. One oxygen atom must be shared by two nitrogens, which implies two single bonds here at an angle approximating 100°. The bond angle between the two unshared oxygen atoms on each nitrogen must be somewhat greater than the angle between one of them and the shared oxygen atom, because the former bonds have multiplicity. The model of this molecule will show the predictable structure (Fig. C-7).

The combination of fluorine and oxygen can also be predicted by your students quite accurately. They will note that since fluorine in the atomic model has the capacity to form but one covalent bond, and oxygen two, the formula should be F_2O. However, they will also note that here is a situation where oxygen encounters an element more electronegative even than itself. Consequently, they can predict a small polarity with oxygen positive, and fluorine negative, and they can understand that this is not actually an "oxide," but rather, a fluoride, whose formula more conventionally should be written OF_2. The bond angle, a little less than tetrahedral, suggests that the two lone pairs of electrons on the oxygen may repel one another most strongly of the four pairs (counting those used in the bonding), thus forcing the two fluorine bonds a little closer together. The model of this molecule (Fig. C-7) will confirm their predictions.

With sodium again, the capacity to form covalent bonds is one and the electronegativity is very low, as shown by the atomic model. You may be somewhat hard put, then, to explain why when sodium is burned in air or oxygen, the chief product is Na_2O_2 instead of Na_2O. However, you can point out at least that Na_2O is also an oxide of sodium and has the properties of high polarity and condensing to a crystalline aggregate which one could predict from the atomic models. By way of apologizing for nature's seeming incongruity in the normal peroxide formation, you can observe that an electron is lost from a sodium atom with somewhat greater ease than from lithium, and that if each of two oxygen atoms could acquire an electron from a sodium atom without the need of breaking the single bond portion of their bonding, this might happen more easily. Furthermore, the crystal energy of a peroxide so formed of sodium might happen to be considerably greater than of lithium, owing to the larger size of the sodium atoms.

An atomic model of magnesium shows it to be more electronegative than sodium but less so than beryllium, and the prediction of the formula, MgO, is quite straightforward. So, also, is the high polarity of the bonds. An "atom-pair model will show, as in the case of beryllium oxide, two vacant orbitals on the magnesium, and a prediction of condensation is therefore in order. The crystal structure is not the same, however, for with the larger magnesium and greater polarity comes 6:6 instead of 4:4 coordination. In other words, each magnesium is surrounded by six oxygen atoms and each oxygen by six magnesiums instead of each by four as in beryllium oxide. This is the "rock salt" structure typical of the alkali metal halides.

Aluminum, as shown by the atomic model, is more electronegative than magnesium, but still should form quite polar bonds with oxygen. In fact, you may wish to point out that the stability of such bonds contributes notably to the success of the thermite process, in which a less polar oxide such as of iron or chromium has its oxygen "wrenched away" by metallic aluminum, with the evolution of a large amount of energy signifying the greater stability of the new bonds. The formula Al_2O_3 can easily be predicted, and an "atom-pair" model (Fig. C-7) will show the possibility of the fourth orbital of the aluminum becoming involved in condensation to a crystalline lattice. Here a stable network of aluminum and oxygen atoms is formed, in which each aluminum is surrounded by six oxygens and each oxygen is surrounded by four aluminums. This resembles a rock-salt structure in which one third of the six aluminums that should surround each oxygen are missing from the lattice, in symmetrically located positions. (See Fig. B-12.)

The atomic model of silicon will show it to be substantially less electronegative than carbon, and consequently capable of forming more polar bonds to oxygen. This, coupled with the lesser ability of silicon to form ordinary multiple bonds, results in a "giant molecule" type of condensation, instead of single molecules of SiO_2 like those of carbon dioxide.

The phosphorus model shows only four orbitals, one of which contains an electron pair and is therefore unavailable for ordinary covalence. One could then predict the formula P_2O_3 and that the bonds would be somewhat polar, with phosphorus positive. It would not be possible, however, to predict the molecular structure, except to observe that the three bonds formed by a phosphorus atom are directed toward the base of a low pyramid. You can, if you wish, begin with a model of P_4, and point out how oxygen atoms could become attached to the edges of the regular tetrahedron of phosphorus atoms, since the bonds in the latter are compressed into angles of presumably high strain. Instead of each phosphorus atom forming three bonds to other phosphorus atoms, with bond angles only 60°, it can, with the help of oxygen bridging, remain in connection with the other phosphorus atoms yet with more reasonable bond angles more nearly tetrahedral. Oxygen bridges on each edge of the tetrahedron would require six oxygen atoms and a separation of the phosphorus atoms from one another to make room for the oxygens. The model of the molecule, P_4O_6 (Fig. C-7), will show the nature of this combination.

Invisible on the phosphorus atom model, however, are the outer *d* orbitals. These must be considered to explain the fact that P_4O_6 molecules can acquire extra oxygen atoms, one on each corner phosphorus atom. The explanation that these additional oxygens are attached by a coordinate covalent bond, the phosphorus electron pair joining with the vacant orbital available on an oxygen atom, is incorrect, as shown by the experimental observation that the bond is very short, much shorter than expected for a single covalent bond. Utilization of an outer *d* orbital of the phosphorus, on the other hand, could permit double bonding to the oxygen, with resultant bond shortening. A model of P_4O_{10} (Fig. C-7) shows the result, and helps the students see why "P_2O_5" is incorrect.

To explain the common sulfur oxides, too, outer *d* orbitals must be invoked. If any of you can think of a good way to represent these orbitals in an atomic model, please let me know. For the present discussion your students will have to imagine them. As they view the sulfur atomic model, they must keep in mind that each of the two electron pairs left after the expected divalence is shown, may produce further bonding capacity by promotion of one electron out of the pair into an outer *d* orbital. This creates capacity for *two* new bonds at a time. Thus sulfur can form two single bonds or four or six, but not ordinarily three or five.

Sulfur with oxygen then might most directly (assuming no S—S bonds) form SO, SO_2, or SO_3. Early reports of SO appear unconfirmed, and at present it may be regarded as unknown. Efforts to avoid expanding the "valence octet" have led to statements that SO_2 is a "resonance hybrid" of :Ö—S̈=Ö: and :Ö=S̈—Ö:. However, sulfur can certainly "exceed the octet," as in SF_4 for example, and there seems to be no good reason to suppose it does not do so in SO_2. In fact, the bonds are short enough to be double bonds. Similarly, SO_3 seems more reasonably described as having three double bonds, whose length incidentally is the same as in SO_2.

The higher oxides of chlorine likewise require either use of *d* orbitals for double bonding or that the electron pairs of the chlorine be donated to the oxygen. The former seems more reasonable. A model of Cl_2O_7 (Fig. C-7) can be shown as an example of a compound in which, as in SO_3, all outer electrons of a nonmetallic atom are used in bonding by aid of the outer *d* orbitals.

If you now go back over these models representing the oxides and let the students suggest the physical properties that might well result from these structures, you should find them beginning to understand some of the simpler relationships. They will probably be able to predict relatively strong forces among the atoms in the more polar oxides and recognize that such forces will contribute to relatively high melting points and low volatility. They will be able to study those aggregates which present to their neighbors an exterior of electron pairs only, and thus can have mainly van der Waals type attractive interactions. These they should recognize as leading to relatively low melting temperatures and high volatility. They will probably notice then that the physical differences between nonmetal oxides and metal oxides originate very logically with the differences in nature between nonmetal and metal atoms.

ACID-BASE PROPERTIES

One of the most important distinctions between metal oxides and non-metal oxides has been that the former are basic and the latter, acidic. With the help of models, your students can understand what this means and why it should be so.

Let us consider first aqueous systems. Water, as previously discussed and as evident among the models (Fig. C-7), is intermediate among the oxides in the charge on oxygen, and it can act as electron donor through the unshared electron pairs on the oxygen. It can also act as electron acceptor, through losing a proton to some donor. Water is thus amphoteric. Oxides having more negative oxygen than water can take a proton from water, leaving the hydroxide ion, which is now a better donor and can add to the oxide.

For example, the oxygen in CaO is more negative than the oxygen in water (show the models), permitting a proton to be drawn from the water. The hydroxide ion then donates an electron pair to the positive calcium:

$$CaO + H_2O \rightarrow CaOH^+ + OH^-$$
$$CaOH^+ + OH^- \rightarrow Ca(OH)_2$$

We call this particular product "calcium hydroxide," but it is only one of a class of complex oxides. In such oxides combination of an oxide of a less electronegative element with an oxide of a more electronegative element results in a complex with the more electronegative element now part of the anion, the less electronegative element the cation. Here hydrogen is the more electronegative and becomes part of the complex anion, OH^-.

Water is also the oxide of a less electronegative element compared to most of the nonmetals. In combination with the oxide of an element more electronegative than hydrogen, water oxygen acts as donor, adding to the other element, again forming a complex oxide, but here the hydrogen is the cationic portion, and the other element is in the anion. For example:

$$H_2O + SO_3 \rightarrow H_2SO_4$$

Now, when water has already lost a proton to an oxide, forming a hydroxide, it is unlikely to be very able to take the proton back again. This would be required of water if the hydroxide were to have acidic properties in aqueous solution. On the other hand, if the hydroxide could coordinate hydroxide ions from water, this would have the effect of leaving behind hydronium ions and thus giving acidity to the solution.

Thus oxides of elements less electronegative than hydrogen can at most be slightly acidic in their aqueous reaction. However, if the element is much less electronegative than hydrogen, its electrons must be largely removed by the OH oxygen, making the bonds very polar and the separation of OH^- ions easy. These hydroxides are therefore basic, and the more so, the more polar the E—OH bonds.

But when water acts as electron donor, its oxygen loses some of the electrons it did control to the element that is more electronegative than hydrogen. Consequently the oxygen becomes more electronegative than it was in water, and withdraws more charge from the hydrogen than it did in water. The H—O bond is more polar, and it becomes easier for other water molecules to remove a proton than when the proton was part of water. In other words, the complex oxide is acidic in water solution. And since, as you can easily demonstrate in the models of the free acids such as HNO_3 and H_2SO_4, the bond between oxygen and the other element is less polar than in water, the chance of separation of a hydroxide ion diminishes to practically zero.

The chief reason for the importance of the position of water in the oxide system, however, is that it is liquid and a common solvent. Fundamentally, there is no difference between complex oxides formed by water and those formed by non-hydrogen oxides. For in general oxygen of higher negative charge can act as donor to oxides in which the oxygen has lower negative charge, forming complexes with the more electronegative other element centered in the complex anion and the less electronegative other element cationic. In these terms basic hydroxides, oxyacids, and oxysalts differ mainly in nomenclature. For example, ZnO, which forms an amphoteric hydroxide in water, is amphoteric on its own account:

$$ZnO + SO_3 \rightarrow ZnSO_4$$
$$ZnO + Na_2O \rightarrow Na_2ZnO_2$$

Highly polar oxides can react with slightly polar oxides in only one way:

$$CaO + SO_3 \rightarrow CaSO_4$$

From the models your students can easily predict the nature of the reaction between metal oxide and nonmetal oxide to form salts. They will then find it easy to understand why the more oxygens that compete for the same electrons, the less negative charge each can acquire and therefore the less basic and the more acidic the oxide is. Models of SO_2 and SO_3 unfortunately will not show this well because the charge on oxygen does not differ sufficiently to show on the color scale. However, a comparison of CrO and CrO_3, for example, will illustrate this trend.

The stability of the complex oxides appears to depend largely on the extent to which the anion can control the bonding electrons without being distorted. If the proton with its high electronegativity and high polarizing power is the cationic part of the salt, it is likely to be relatively unstable. This is shown by the common phenomenon of free acids decomposing more readily than many of their salts, some, like carbonic acid, even being unknown in isolated form. With a model of a hydrated cation you can demonstrate how the anion is protected by the hydration from the charge and polarizing power of the cation. This explains why hydrated salts of oxyanions are more plentiful than the anhydrous salts.

The structure of a typical complex oxide can profitably be shown, because the concept of alternating cations and anions leads to misunderstanding of the real situation. If, for example, you have a crystal model of $CaCO_3$ (Fig. C-8), you can point out that actually each Ca is surrounded by six oxygen atoms, and each oxygen is attached to two calciums as well as to a carbon.

OXIDIZING PROPERTIES

The oxygen in any oxide can be caused to unite under the right conditions with a reducing agent such as hydrogen, but this does not mean that the oxide is necessarily classified as an oxidizing agent. Under ordinary conditions if the combined oxygen has a reasonably high negative charge, the oxide is not an oxidizing agent. As the negative charge diminishes, however, the oxidizing powers increase. All oxides in which the oxygen is not highly negative are therefore at least potentially oxidizing agents. Study of the models will disclose which compounds these are. Compounds like Cl_2O_7, in which the oxygen has scarcely any negative charge (Fig. C-7), are naturally stronger oxidizing agents than oxides like carbon dioxide, but the yellowish-green color of the oxygen even here (Fig. C-7) will suggest that carbon dioxide is potentially an oxidizing agent. Indeed, its use to extinguish fires is quite in contrast with the fact that actually the most reactive of organometallic compounds are spontaneously inflammable in carbon dioxide.

PERIODICITY OF BINARY OXYGEN COMPOUNDS

Models of oxides across the periodic table can serve very well to solidify your students' concepts of the meaning of chemical periodicity. In such a collection of models, the intermediate position of water is quite clear. They can see at once that in a period, such as from lithium to fluorine, the condition of combined oxygen changes steadily, becoming less negative from left to right. Associated with this change, they will recognize the trend from stable, solid crystalline oxides to volatile, less stable covalent oxides of much lower polarity. The trend is also from strongly basic to strongly acidic oxide, from nonreducing to strongly oxidizing compounds. Not only the trends across periods but also the similarities and occasional differences within major groups of the periodic table are clearly evident from the models (Fig. C-7) and an understanding of what they represent. A collection of models of oxides over the periodic table can do much to demonstrate the importance and the real meaning of the periodic law. When your students begin to acquire the fundamental understanding of oxygen chemistry that is so much more easily available with the help of such models, they will be well on their way to developing an understanding and appreciation of chemistry in general.

CHAPTER

7

CHEMISTRY OF HYDROGEN

The intermediate position of hydrogen among the elements in electronegativity makes models of the binary hydrogen compounds especially interesting, because they show in the combined hydrogen a wide range from blue-green for highly negative charge to red-orange for quite positive charge. A collection of models of molecules, hypothetical or real, of all the binary hydrogen compounds of the inert-shell and 18-shell elements can be used to demonstrate spectacularly the periodicity of the elements, as well as to help correlate and explain the properties of the hydrogen compounds. I would recommend at least the following: (gaseous molecules where the compound under ordinary conditions is ionic or highly polymeric solid) LiH, BeH_2, B_2H_6, CH_4, NH_3, H_2O, HF, NaH, MgH_2, AlH_3, SiH_4, PH_3, H_2S, HCl, HBr, HI, ZnH_2.

In addition, you will find crystal models of LiH or NaH helpful and also BeH_2 or AlH_3. You may wish also to have models of B_4H_{10}, B_5H_9, and $B_{10}H_{14}$, and perhaps H_2O_2 and N_2H_4. Other hydrocarbon models may also be useful; these will be mentioned more specifically in a brief discussion of organic chemistry in Chapter 9.

PREDICTION OF COMPOUNDS FROM ATOMIC MODELS

Before displaying the molecular models of binary hydrogen compounds to your class, you may find it very helpful to begin with the corresponding atomic models and let your students, under your guidance, predict the probable nature of the compounds with hydrogen. From the model of lithium, for example, they can see its capacity to form but one covalent bond, and the similar capacity for hydrogen is noted from the hydrogen model. They can easily predict that the two elements will unite one to one. From the obviously higher electronegativity of hydrogen (yellow-green in contrast to red), they can predict that the bond will be highly polar, the hydrogen withdrawing electron charge from the lithium. They can predict that this should result in expansion of the hydrogen sphere and contraction of the lithium sphere. Now if you show them the model of a single molecule of lithium hydride (Fig. C-9), they will be pleased and impressed to find it meeting exactly the specifications which they were able to predict from the atomic models alone.

Examination of the atomic model of beryllium will disclose that this atom can form two covalent bonds, that these must be located at opposite sides of the atom if the two vacant orbitals are not to be used in the bonding. The students can see that although the electronegativity of beryllium is substantially higher than that of lithium, it is still much less than that of hydrogen. Consequently, they can predict that the bonds to the two hydrogen atoms that will unite with each beryllium atom will be quite polar, but not so much so as in lithium hydride. The expansion of the hydrogen and the contraction of the beryllium can also be predicted. If you will now show them the model of beryllium hydride (gas molecule) (Fig. C-9), they will see its linear shape, the blue-green of the hydrogen and the orange-red of the beryllium, and feel the gratification that comes from successful prediction and a feeling of understanding.

From the model of boron, they can see that it can form three bonds toward the corners of an equilateral triangle about the boron nucleus, and will therefore unite with hydrogen in a one to three ratio. From the boron electronegativity, they can see that the bonds will be less polar than in the beryllium hydride, but still somewhat polar since the hydrogen is clearly more electronegative than the boron. Unless they know about hydridic bridging, discussed below, they will not be able to predict that two BH_3 groups will dimerize and thus each will become nonplanar, using the fourth boron orbital. This they need not be ashamed of, for the best of chemists would not have predicted this either at the time of its discovery. In fact, the dimeric nature of boron hydride gave the theoretical chemists a shock from which they have not yet altogether recovered. But your students will see, when you show them the diborane model (Fig. C-9), that their predictions about bond polarity and relative numbers of atoms were entirely correct.

A model of a carbon atom will show your students very clearly that it is capable of uniting with four hydrogen atoms, to be located at the corners of a regular tetrahedron around the carbon. They will predict that the bonds will be very close to nonpolar—in fact, from the carbon and hydrogen models, unless their eyes are delicately color sensitive, they may think the electronegativity difference is zero. Actually the carbon should be just a little greener yellow than the hydrogen. Your model of methane (Fig. C-9) will confirm their predictions. The carbon is yellow-green indicating slight negative charge. The partial charge on hydrogen, although positive, is too small to be shown by the color scale, and the atoms are therefore yellow for nearly neutral.

From a model of a nitrogen atom they will see that although five electrons are available, only three vacancies to accommodate electrons from hydrogen atoms are there. Consequently only three hydrogen atoms can unite from one nitrogen atom. They will easily see that the electronegativity of nitrogen is higher, and therefore will be able to predict that in the compound hydrogen will acquire a partial positive charge, contracting a little, while nitrogen expands a little as the result of its negative charge. Furthermore, noting the extra pair of electrons, judging its availability from the negative charge on the nitrogen, and noting the positive nature of hydrogen, they will be able, if they know about protonic bridging, to predict its possibility here. The model of ammonia (Fig. C-9), of course, confirms all these predictions.

Water has already been thoroughly discussed (Chapter 5).

From the model of fluorine your students can observe its limitation to the forming of one covalent bond and infer that its compound with hydrogen will be one to one. From the very high electronegativity of the fluorine they will guess, and rightly so, that the bond will be very polar, although not at all comparable to the polarity in something like sodium fluoride. Again the model of hydrogen fluoride (Fig. C-9) shows the predictable features, including extra pairs of electrons which, combined with the negative charge on fluorine and the relatively high positive charge on hydrogen, suggest strong protonic bridging which is very characteristic of this compound.

There is no need here to continue in this vein through the rest of the periodic table, but it seemed desirable to emphasize strongly how easily your students will be able to grasp the fundamentals of chemical combination and the nature of compounds when this type of approach to the presentation of chemistry is made.

PHYSICAL PROPERTIES

With the models of the molecules you can point out that toward elements of lower electronegativity hydrogen acts as oxidizing agent, becoming negative. When it is highly negative, as in combination with the alkali metals, no discrete molecules result, but instead ionic crystals which resemble the lattice of sodium chloride. A model of a crystalline hydride (Fig. C-10) will show that hydrogen in this highly negative state, when placed in the environment of cations, occupies a relatively very large volume. (The size chosen for hydrogen in the models of gaseous molecules is much smaller and actually not intended to be taken literally. The only intent is to show that positively charged hydrogen is smaller and negatively charged hydrogen larger than neutral hydrogen, which is the only form for which a reasonably accurate covalent radius is known. How much smaller or how much larger is not known and therefore only arbitrarily represented in the models.) With less negative hydrogen the compounds are less ionic and tend to solidify, it is believed, through hydridic bridging. This is probably the structure of solid BeH_2. With boron the bridging is limited to a double bridge between two borons such that the expected BH_3 has no stable existence but forms the dimer, B_2H_6. In methane the hydrogen is no longer negative, since carbon is slightly more electronegative than hydrogen. No longer is there appreciable association under ordinary conditions until the hydrogen becomes sufficiently positive, as in NH_3, H_2O, and HF, to produce molecular association through protonic bridging.

The states of aggregation of these binary hydrogen compounds thus largely as usual determine the physical properties. Ionic hydrides are nonvolatile and high melting (or decompose before melting). Volatility increases and lower melting points result with decreased association corresponding to decreased negative charge on hydrogen. Then, as hydrogen becomes partially positive, its ability to form protonic bridges increases, and although ammonia, water, and hydrogen fluoride are very volatile, they are not nearly as volatile or as low melting as would be expected if protonic bridging did not occur. A similar trend is noted going across the periodic table from sodium to chlorine, with certain significant dfferences and exceptions. Like lithium hydride, sodium hydride forms ionic crystals. Magnesium hydride is probably somewhat more ionic than the beryllium compound, but still largely associated through hydridic bridging. Aluminum hydride differs from boron hydride in two significant ways: its hydrogen is more negative, since aluminum is less electronegative than boron, and it has more than one vacant orbital that might be employed in the hydridic bridging. Instead of forming a dimer, aluminum hydride forms a polymeric solid presumably by hydridic bridging using outer *d* orbitals as well. Silane, SiH_4, has negative hydrogen, in contrast to methane, but is so symmetrical that it is very volatile and shows no evidence of hydridic bridging. In phosphine, PH_3, the hydrogen is believed to be only slightly negative, and instead of available empty orbitals, the phosphorus has an unshared electron pair. Thus there is no possibility of protonic bridging such as occurs in ammonia, and phosphine has much lower melting and boiling points than ammonia. Hydrogen sulfide has slightly positive hydrogen, but it is not sufficiently positive, and the sulfur is not sufficiently negative, nor small enough, for appreciable protonic bridging. The contrast in properties between water and hydrogen sulfide is therefore very striking. In hydrogen chloride the hydrogen is now more positive, but again the chlorine is too large for effective protonic bridging to occur, and the contrast in physical properties between hydrogen fluoride and hydrogen chloride is nearly as striking as between water and hydrogen sulfide.

My interpretation of what I choose to call "hydridic bridging" is at present somewhat controversial. Some may doubt that there is any fundamental cause and effect relationship between this kind of bridging and any fancied or real partial negative charge on hydrogen. The empirical relationship cannot be challenged, however, for to the best of my knowledge, no "hydridic bridging" is known where the charge on hydrogen would be calculated to be neutral or positive, or where an available orbital on a positively charged atom does not exist. Hydridic bridging seems always to occur when the hydrogen is calculated to bear negative charge and the adjacent atom has positive charge and a vacant orbital. The degree of association of binary hydrogen compounds seems very definitely to be related to, and to increase with, increasing negative charge on hydrogen.

The self-consistency of the interpretative scheme on which these models are based is one of its most satisfying features.

CHEMICAL PROPERTIES

Hydrogen in the free state is both an oxidizing and a reducing agent. It oxidizes the alkali metals, for example, and it reduces oxygen, both vigorously. In Chapter 4 certain principles relating partial charge on a combined atom to its chemical properties were stated. In general, hydrogen follows these principles closely. As it changes from the free or neutral state toward increasing partial negative charge, it loses its oxidizing powers and becomes more and more strongly reducing. As it becomes increasingly positive, its oxidizing powers become enhanced and its reducing power diminishes. Closely related to oxidation-reduction, as stated previously, is electron acceptor-donor interaction. Neutral hydrogen cannot act either as donor or acceptor. Negative hydrogen, however, to the extent that it has acquired control of an electron pair, can act as donor. Positive hydrogen, to the extent that it can "shake loose" from the pair of electrons that holds it imperfectly, can act as acceptor. Complex as well as simple hydrogen compounds are therefore known. Closely related to donor-acceptor action is, of course, acid-base reaction, of which donor-acceptor action is sometimes classed as a more general category. Negative hydrogen is basic, and positive hydrogen acidic.

Armed with these principles, all one really needs to do to predict the chemical properties of binary hydrogen compounds is to study the molecular models (Fig. C-9). If these show the hydrogen to be highly negative, the compounds will be easily oxidizable, basic, and can form complex hydrides by acting as donors toward Group IIIA hydrides in which the hydrogen is less negative. Thus, lithium hydride can donate to aluminum hydride to form the important reducing agent, $LiAlH_4$. If the models show the hydrogen to be essentially neutral, the compound can be predicted to be relatively unreactive, as for example, methane. If the hydrogen is positive, the compound will be relatively difficult to oxidize, show some acidic and therefore oxidizing properties, and tend to lose a proton readily, at least to form complex hydrogen compounds by acting as acceptor. For example, HF cannot be oxidized by any chemical agent, is definitely acidic, can oxidize reducing agents such as metals, and can lose its proton to a donor such as ammonia, forming the complex ion, NH_4^+.

The basic properties shown by ammonia and, to a lesser but still important degree, by water arise from the unshared pairs of electrons on the nitrogen and oxygen; these compounds are also acidic by virtue of their positive hydrogen.

If positive hydrogen is oxidizing and negative hydrogen is reducing, small wonder that when they come together, reaction to liberate hydrogen gas is typical. The familiar reaction of water with metallic hydrides is only a special example of this general type of reaction, and your students can predict that it can happen when any compound of negative hydrogen encounters a compound of positive hydrogen. About the only significant exception seems to be phosphine, whose slightly negative hydrogen does not react in this way, but here a pair of unshared electrons is available to the proton more readily than the pair of electrons associated with the hydrogen—phosphorus bond. In a similar manner, certain ions in which hydrogen is negative, such as hydroxide ion, furnish unshared electron pairs to protons rather than hydrolyze to liberate hydrogen gas.

The above is the chemistry of binary hydrogen in a nutshell, and there are many interesting details which are more complex and perhaps not so easily interpreted. However, it does provide a better basis by far for the consideration of hydrogen compounds as a group than the familiar classification of these compounds as saline and covalent hydrides.

PERIODICITY OF HYDROGEN CHEMISTRY

The intermediate electronegativity of hydrogen permits an unusually vivid display of chemical periodicity through the models of its binary compounds (Fig. C-9). In these the hydrogen ranges from relatively large and greenish-blue in color, in the alkali metal hydrides, to relatively small and red-orange in color, in hydrogen fluoride. The nature of all the elements that form the expected hydrogen compounds, which includes all the inert-shell and 18-shell elements, is disclosed by the nature of these hydrogen compounds and by the condition not only of the combined hydrogen but also of the other element in the hydrogen compound. Since hydrogen is only intermediate in its oxidizing power, elements made highly positive by reaction with hydrogen must initially have been highly reactive, strongly reducing metals. This is shown in the models of alkali metal hydride gas molecules, in each of which the metal atom is red and the hydrogen greenish-blue. Proceeding to major groups of higher number, the hydrogen approaches neutrality and then becomes increasingly positive, but even in the extreme never so positive as it is negative at the other extreme. The reason for this lies in the fact that although hydrogen is classed as intermediate in electronegativity, it is actually somewhat on the high side; there is less difference in electronegativity between even hydrogen and fluorine than there is between hydrogen and the alkali metals.

The effects of similarities and differences within major groups can also be pointed out in the models, or with their use. For example, the alternations in electronegativity that result when the electronic type of atom, descending a major group, changes from inert-shell to 18-shell is clearly shown. The simplest hydride of boron is dimeric, B_2H_6. Aluminum, being less electronegative than boron and therefore differing more from hydrogen, forms a hydride in which the hydrogen has higher negative charge, giving it a greater tendency to associate through hydridic bridging. Instead of Al_2H_6, a polymer $(AlH_3)_x$, results. This tendency toward further association is probably aided by the larger size of the aluminum and possibly by its ability to use outer *d* orbitals. If gallium, the atoms of which are larger, were to continue the trend, its hydride would be even more closely associated. In fact, however, it appears to be dimeric, Ga_2H_6, more like B_2H_6, although solid polymers are also known. This is consistent with a higher, rather than lower, electronegativity of gallium.

In Group IVA a similar situation exists. Methane, with practically neutral hydrogen, is not spontaneously inflammable nor hydrolyzable. Silane, SiH_4, in which the hydrogen is now appreciably negative, is both spontaneously inflammable and hydrolyzable. Under ordinary conditions, neither oxygen nor water attack germane, GeH_4, which is more like methane. This would not be easy to account for if germanium followed the trend set by carbon and silicon, but its alternation in electronegativity back toward carbon is quite consistent with the observed return toward the properties of methane. The model of GeH_4 shows the hydrogen to be neutral.

Surveying the whole periodic table of binary hydrogen compound models, one can visualize the periodic trends in all directions with great clarity. An advantage of hydrogen compound models over oxygen compound models in this respect is that they cover a wider range of chemical activity. Whereas the oxides go, left to right, from nonoxidizing to oxidizing, the hydrogen compounds go from actively reducing to oxidizing. The hydrogen compounds cover, in fact, a wider range of variation in properties than perhaps any other class of compounds, except the alkyl derivatives of the elements which in some respects are quite similar.

CHAPTER

8

CHEMISTRY OF HALOGENS

CHLORINE

An examination of the atomic models of the elements will disclose that chlorine is third highest in electronegativity, exceeded only by oxygen and fluorine. In its compounds, therefore, chlorine is always partially negative, except when combined with oxygen or fluorine. Models of gaseous molecules of the following will be useful: HCl, $LiCl$, $BeCl_2$, BCl_3, CCl_4, NCl_3, Cl_2O, ClF, $NaCl$, $MgCl_2$, Al_2Cl_6, $SiCl_4$, PCl_3, PCl_5, S_2Cl_2, SCl_2, Cl_2, and perhaps others. Crystal models showing the various structures of solid chlorides may also be useful.

Starting with atomic models, you may wish to have your students predict the nature of the above molecular models before you show them. Thus the chlorine and hydrogen models will show that each atom can form only one covalent bond, and the formula, HCl, is thus predetermined. Its polarity is likewise easily predictable from the electronegativities, as indicated by the blue-green of chlorine and the yellow-green of hydrogen. The orange (H) and green (Cl) model of HCl (Fig. C-9) will then confirm your students' expectation.

The lithium model again makes easy the prediction of a 1:1 formula, and its red color showing very low electronegativity suggests high bond polarity, which the red and blue model of LiCl will confirm (Fig. C-11).

The beryllium model will indicate not only the $BeCl_2$ formula, but also the expected linear configuration of the molecule. Again, the bond polarities can be predicted to be high although not as high as in LiCl. The $BeCl_2$ model of course has no surprises when the component atoms have first been thoughtfully studied.

In a similar manner, the nature of all the other molecular models can be predicted, except the dimeric quality of $AlCl_3$, which can be discussed in a general treatment of the physical and chemical properties.

Following the general principles established earlier, you can now indicate the relationship between bond polarity and state of aggregation of the chloride. The highly polar bonds will correspond to ionic crystal lattices of high stability. As polarity becomes less, association diminishes. In $AlCl_3$ the empty orbital on the aluminum together with the relatively high chlorine charge and therefore availability of unshared electron pairs for bonding, cause, in liquid and vapor state, dimerization to Al_2Cl_6 (Fig. C-11). One chlorine atom on each of two aluminum atoms serves as donor to the other aluminum, the two aluminums thus becoming attached through a double chlorine bridge. Doubtless you will wish to point out that this coordination increases the bonding electron pairs around the aluminum from three to four, and consequently changes the geometry from planar to tetrahedral. Some bright student will be likely to ask why a similar dimerization of BCl_3 does not occur. You will be able to point out that the boron is not as highly positive as the aluminum in their respective chlorides and that the chlorine is more negative in the aluminum compound and therefore a better donor than the chlorine in BCl_3, but this will not explain the gallium halides which are dimeric and the fact that even BF_3 is not. You may perhaps suggest that "back coordination," which means donation of a pair of electrons not already involved in the single bonding from the chlorine, can possibly occur more readily with the smaller boron atom than with the larger aluminum and gallium atoms, thus utilizing the extra orbital of the boron. But no complete and clear-cut answer appears to be available.

Carbon tetrachloride is very symmetrical so that even with its polar bonds the molecule as a whole is nonpolar. Intermolecular attractions are therefore relatively low, giving the compound relatively low melting and boiling points. These values are, nevertheless, considerably higher than for Cl_2 itself, and you may wish to consider possible reasons for this, with your class.

The notorious instability of NCl_3 is not something readily explained from the NCl_3 model, except in terms of weaker bonds between atoms of different size plus the very high energy of the N≡N bonds formed by its decomposition. However, from here on, through Cl_2O and ClF, the diminished intermolecular association corresponds to lower bond polarity as clearly shown by the models.

In a similar way, the physical trend from NaCl to Cl_2 can be discussed. If vacant orbitals and unshared electron pairs are indicated on all these models, the condensation to crystalline solids can be predicted better than just from observed geometry and bond polarity. The models of LiCl and NaCl gas molecules, for example, will then show three vacant orbitals on each metal atom and three unshared electron pairs on each chlorine atom. If your students have in mind the general principle that chemical combination tends to continue until all exposed vacancies are utilized in bonding or physically shielded from bonding, they will see why, in addition to the reason of the electrostatic forces, these molecules will tend to condense as they do. Similarly, when they observe that such models as those of CCl_4 or ClF show no outer orbital vacancies but only electron pairs, they can understand why these molecules do not condense except weakly as permitted by van der Waals and sometimes dipole-dipole interactions. You will find it helpful, indeed, to consider in detail each chloride molecule with respect to its likelihood of intermolecular association or other condensation and with respect to the physical properties that have been observed. You will find that your students cannot—nor can you—predict exactly what these properties will be, but they can at least predict approximately, and any specific physical property can be rationalized in terms of the nature of the component ions or molecules.

Chemically, the general principles stated earlier can be illustrated very well by the properties of binary chlorides. Chlorine which in combining has failed to acquire high negative charge retains its potential ability to do so by breaking loose and attaching to some less electronegative atom. From left to right across the periodic table, therefore, oxidizing (chlorinating) power of binary chlorides increases. Even so apparently inert a compound as carbon tetrachloride, in which the chlorine can be seen to be only slightly negative, can react explosively with finely divided metals if the reaction is initiated. At elevated temperatures carbon tetrachloride is an effective chlorinating agent. With increasing negative charge, however, the combined chlorine naturally loses electronegativity, and all compounds wherein the chlorine of the models is blue-green or blue (as in NaCl) are relatively inert and ineffective as chlorinating agents.

Displacement and double decomposition reactions involving chlorides can be explained quite well by use of the models, for these involve the important general principle that highly electronegative elements tend to become as negative as possible and that reactions tend to proceed spontaneously or exothermically in the direction of forming the most polar bond possible. Your students can see from the models that if a given element would, by forming a chloride, give to the chlorine a lower negative charge than would be supplied by some other element, the first element is certainly not expected to displace the second from its chloride. The converse is true, and any element that forms a chloride in which the chlorine is more negative will displace from its chloride another element which gives electrons to the chlorine less completely. Double decompositions are similarly explained. For example, the lithium-chlorine bond is more polar than aluminum-chlorine or lithium-hydrogen. When lithium hydride and aluminum chloride are warmed together, a double decomposition (metathetical) reaction could result in aluminum hydride and lithium chloride. One would predict essentially no reverse reaction.

Another general principle is that of donor ability increasing with negative charge acquired. Chlorine in the less polar chlorides has essentially no donor ability, despite its unshared electron pairs. However, chloride ion, or even chlorine only as negative as in aluminum chloride as discussed earlier, can act as donor in formation of many complex compounds. Where less polar chlorides have available outer orbitals, they may become joined to polar chlorides, forming, for example, PCl_6^-, $SnCl_6$, and so on. Large numbers of such complex chlorides are known. They are analogous to the complex oxides in that the more electronegative of the two other elements becomes part of the anion, leaving the other element as the cation.

In general, the binary chlorides over the periodic table show interesting and rather close resemblances in trends and similarities to the oxygen and hydrogen compounds discussed in preceding chapters. A set of models of molecules of chlorine compounds, arranged in the form of a periodic table, will display the facts of periodicity very well.

FLUORINE

Fluorine is the most electronegative element, and consequently all models of fluorides will show the fluorine as having partial negative charge. You may find it helpful to have a set of fluoride models corresponding to your set of chloride models, for a comparison of the two sets will show very well the similarities as well as the effects of the higher electronegativity of fluorine.

The procedure of beginning with atomic models can be followed here. Thus the hydrogen model and the fluorine model will permit the students to predict without hesitation a formula of HF, and that this molecule will be quite polar, with hydrogen positive and fluorine negative. A model of HF (Fig. C-9) will show that the prediction is correct. In a similar manner, just as described in detail for oxygen and hydrogen compounds in preceding chapters, the formulas and molecular structures for other fluorides can be predicted from the atomic models and verified by demonstration of the molecular models. The relationships between the simple molecules and the states of aggregation, and thus the physical properties of fluorides, will all be shown by the models. The chemistry of the fluorides closely resembles that of the chlorides, and therefore will not be covered completely here.

Rather, some points of special interest will be discussed here.

First, the protonic bridging of hydrogen fluoride is of interest. From the model of HF, especially if it includes the three unshared electron pairs of the fluorine, one can see that with the high negative charge on the small fluorine atom and the high positive charge on the hydrogen, conditions are optimum for the formation of hydrogen bonds (protonic bridges). It is not surprising, therefore, that protonic bridging occurs in hydrogen fluoride, even in the vapor state at ordinary temperatures, causing polymerization to linear, and possibly cyclic, structures of significant but not high stability. The physical properties of hydrogen fluoride, as influenced by this high degree of association not observed in the other hydrogen halides, are therefore different from those other halides to a degree that is noteworthy, and has led to classification of hydrogen fluoride as anomalous. Thus, hydrogen fluoride has a much higher boiling point (nearly 20°) than would be expected from the low values for the other hydrogen halides. In general, it differs from the other hydrogen halides in much the same way and for much the same reasons as does ammonia from other group IIIA hydrogen compounds and water from the gaseous hydrogen sulfide, selenide, and telluride. You may wish to point out that this high attraction between proton and fluoride ion, as shown by the stability of HF and the extent of protonic bridging, results in weakness of aqueous solutions of hydrogen fluoride (hydrofluoric acid) as an acid.

A model of the bifluoride ion, FHF^-, will show that the hydrogen is equally distant from each fluorine, an observation interpreted as meaning that the two bonds must be exactly equivalent. In other words, here is not the usual "hydrogen bond" in which the proton remains attached to its original molecule and remains at a considerably greater distance from the atom of the second molecule that attracts it. Here seems to be truly divalent hydrogen, and as the model shows, if the electronegativity becomes equalized by distribution of the charge among the three component atoms in accordance with their relative initial electronegativities, the hydrogen does not even remain positive, but bears a small negative charge. The bond energy is found to be four or five times as great as that of an ordinary protonic bridge, another important bit of evidence that the bonding here is quite unusual.

Boron trifluoride (Fig. C-11) is interesting in its physical properties, as, although the individual bonds are quite polar, it is a gas with no evidence of the kind of association that makes aluminum fluoride a nonvolatile, high melting solid. The bond lengths are somewhat shorter even than would be calculated from the polarity, and very possibly the extra orbital of the boron is employed to use otherwise unshared electrons of the three fluorine atoms in a partial multiple bonding which thus leaves little opportunity for intermolecular association. However, such use of the fourth boron orbital does not prevent its use in the forming of coordination compounds, boron trifluoride being strongly acidic, acting as electron acceptor in many stable complexes.

A model of nitrogen fluoride (Fig. C-11) will show the bonds to be somewhat polar, with the nitrogen end positive and the fluorines negative, and one would expect from the pyramidal structure that the molecular dipole moment would be quite high. On the contrary, it is quite low, and one may suppose that the unshared electron pair on the nitrogen is caused to adjust its average position in such a way as to counteract much of the polarity induced by the fluorines. However, this electron pair certainly does not thereby become more available for the formation of coordination bonds. With the positive charge on nitrogen, one would expect these electrons to be less available—the nitrogen to be a much poorer donor—and indeed it is. Nitrogen trifluoride appears to lack almost completely the basic properties shown by ammonia and amines.

Sulfur hexafluoride is an interesting compound to show by model (Fig. C-11). In it, none of the fluorine atoms have succeeded in acquiring much negative charge, and hence, in principle, the compound should be a powerful fluorinating agent. Actually, it is amazingly inert. There seems to be no question about the potential for high chemical reactivity being present, but here is a good example of how the lack of a reasonably available mechanism for a reaction results in a seeming inertness. The molecule is highly symmetrical, and the sulfur is so thoroughly shielded from the outside world that under ordinary conditions no outside reagent can attack it. All such a reagent "sees" when it approaches the SF_6 is the unreactive sides of fluorine atoms; the bonds themselves appear to be completely protected.

Across the periodic table, the fluorides vary in much the same way as do the oxides and the chlorides. At the left, the compounds are ionic crystals, ordinarily very stable, high melting, low in volatility. The fluorine, being already negative, has no tendency to become more so, and the fluorides in this region are nonoxidizing (not fluorinating agents). Fluoride ion can serve as electron donor, and there are large numbers of complex fluorides and related compounds. Then proceeding toward the right-hand side of the periodic table, one observes that the fluorinating ability begins and increases, that the electron donor activity of the combined fluorine decreases, that as the bond polarity decreases, the strength of association decreases and the volatility increases, with lower melting and boiling points resulting. In short, a collection of models of binary fluorides across the periodic table can show the principles and trends of chemical periodicity very well.

BROMIDES AND IODIDES

These compounds resemble the fluorides and chlorides quite closely, so that discussion of them individually should not be needed here. In general, the trends in oxidizing power increasing from iodine to fluorine, and in reducing power increasing from fluoride to iodide, must be taken into account in any comparison among the different binary compounds of halogen.

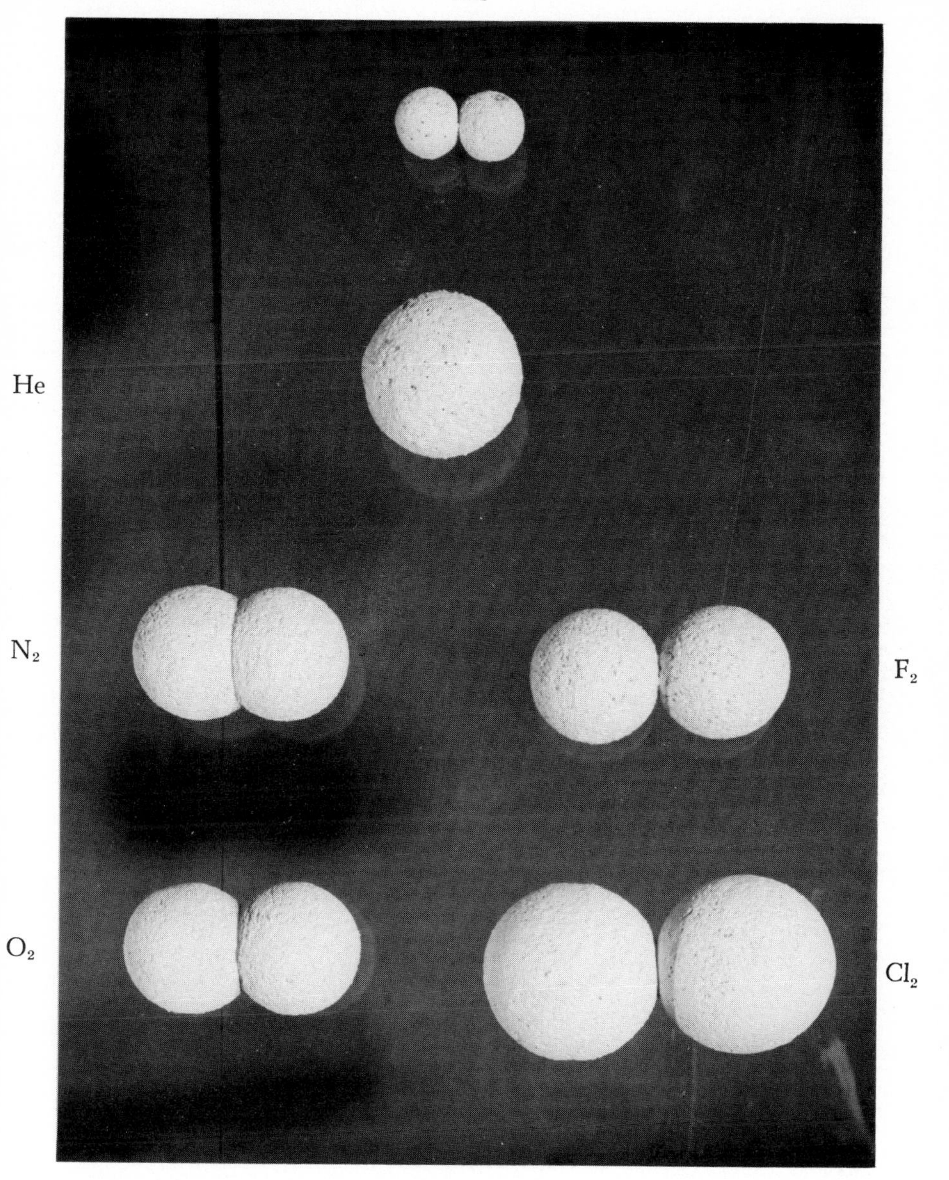

FIG. B-1. MOLECULAR MODELS OF SOME NORMALLY GASEOUS ELEMENTS. Observe how bond multiplicity is represented by the closeness of contact of the atoms.

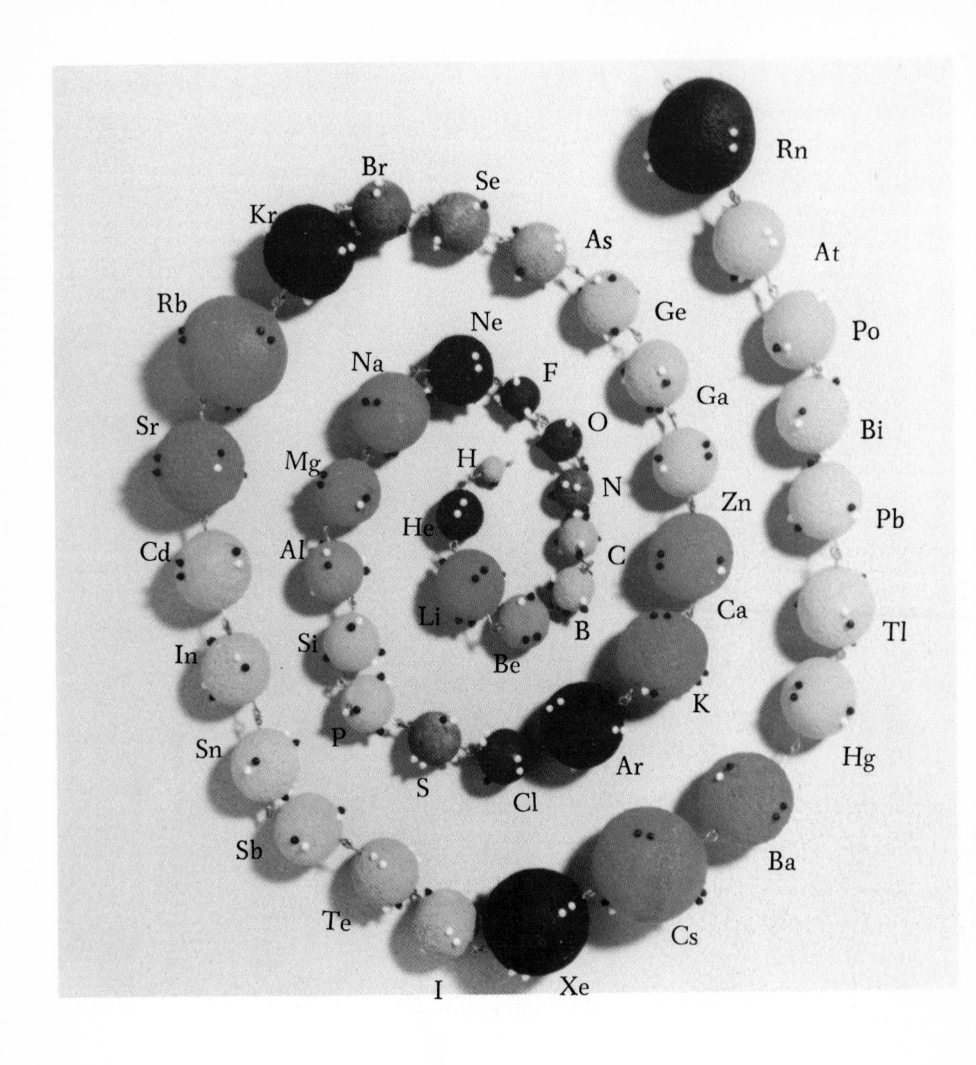

FIG. C-1. ATOMIC MODELS IN ORDER OF INCREASING ATOMIC NUMBER. These are the miniatures; extended, the chain is about 40″ long. On the medium scale, the length would be about 17′; on the large scale, 34′.

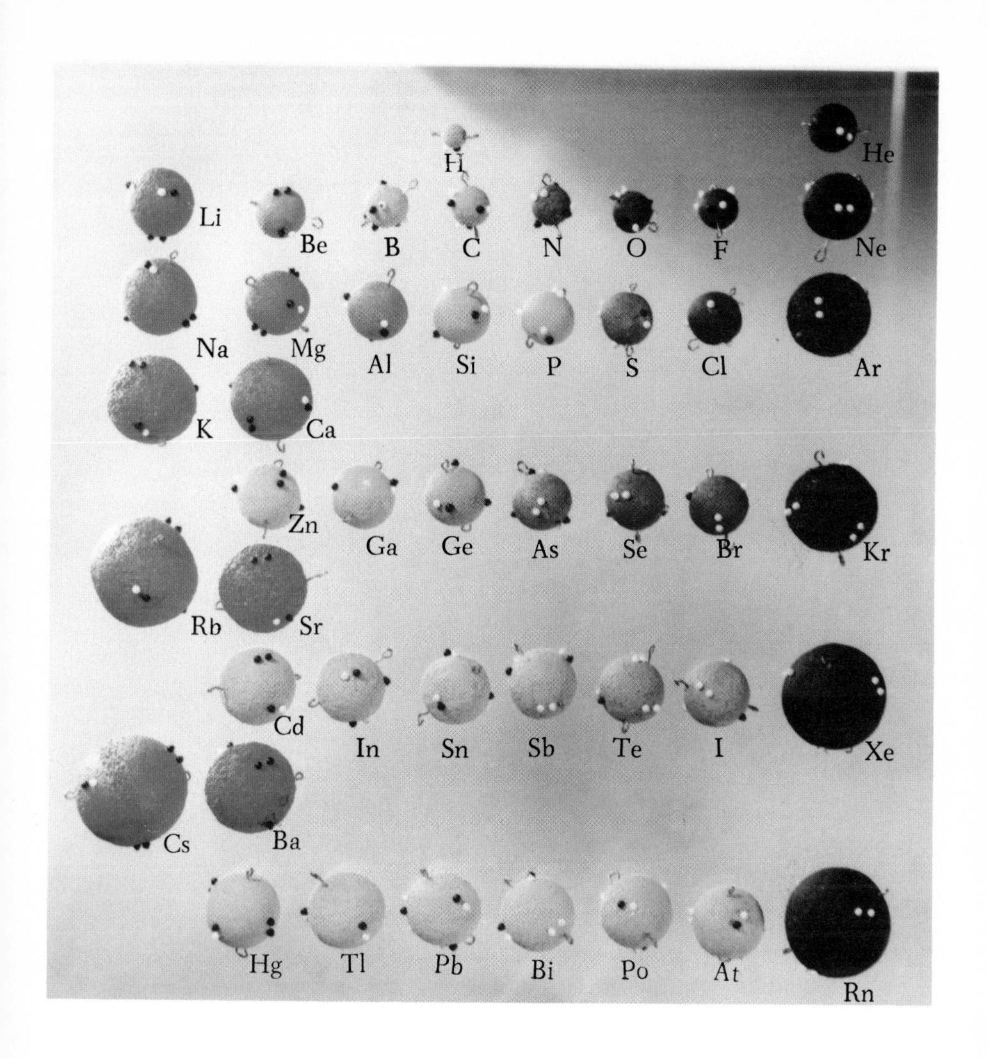

FIG. C-2. THE SAME MODELS IN PERIODIC TABLE ARRANGEMENT.

FIG. B-2. ALLOTROPIC FORMS OF CARBON. Upper: diamond. Lower: graphite.

FIG. B-3. UPPER: WHITE PHOSPHORUS, P_4. LOWER: SULFUR MOLECULE, S_8. Basic unit of both rhombic and monoclinic forms.

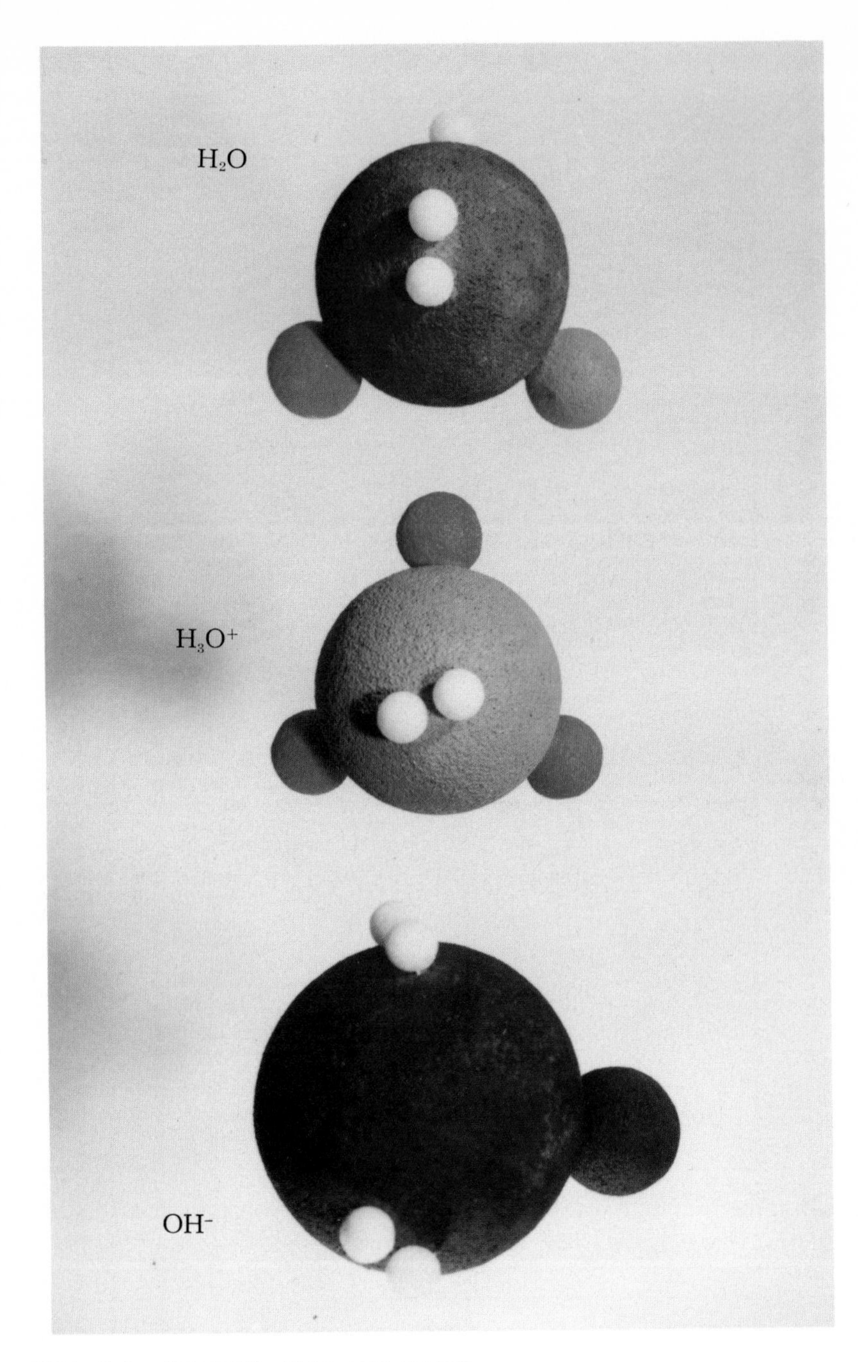

FIG. C-3. WATER AND ITS IONS.

FIG. C-4. UPPER: SOLID CARBON DIOXIDE (DRY ICE); LOWER: SOLID WATER (ICE). The black sticks represent protonic bridges; they are attached to oxygen at the sites of outer electron pairs.

FIG. B-4. HEXAGONAL CLOSEST PACKING. Upper right: in a plane, the closest possible packing of spheres equal in size brings 6 spheres around one. Three more neighbors are possible above and below. Placing this group of 10 on top of the trio at the left gives a cluster of 12 closest neighbors about a central atom: bottom photo.

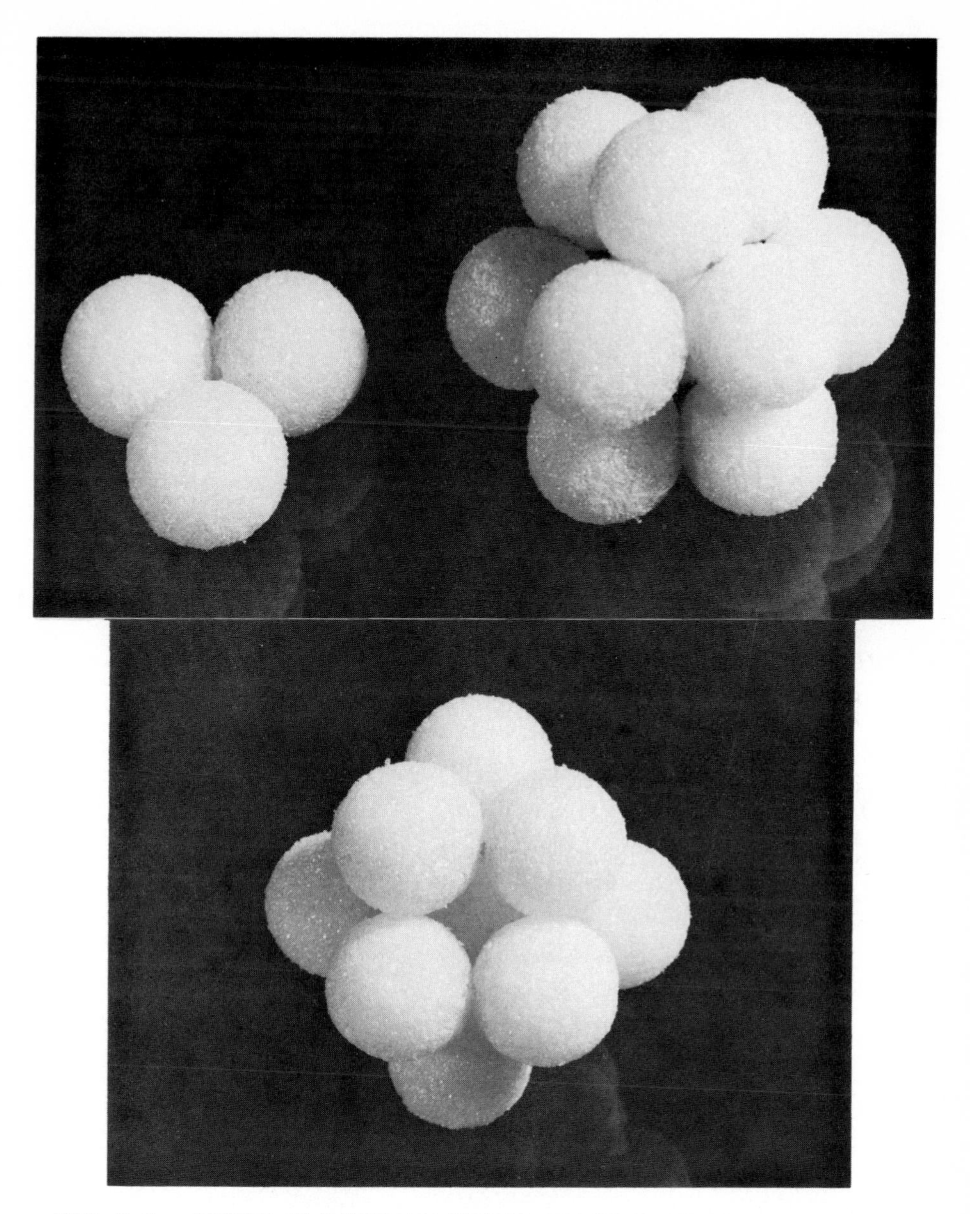

FIG. B-5. CUBIC CLOSEST PACKING (FACE CENTERED CUBIC). This differs from hexagonal packing only in the orientation of the lower triangle (upper left). If the group of 10 is placed on top of this trio, the cluster of 12 closest neighbors about a central atom shown in the lower photo results. The diamond is the cube face. The four atoms of the square are at the centers of cube faces perpendicular to the page.

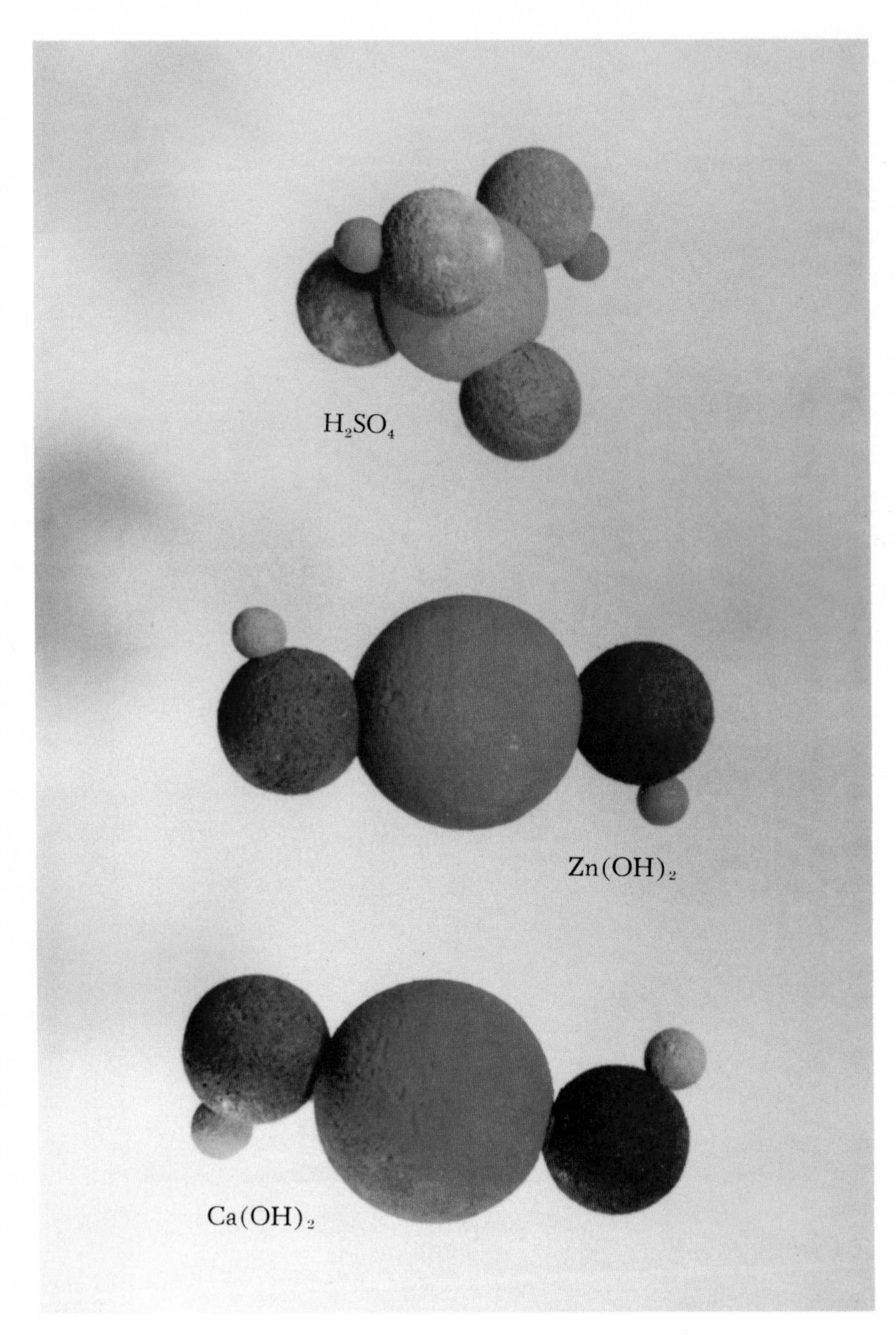

FIG. C-5. HYDROXY COMPOUNDS. Notice the difference in condition of OH, from acid to base.

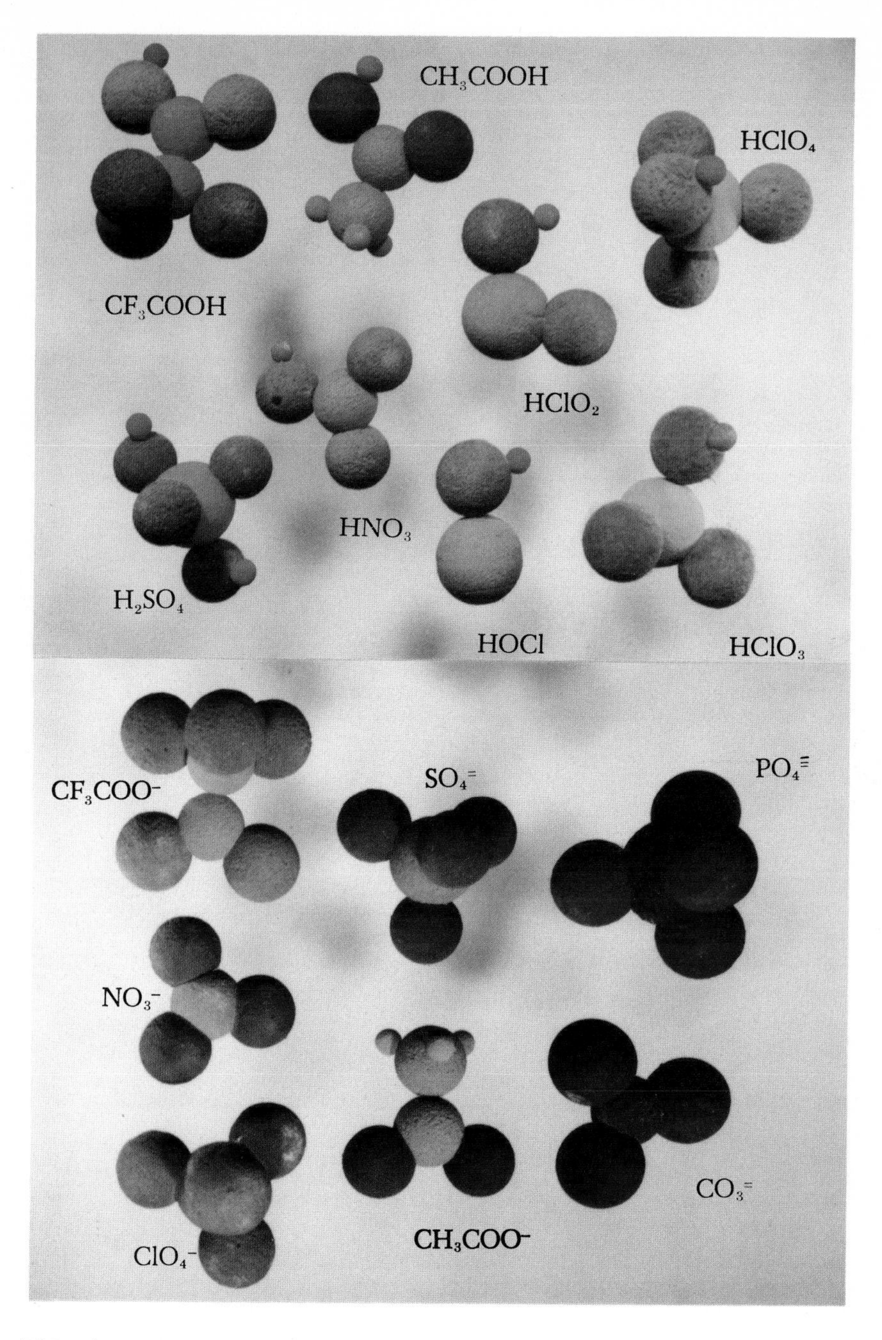

FIG. C-6. UPPER: SOME ACID MOLECULES. LOWER: SOME OXYANIONS OF ACIDS.

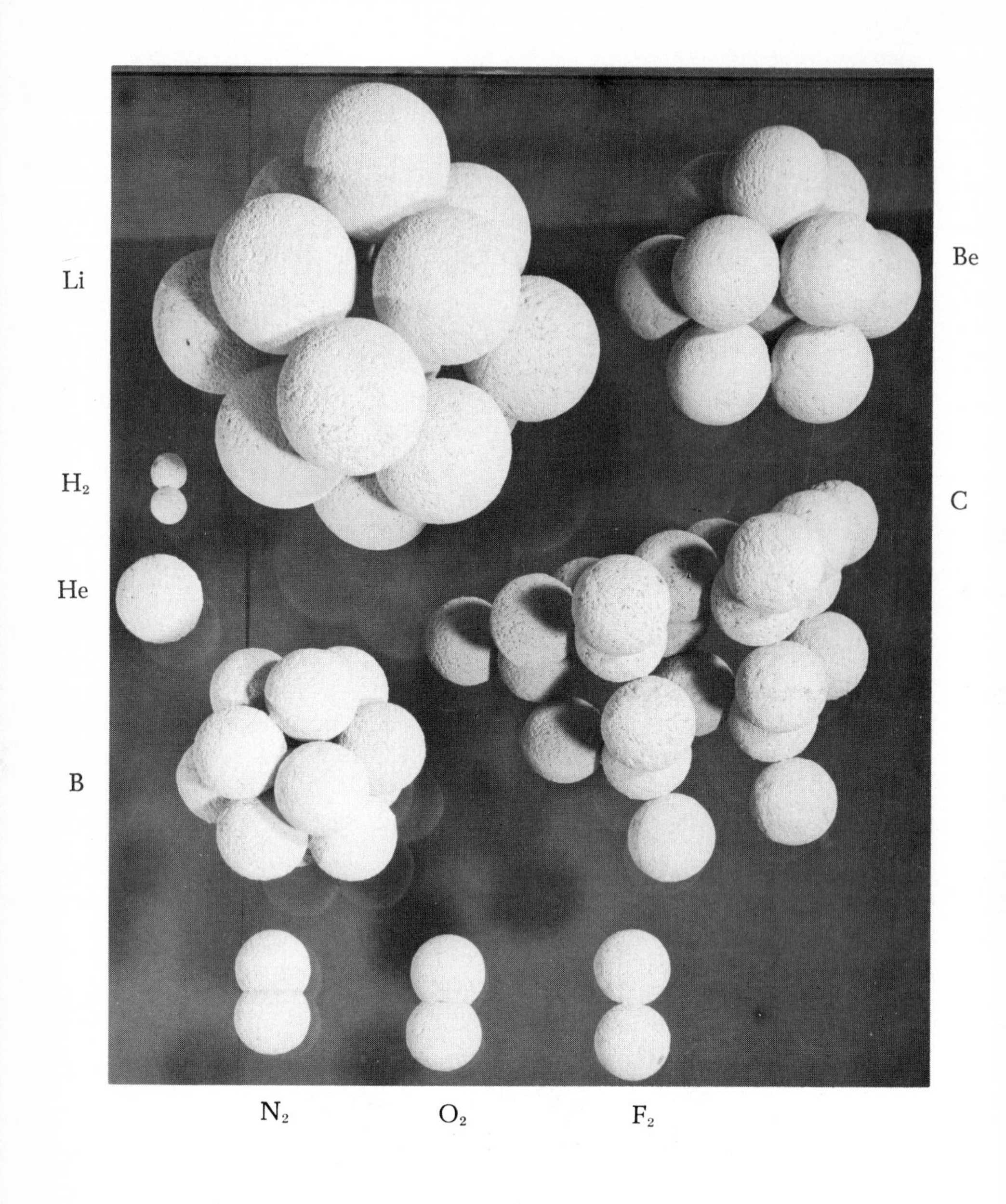

FIG. B-6. USUAL AGGREGATES OF SOME ELEMENTS WITH INCREASING ATOMIC NUMBER — ACROSS THE PERIODIC TABLE.

FIG. B-7. UPPER: BODY CENTERED CUBIC PACKING. Each interior atom has 8 closest neighbors. Six more are at the centers of the 6 neighboring cubes. See Li, Fig. B-6. LOWER: SODIUM CHLORIDE LATTICE. Each atom (ion) is surrounded by 6 atoms (ions) of the other element.

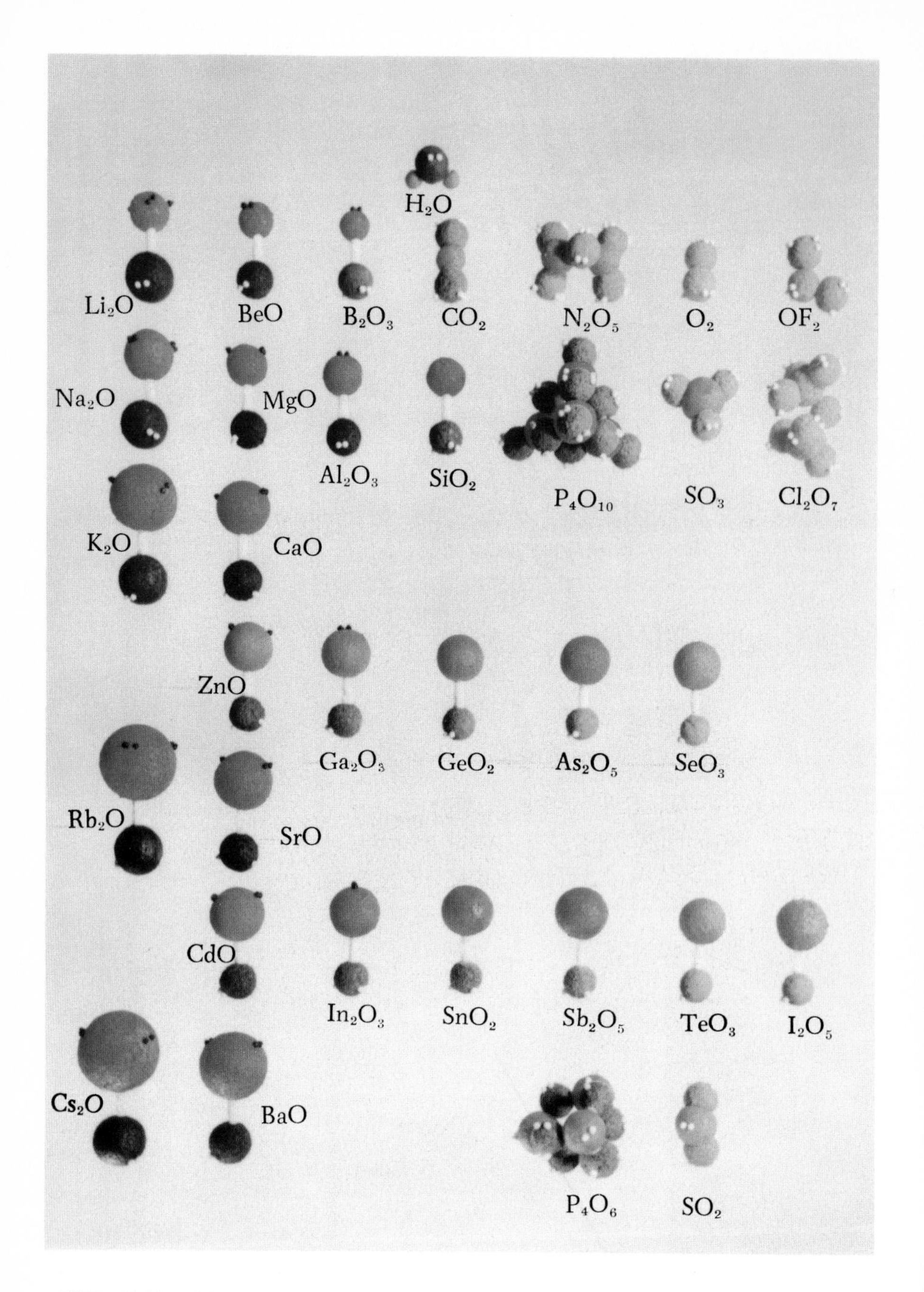

FIG. C-7. SOME BINARY COMPOUNDS OF OXYGEN. Atom-Pair Models and Molecular Models.

FIG. C-8. UPPER: CALCIUM CARBONATE CRYSTAL. LOWER: PHOSPHOTUNGSTATE ION, $PW_{12}O_{40}$. Phosphorus at the center.

FIG. B-8. CESIUM CHLORIDE LATTICE. 8:8 coordination.

FIG. B-9. NICKEL ARSENIDE LATTICE. 6:6 coordination.

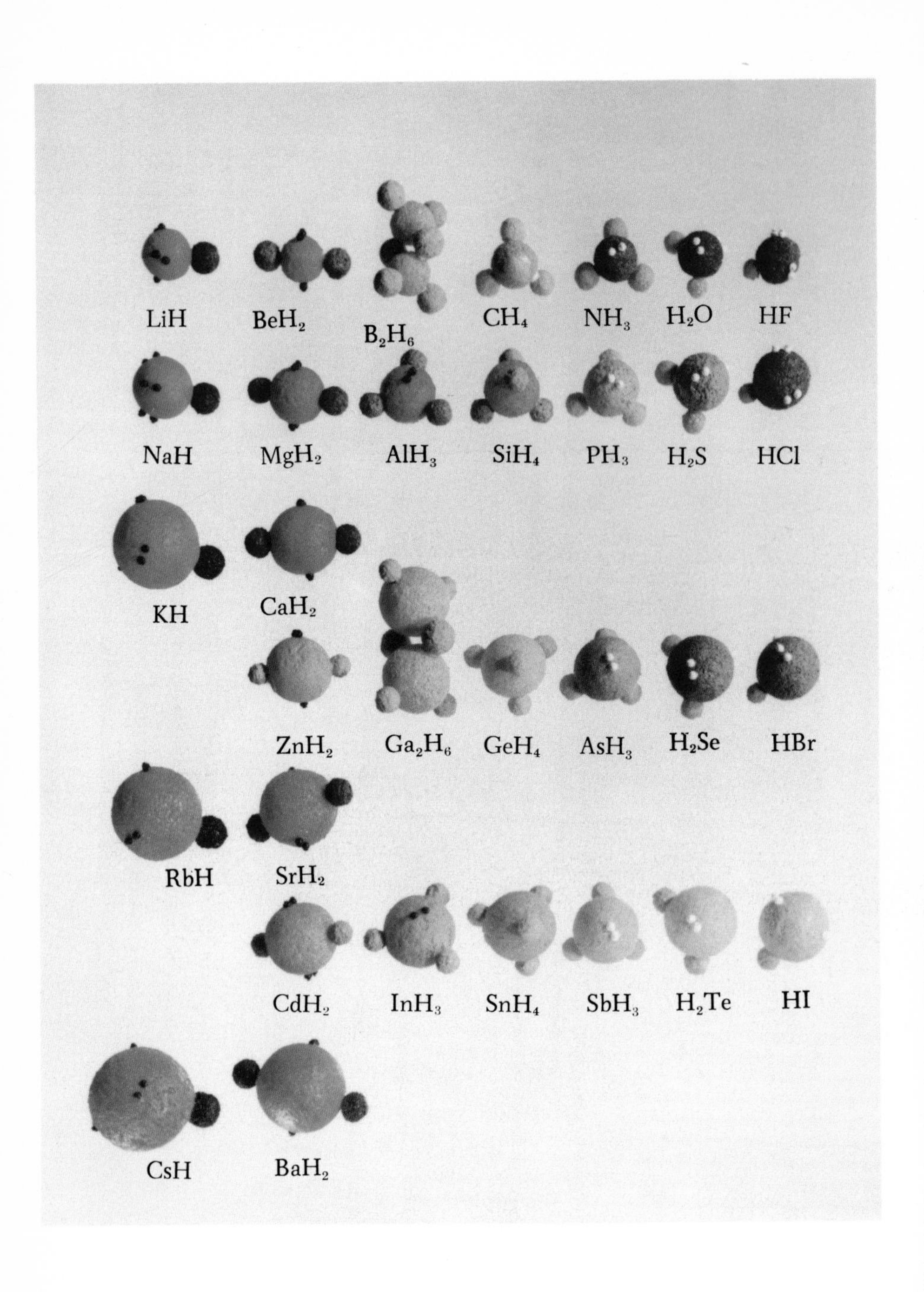

FIG. C-9. SOME BINARY HYDROGEN COMPOUNDS.

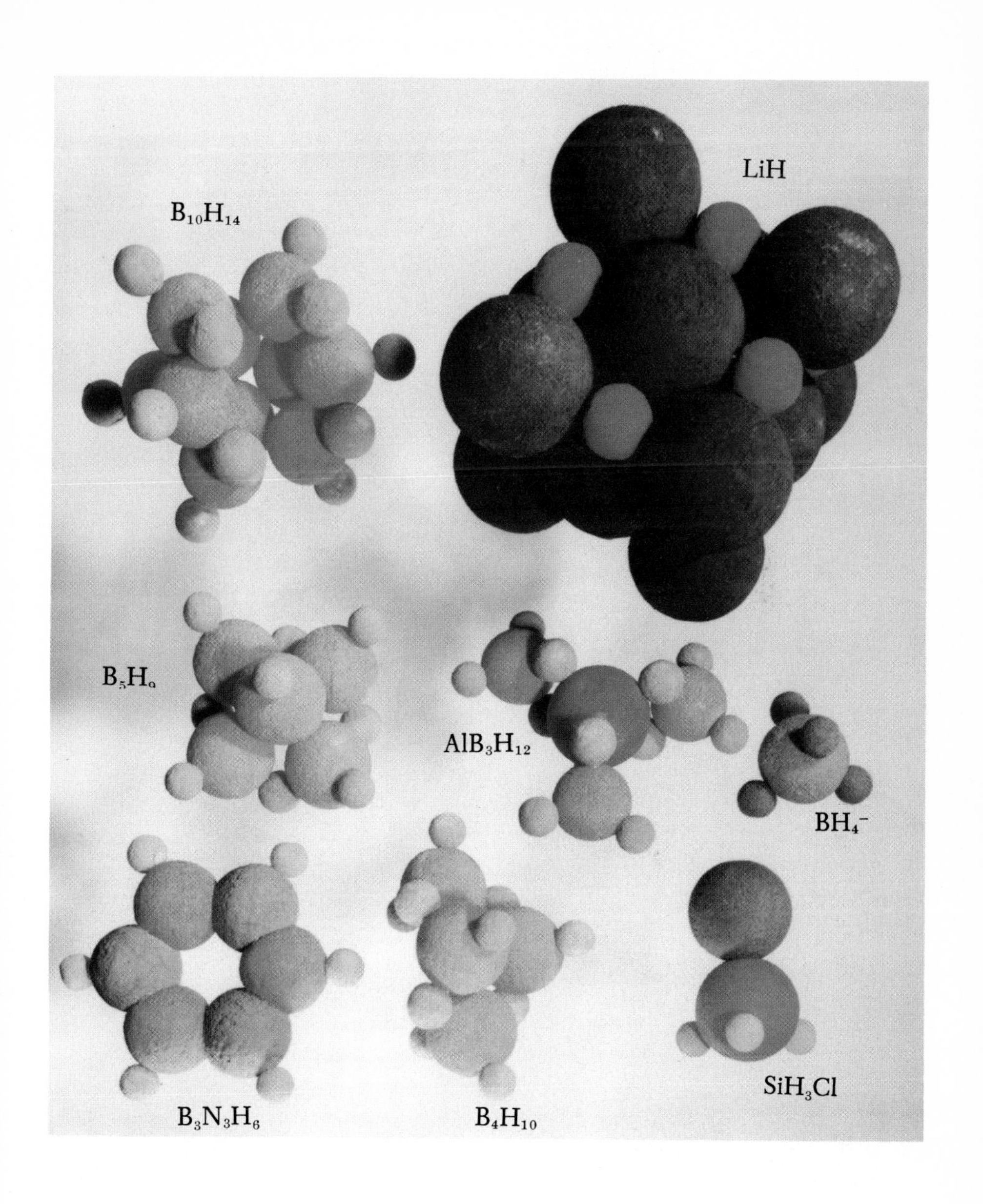

FIG. C-10. MISCELLANEOUS HYDRIDES AND DERIVATIVES.

FIG. B-10. SPHALERITE (ZINC BLENDE) LATTICE. This form of ZnS resembles diamond; 4:4 coordination. Each atom is attached at the corners of a regular tetrahedron to four of the other kind.

FIG. B-11. WURTZITE LATTICE (ZnS). This too shows 4:4 co-ordination, differing from diamond in the relative positions of the layers. Compare upper view with upper view of Fig. B-10, in which the holes are blocked.

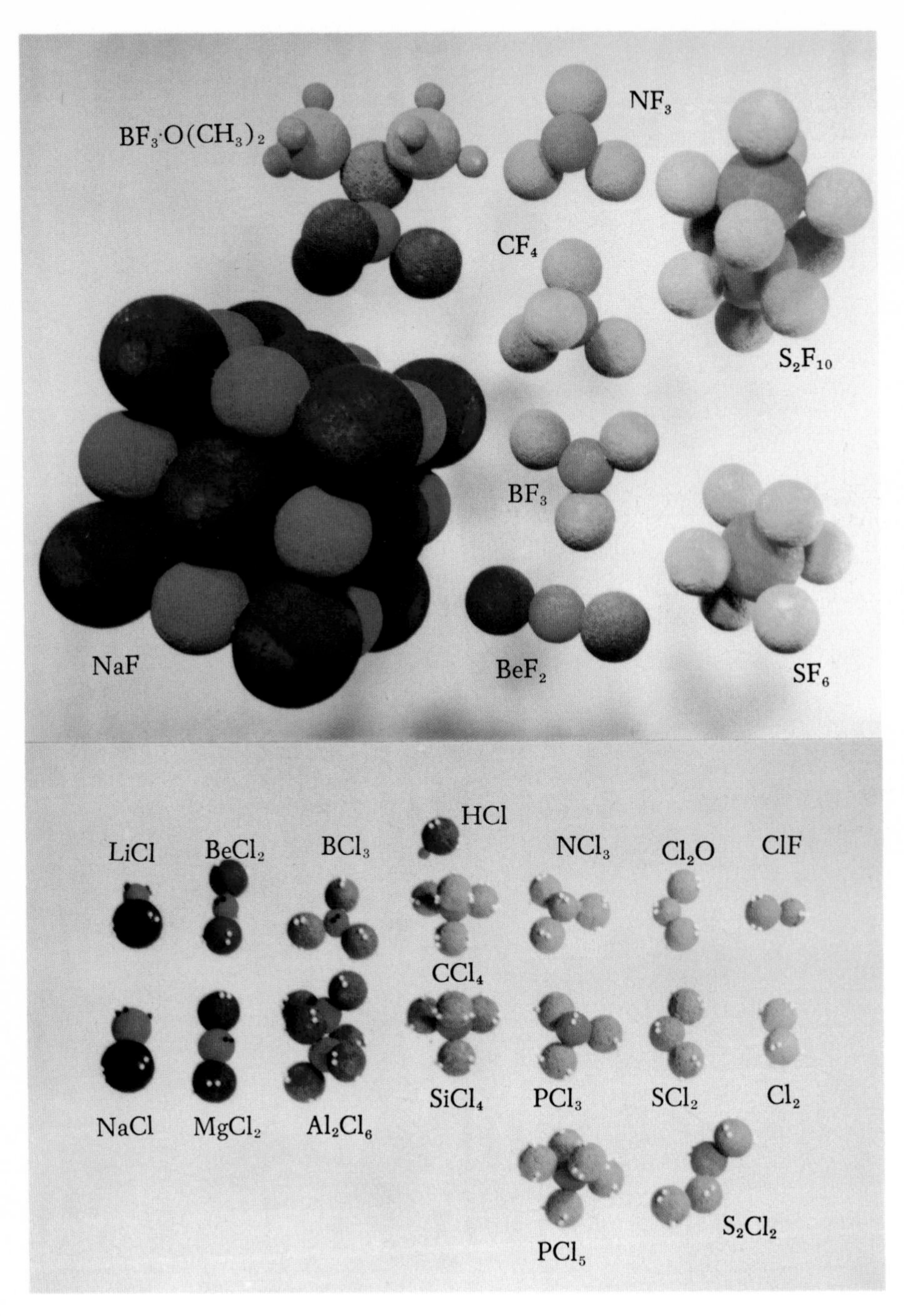

FIG. C-11. UPPER: SOME FLUORIDES. LOWER: SOME BINARY CHLORINE COMPOUNDS.

FIG. C-12. MISCELLANEOUS CHLORIDES. The $ZnCl_2$ is one layer of the lattice.

FIG. B-12. CORUNDUM (α-Al_2O_3) LATTICE. Lower left is rear view of upper. Lower right is view at angle showing similarity to sodium chloride structure (Fig. B-7).

FIG. B-13. FLUORITE (OR ANTIFLUORITE) LATTICE. The black atoms here show 8 coordination, the white atoms 4 coordination.

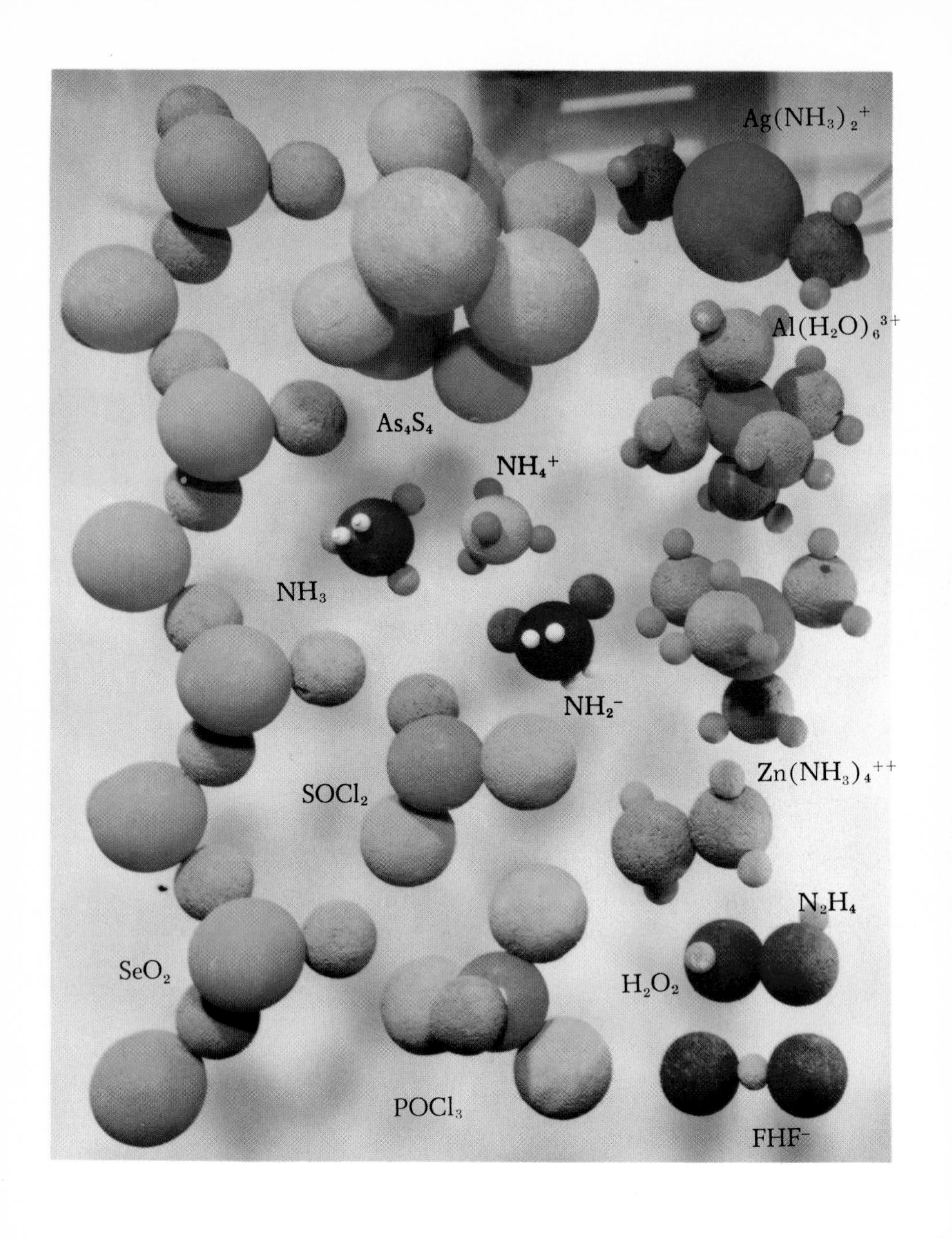

FIG. C-13. MISCELLANEOUS INORGANIC COMPOUNDS AND IONS. Compare NH_3 and Ions with Fig. C-3.

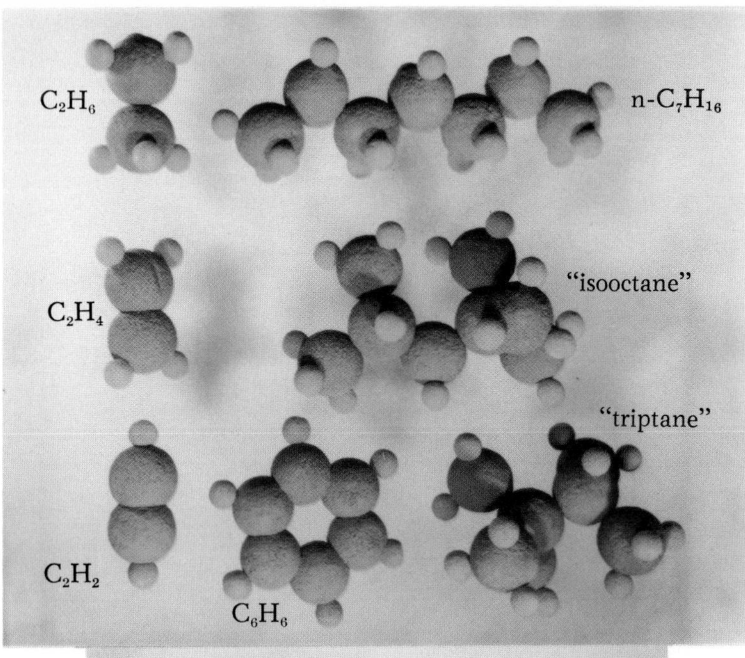

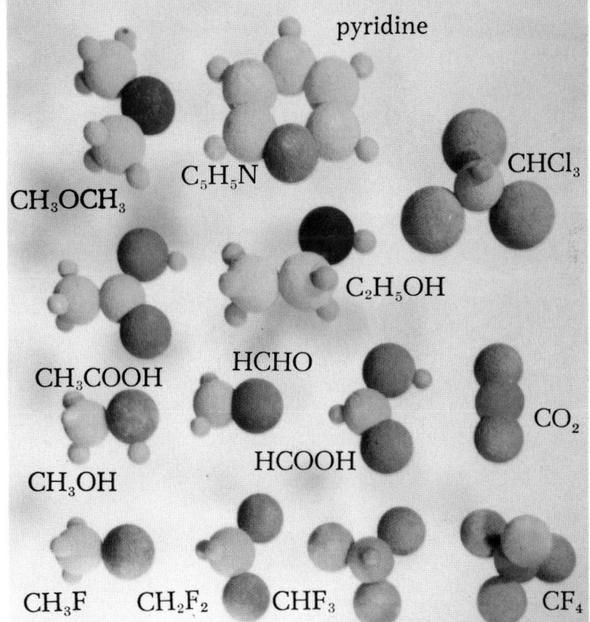

FIG. C-14. UPPER: SOME HYDROCARBONS. LOWER: SOME SIMPLE DERIVATIVES. Note especially the methane oxidation and fluorination series.

FIG. B-14. RUTILE (TiO_2) LATTICE. The white atoms show 6-coordination, the black, 3.

FIG. B-15. MX_2 LAYER LATTICE. Upper: top view of layer. Lower: side view of layer. White atoms show 6-coordination; black atoms, 3. Alternative ways of packing the layers produce different crystal forms.

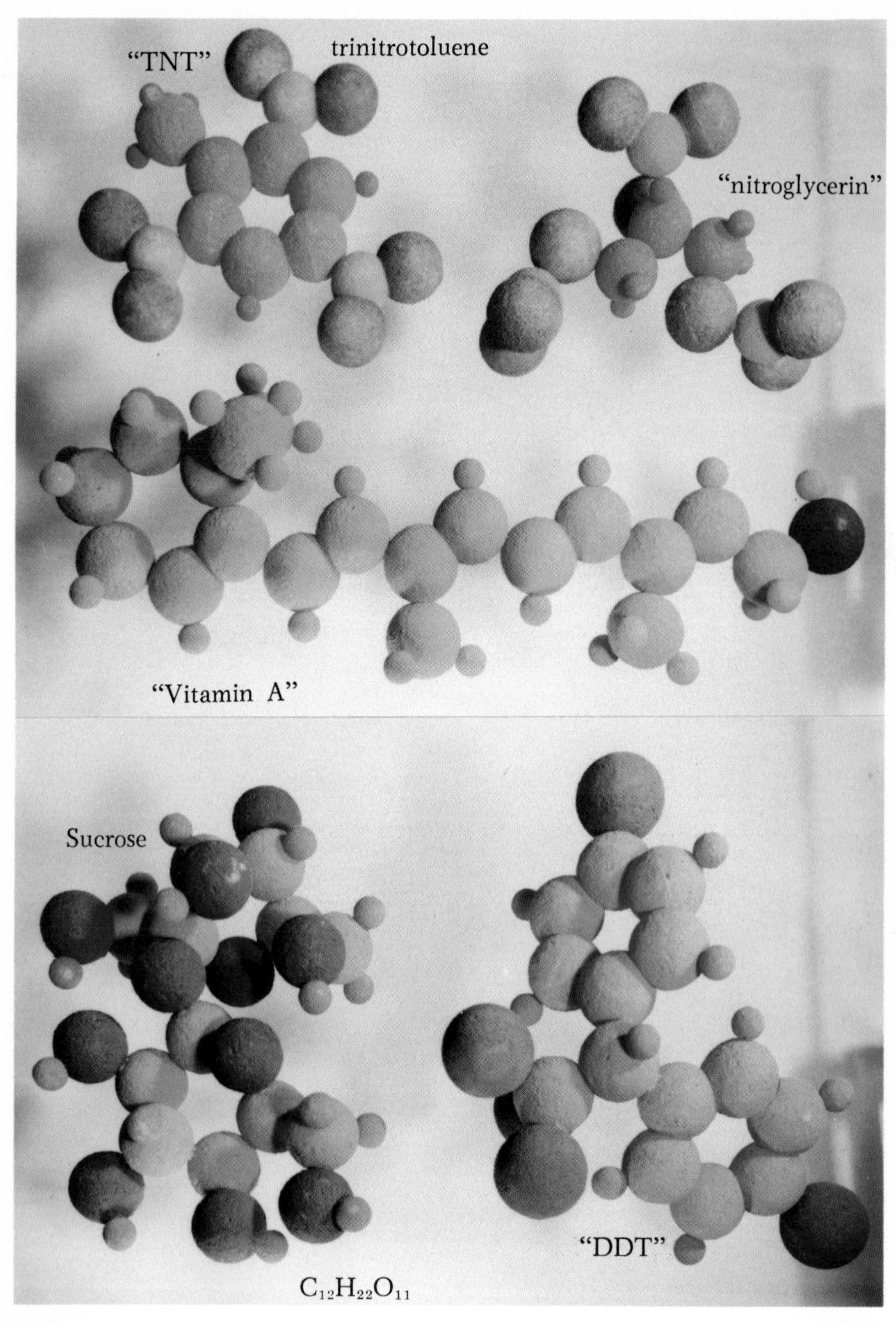

FIG C-15. SOME ORGANIC COMPOUNDS OF SPECIAL INTEREST.

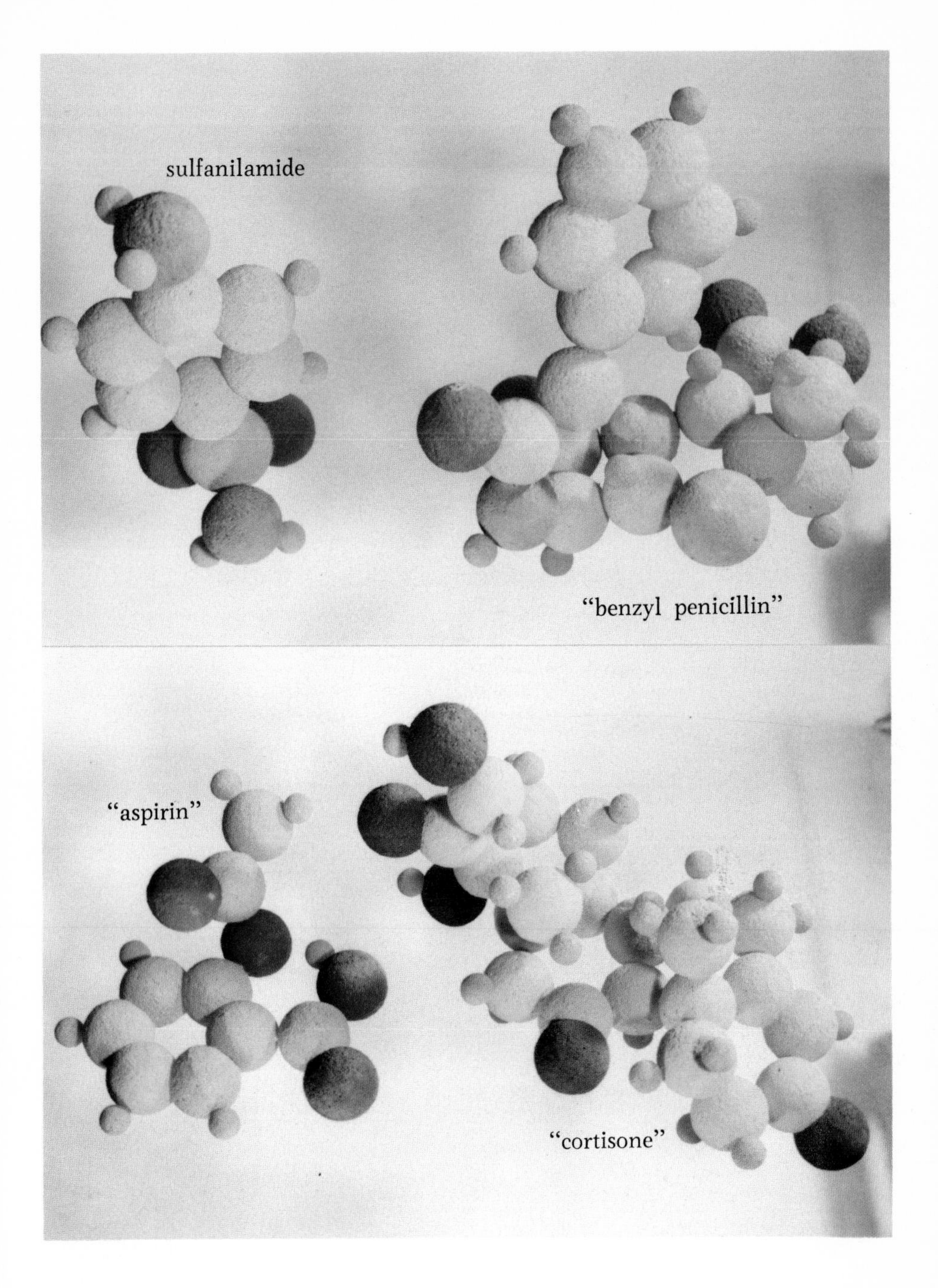

FIG. C-16. SOME COMPOUNDS OF MEDICAL INTEREST.

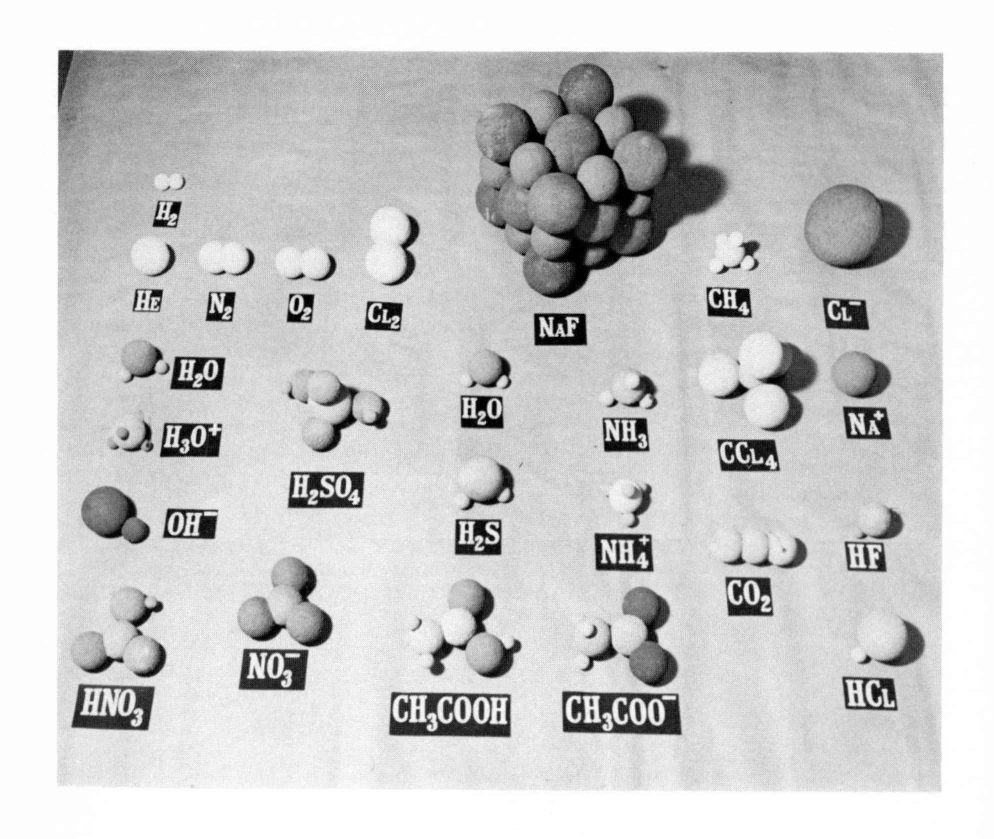

FIG. B-16. SET OF MODELS SUGGESTED FOR ELEMENTARY INSTRUCTION. Such a set can give introductory teaching experience with models on the basis of which additional models can be selected. Also needed: Atomic models.

CHAPTER

9

MISCELLANEOUS MODEL APPLICATIONS

COORDINATION CHEMISTRY

Addition Compounds

The planar configuration of Lewis acids of Group IIIA, such as BF_3 and $AlCl_3$ monomer, is changed to tetrahedral by the formation of a fourth coordination bond. This can be demonstrated, for example, by showing models of BF_3 and $(CH_3)_2O$ and then of their 1:1 addition compound (Figs. C-11 and C-14). The structural change could, of course, have been predicted easily from the idea that the bonds separate from one another as far as possible.

You may wish to point out that a similar change in structure of the donor molecule does not occur, because the full octet of electrons is already present around the donor atom even before coordination. A model of NH_3 or $N(CH_3)_3$ will serve to demonstrate this.

Crystal Coordination

When the formation of an individual molecule would leave stable outer orbitals unshielded and unoccupied, as, for example, in ZnO, individual molecules do not persist, but rather condense to a crystalline form in which the otherwise vacant orbitals appear to be utilized in the bonding. A model of the "wurzite" structure (Fig. B-11), characteristic of ZnO, will demonstrate one way in which such condensation can occur. In it the tetrahedral bonds to zinc, whose two single bonds are normally linear, are clearly evident.

One cannot always explain crystal bonding, especially in the more ionic crystals, in terms of specific orbitals and electron pairs in localized bonds, as was just done for ZnO. For example, LiCl has only four otherwise vacant orbitals around the lithium, but six chloride ion neighbors. With very few exceptions, however, molecules that would contain both vacant orbitals and unshared electron pairs condense to ionic or polymeric solids. Your students will be able to predict from any "atom-pair" model, the probable state of aggregation of the compounds. If all the atoms of a molecule exhibit an exterior of unshared electron pairs but no vacancies, your students can then predict that the compound, if solid, will be held together only by relatively weak forces and will probably therefore have a low melting point and be relatively volatile. The compound, depending on the number of atoms per molecule, in part, is quite as likely to be either liquid or gaseous at ordinary conditions.

Complex Ions and Their Compounds

You may wish to demonstrate by models both structure and isomerism of complex ions. For the latter purpose special models as described here have some advantages. Instead of glued connections for bonds, magnetism may be used. To each of four large spheres of styrofoam, perhaps 4 to 5 inches in diameter, attach six small magnets, imbedding them flush with the surface and gluing in place in positions at the 6 corners of a regular octahedron (90°-bond angles). Two inch diameter spheres of various colors—to distinguish them as representing different ligands—are each equipped with a small thin piece of sheet iron glued flush to the surface and partly imbedded for greater strength.

With such models you can easily demonstrate positional isomerism. For example, when two different kinds of ligands are attached in square planar configuration, your students can easily see that if the complex is MA_2B_2, two isomers are possible: one where the like ligands are adjacent, or "cis," the other where the like ligands are diagonally opposite, or "trans." Similarly, when six-coordination is involved, one can easily demonstrate the equivalence of all the "cis" positions and the difference from cis, but mutual equivalence of the three possible trans combinations. Isomerism involving more than two kinds of ligand can similarly be demonstrated.

For all these demonstrations, several of the magnetic spheres can be useful so that different or apparently different structures can be compared.

SOME APPLICATIONS TO ORGANIC CHEMISTRY

For many purposes and especially those involving the teaching of stereochemistry wherein "hindered" rotation must be explained, the conventional commercial models, which represent both van der Waals and bonding radii, are very satisfactory, and superior to the models described herein, in which nonbonding distances are not shown and the bonds are usually assembled to be rigid and nonrotating. Where it is desirable to show charge distribution, as in teaching about inductive effects, the new models are superior. For permanent displays or even for comparison of a number of molecules at once, the new models, being much cheaper, have great advantages. For example, one would hesitate to tie up many expensive atoms of the interchangeable type in a permanent model of cortisone, or sucrose, and one would also be reluctant to assemble such a model for one brief showing and then take it apart again. The only problem presented by the new type of permanently assembled models is one of storage, and this is not too serious, especially where classes are small and the smaller scale models are adequate.

Isomers

A collection of models of isomeric hydrocarbons or derivatives can be helpful in discussing this subject. For example, one might exhibit all the isomeric octanes and point out the differences.

Nomenclature

A set of hydrocarbon models and models of their derivatives could be very useful in a student exercise on the naming of organic compounds. Simply turn the students loose with a dozen or more molecular models that are labelled only by code, and let them assign names. This should be far superior visually to using a collection of graphical formulas on paper.

Functional Groups

A set of molecular models representing various types of organic compounds can be a valuable lecture aid as well as good material for student exercises. For example, one might have students identify the functional group and therefore the kind of compound for each of a series of models representing ethanol, ethane, diethyl ether, ethylamine, acetaldehyde, diethylketone, ethyl acetate, ethyl chloride, ethyl mercaptan, ethylene glycol, acetic acid, and as many more as desired. At a penny an atom, even the smallest budget should find room for a useful number of such models.

Partial Charge Effects

By the methods of charge calculation described herein, all atoms of the same element in the same molecule are assigned equal charge, no matter how or to what other atom they are attached. Some may object to this, claiming, for example, that the hydrogen on carbon in HCOOH is not the same as that attached to oxygen. This is true, but the difference is in the nature of the other atom to which the hydrogen is attached, and not necessarily a difference in charge. Unless each bond to an atom is independent of all other bonds to the same atom, a supposition that seems highly illogical and unacceptable, and unless the Principle of Electronegativity Equalization, for reasons not evident, is invalid, there seems to be no alternative to the assumption that all atoms of the same element must have the same charge in a given molecule.

Oxidation. A set of models showing the methane oxidation series can be instructive by showing the change in condition of the combined carbon and hydrogen with increased degree of electron withdrawal. These models should be CH_4, CH_3OH, HCHO, HCOOH, and CO_2 (Fig. C-14).

The methane fluorination series can similarly be usefully represented: CH_4, CH_3F, CH_2F_2, CHF_3, and CF_4 (Fig. C-14).

Acids. A comparison of models of any alcohol and the corresponding acid, for example, methanol and formic acid, will show how the nature of the hydroxyl group is changed by substitution of an oxygen for two hydrogens on the hydroxyl carbon. The O—H bond is made much more polar, with the result that the very slightly acidic properties of the alcohol become much enhanced in the carboxylic acid. (Association through protonic bridging also seems to increase, judging by the higher boiling points of the acids.)

The "inductive" effect of an electronegative substituent on the alpha carbon of a carboxylic acid molecule can also be shown by models of both acids and anions. For example, the O—H bond in chloroacetic acid is shown to be more polar than that in acetic acid. Also, the oxygen in the acetate ion is seen to be more negative than that in the chloroacetate ion. Both show the greater acidity of the chloroacetic acid. Successive substitution can similarly be shown to increase the acidity, and trifluoroacetate ion contains oxygen of very low negative charge and therefore poor electron donor ability, which is characteristic of a strong acid.

Thermal Stability. In some compounds a considerable degree of thermal instability appears to be associated with partial positive charge on two covalently attached atoms. In oxalic acid, for example, the two carbon atoms have fairly high positive charge, and the molecule decomposes easily. This result is to be noted especially in models of TNT and nitroglycerine (Fig. C-15), whose explosiveness may well be enhanced by the instability caused by adjacent high positive charges. (Fluorocarbons are notable exceptions; it seems possible that electrostatic attractions between each carbon and the fluorine atoms on adjacent carbons may compensate for the expected weakening of carbon-carbon bonds.)

Other Applications. The above discussion suggests only a few of the possible applications of these models to the teaching of organic chemistry. Many other applications are likely to occur to those actively concerned with organic chemistry.

SOME SUGGESTIONS FOR STUDENT EXERCISES

You have already read, in preceding chapters, various suggestions for stimulating student participation in the classroom by having students predict compounds from examination of models of atoms of the different elements. Here are some variations and extensions that you might find helpful for student activity in the laboratory. For most, if not all, of these exercises the smallest scale model should be quite satisfactory except that these may be too easily misplaced, lost, or pocketed. Perhaps relatively large, transparent plastic boxes, inside which each model can be permanently mounted where it can be inspected from all angles but not directly handled may be obtained.

1. Valence

This is a laboratory exercise which has been used in Iowa general chemistry courses several times now with very satisfactory results. The following information on mimeographed sheets is given to each student some time in the week preceding the laboratory period.

VALENCE

A Laboratory Exercise

In order to help you to become familiar with the electronic meaning of the term "valence" and to understand differences among the chemical elements in their ability to form bonds, you will be provided with a set of 13 models representing atoms of various elements. These models are styrofoam spheres, on the surface of which the outer four orbitals (one *s* and three *p* orbitals) are represented by black-headed and white-headed tacks.[1] (Please do not loosen these tacks.) A white tack head represents an electron; a black tack head represents an available space in an orbital which is capable of accommodating an electron. Any one orbital can accommodate two electrons. A pair of white tack heads then represents a pair of electrons, or an orbital that is completely filled. A pair of black tack heads represents two vacancies, or an orbital that is completely unoccupied. A pair consisting of one white and one black tack head represents an orbital containing one electron and therefore has one vacancy, to which another electron might be added.

[1] Upholstery nails, pushed through a drop of glue into the styrofoam surface until flush, are satisfactory, but spots could be painted as well and more cheaply.

Bond-forming Capacity: Prediction of Number of Bonds

In considering the distribution of the outer electrons of an atom among the four orbitals, *s* and three *p*, one must distinguish between "ground state" structure and "valence state" structure. In building up of electron energy levels, within any given principal quantum level the *s* orbital always becomes filled before any electron goes into a *p* orbital. Thus, when the number of electrons in the outer shell is more than one, the *s* orbital always contains two electrons, in the ground (or most stable) state of the atom.

However, the amount of energy necessary to promote one of these *s* electrons to a *p* orbital in the same principal quantum shell is relatively low. As will be discussed in more detail below, when an atom combines chemically, it makes use of as many orbitals as possible. Stated differently, the electrons do not remain paired in any one orbital as long as there is any orbital that has no electrons (this discussion concerns only the four outer orbitals). Specifically, then, the valence state of an atom differs from the ground state if the ground state contains both fully occupied and fully vacant outer orbitals. The difference is that in the ground state an atom contains a pair of electrons in the *s* orbital but in the valence state, which is the state significant in chemical reaction, one of these electrons is promoted from the *s* orbital to an otherwise vacant *p* orbital. *This set of atomic models includes both ground state and valence state electronic representations.* Thus, two different models may represent the same element. For example, in the ground state an atom might have a pair of electrons in one orbital and one electron in another orbital, leaving two more orbitals completely vacant. In the valence state the same atom would have but one electron in the first orbital and one electron in each of two other orbitals, leaving but one more orbital completely vacant.

There are two kinds of covalence, one involving an electron-vacancy combination on each of the combining atoms and the other involving a pair of electrons in the outer orbital of one of the combining atoms and a vacant outer orbital of the other. The electron sharing, 2 electrons held mutually by two atoms each using one of its orbitals for the purpose, produces a chemical bond. This bond is called just a "covalent bond" if each atom supplies one of the electrons, or a "coordinate covalent" or simply "coordinate" or "coordination" bond if both of the shared electrons came originally from just one of the atoms. The number of single covalent bonds that an atom can form is then shown by the number of electron-vacancy combinations—half-occupied outer orbitals—that exist, or could be created by promotion of one electron on the surface of the model. The number of coordinate covalent bonds and the function of the atom as either electron donor or electron acceptor is shown on the models by the number of pairs of outer electrons that are, or would be, *in the valence state,* or by the number of empty outer orbitals that are, or would be, unoccupied *in the valence state.*

Atoms in which the outer low-energy orbitals are all filled—with 2 or 8 outer electrons and no vacant orbitals indicated—are unable to form bonds and are therefore chemically inert.

Prediction of Empirical Formulas

Practically always an atom will form as many covalent bonds as it can, or at least use all available electrons, rather than form fewer bonds leaving one or more electron-vacancy combinations unutilized. Reliance on this rule permits the prediction of the composition of compounds of two different elements on the basis of the bond-forming ability of their atoms. For example, if atom A has an outer electronic structure that in the valence state indicates the ability to form two single covalent bonds, and atom B similarly can form three, the compound most likely to form when A and B react can be predicted to be A_3B_2.

In this exercise we are interested only in combinations that would contain covalent bonds (or ionic bonds). When both of two atoms have fewer outer electrons than they do vacancies, the bond between them is metallic, not covalent. For the purposes of this exercise we will consider only those possible combinations in which at least one of the combining atoms has at least 4 outer electrons. We shall assume that covalent bonds can be formed in all such combinations, and we shall assume that other combinations would form metallic bonds. The number of metallic bonds, and therefore the formulas of intermetallic compounds, cannot easily be predicted.

Remember, in judging from the models how many covalent bonds can be formed, (1) that the same number of bonds will result whether the model shows the "ground state" or the "valence state" of the atoms, and (2) that coordination bonds do not form until all ordinary covalent bonds have been formed. Coordination bonds should therefore not be included in the number of covalent bonds that can be formed.

Directional Nature of Covalence: Prediction of Angles

One more property that is indicated by the models is that of bond direction. Theoretical calculations have indicated that when *s* and *p* orbitals are simultaneously involved in forming chemical bonds, these orbitals do not remain *s* and *p* but "hybridize," become averaged, forming new orbitals of intermediate nature and all equivalent to one another.

These new "hybrid" orbitals are directed in space such that the bonds they can form make definite angles with one another that can be calculated theoretically. A simpler but equally effective view is that the pairs of electrons, *whether or not they are involved in bonding,* tend to become separated as far as possible on the surface of the atomic sphere. Unoccupied orbitals have no apparent effect. When all the outer electrons are involved in forming two bonds, the farthest apart these can be is directly opposite one another, or, they form an angle of 180°. When all the outer electrons are involved in forming three bonds, the farthest apart these can be is at the corners of an equilateral triangle with the atomic nucleus at its center—in other words, the bond angles are 120°. When all the outer electrons are involved in forming four bonds, the farthest apart these can be is at the corners of a regular tetrahedron about the atomic nucleus, thus making bond angles of 109°28′.

On the other hand, when an atom can form two covalent bonds but there are also two electron pairs—two filled orbitals—in the outer shell of the atom, which are not involved in the bonding, then the effect is almost the same as when four bonds are present and the structure is tetrahedral with the two bonds at an angle near to 109°. When an atom can form three covalent bonds, but there is also another outer shell electron pair (filled orbital) uninvolved in the bonding, the structure is again nearly tetrahedral, the three bonds forming angles near to 109°.

In the atomic models you will study, for those representing the valence state, the tack heads are located at approximately the correct positions to indicate the directional characteristics of the bonding, as outlined above.

Electronegativity: Prediction of Bond Polarity

Electronegativity may be defined as the relative attraction which an atom has for the electrons of a covalent bond. When two atoms initially unequal in electronegativity form a covalent bond, the bonding electrons are unevenly shared, the atom which was initially higher in electronegativity gaining more than half share. This means a partial negative charge is acquired by this atom, leaving the other atom partially positive. The bond is therefore *polar,* to a degree dependent on the initial electronegativity difference.

In general, elements of lowest electronegativity are those having fewest outermost electrons, and as the number of electrons in the outermost shell increases, the electronegativity tends to increase. One can therefore predict from the models whether an atom will be high or low or intermediate in electronegativity. On the basis of this prediction, one can also predict the direction and roughly the extent of polarity of a bond between two atoms of different elements.

EXERCISE

This is what you are to do. If you have not read the above discussion carefully, do so first. Then study each model very carefully and fill in the accompanying chart. Each model has a code letter identifying it to the instructor. This code letter is *not* a chemical symbol! First list the code letter. Then indicate whether the model represents the ground state or the valence state or perhaps both. Remembering that the ground state if different must change to the valence state before chemical combination can occur, indicate how many ordinary covalent bonds the atom can form, what would be the bond angle, how many coordinate covalent bonds it can form, and whether in the forming of the latter, it would be expected to act as electron donor or electron acceptor. When you have completed the tabulation of this information for all thirteen models, then predict the empirical formulas of binary compounds of each atom with each of the others (except when metallic bonding would be predicted as discussed above), and write these formulas in the appropriate spaces. In these formulas underline the letter that designates the element which you would predict to have the negative charge.

Finally, identify all the possible actual elements that each of these models *could* represent.

We have found that one set of thirteen models is sufficient for each group of ten students, and that one two-hour laboratory period is about adequate for the exercise.

2. Periodicity—Atomic Models

Perhaps to supplement your own lecture demonstration of the construction of a periodic table, using the atomic models of the elements, you may wish to devise a laboratory exercise in which students, by close personal inspection of the individual atomic models (coded but not otherwise identified), can decide for themselves how best to place these elements in a periodic system. They will be able to identify the elements of the same group by their similar outer electronic configurations and place them in proper sequence within the group according to increasing size.

3. Periodicity—Molecular Models

Your students, by examining a set of models of compounds of the major group elements with any one of the nonmetals, for example, oxygen, should be able to arrange them in a periodic arrangement and identify them by their composition and structure—especially if the outer unshared electrons and vacancies are represented on the models.

4. Predicting Properties of Binary Hydrogen Compounds (or Oxygen or Halogen Compounds) from Atomic Models

By studying the individual atomic models of the elements, your students should be able to make reasonable predictions about their compounds. If you choose one nonmetal, for example, hydrogen or oxygen or fluorine or chlorine or sulfur and assign them the problem of deciding the physical and chemical nature of its binary compounds with each of the other major group elements, they should be able to write a somewhat detailed account of the properties without actually knowing these properties as they have been observed. This exercise or similar ones should give them valuable practice in analytical thinking and help them toward a sound understanding of the cause-and-effect relationships in chemistry.

5. Predicting Properties of the Other Element from Molecular Models of Binary Compounds of One Element

Another valuable student exercise may consist of having them study a relatively large number of molecular models of the same element combined with others. For example, a representation of fluorine compounds across the periodic table, distributed at random and labelled only as fluorides, should serve. Knowing the nature of fluorine, the students should be able to judge from the qualities shown by the molecular model what must be the valence, relative electronegativity, and probable identity of the other element in the compound. You and they will be agreeably surprised to realize how once the general scheme becomes familiar, the properties of compounds are predictable from the properties of the elements and the properties of the elements, from the properties of the compounds.

6. Student Construction of Models

No student can fail to learn useful information about chemistry by building atomic and molecular models himself. In fact, personal construction and possession of such models should add much to a student's interest and enjoyment, as well as success, in chemistry. Furthermore, what they say about "many hands" applies to model construction as well as to other sometimes tedious jobs, and you could, if you wished, build up a good collection of useful models for your own department if you could enlist the enthusiastic help of some of your students. Once materials are assembled, paints mixed, and instructions or structural details are collected, the work should go rapidly. One could not only accumulate a collection of models for lecture demonstration or laboratory exercise purposes, but also establish a sort of chemical museum, which in a few years could be very valuable in attracting interest to chemistry, as well as helpful in study and research. Even for students not majoring in chemistry, the experience of creating for themselves the means of visualizing what would otherwise be very nebulous and abstract should be valuable in suggesting similar approaches to problems of learning and understanding in other fields. One learns much more from personal construction than could ever be learned just from visual study of what someone else has constructed.

SUGGESTIONS FOR DISPLAY DEMONSTRATIONS

If adequate showcase space, well lighted and strategically located, is available, large-scale models can be used for spectacular displays to attract general interest and/or to teach specific lessons. But even if such space is not available, the smallest scale models lend themselves well to poster-type displays that can serve as a supplement to the classroom demonstrations and the laboratory exercises.

The following list is intended merely to suggest some of the kinds of chemistry that can be explained or elaborated on by means of such poster displays, using the small-scale models and attaching them to poster cardboard on which are printed appropriate explanatory captions.

1) Water and its Ions
2) Physical Properties of Water, and Structure of Ice
3) Water as a Solvent
4) Acids and Bases
5) Oxidizing Agents
6) Structural Isomerism in Inorganic Chemistry
7) Displacement Reactions
8) Double Decompositions
9) Chemical Equations
10) Ionization

For example, students may find it helpful to study a poster showing the meaning of complete chemical equations, such as the following:

Synthesis of Water: A Complete Chemical Equation

Here is a model of a molecule of hydrogen. (MODEL)
It contains two atoms; hence its formula is H_2.
Here is a model of a molecule of oxygen. (MODEL)
It contains two atoms; its formula is O_2.
Here is a model of water. (MODEL)

It contains two hydrogen atoms and one oxygen atom; its formula is H_2O. When hydrogen burns in air or oxygen, it combines with the oxygen to form water.

By models and formulas this reaction may be represented:

$$(\text{MODEL } H_2) + (\text{MODEL } O_2) \rightarrow (\text{MODEL } H_2O)$$
$$H_2 + O_2 \rightarrow H_2O$$

However: Because there must be two oxygen atoms (O_2), two water molecules (2 H_2O) must result, to keep from losing (or gaining) any oxygen atoms by the reaction, which would be impossible.

But if there must be two H_2O, four hydrogen atoms or two H_2 are needed. Therefore, the complete reaction must be represented:

$$(\text{MODEL } H_2, \text{MODEL } H_2) + (\text{MODEL } O_2) \rightarrow$$
$$2\,H_2 + O_2 \rightarrow$$

$$(\text{MODEL } H_2O, \text{MODEL } H_2O)$$
$$2\,H_2O$$

The number of useful posters of this type that might be prepared for display conspicuously in your chemistry rooms or in the halls is limited only by your patience and willingness to improvise them. What may not have been clear to your students when presented in one way may suddenly be revealed in all its beautiful simplicity in some other way; it is a wise teacher who makes available to his students as many alternative ways of learning as possible.

CHAPTER

10

MODEL CONSTRUCTION

GENERAL INFORMATION

Scale

Three different scales are recommended for the models, although of course, any convenient scale should be satisfactory. The scales chosen here are based in part on the commercial availability of materials of the right size and shape. For use in large lecture rooms a practical scale is 1.5 inches per Ångstrom unit. On this scale, if covalent radii are represented, a hydrogen atom is about 1 inch in diameter. The linear magnification is 381 millions. By this scale carbon, nitrogen, and oxygen are about 2.5 inches in diameter. The largest atoms, of cesium, are about 7 inches in diameter.

Considerably more expensive and requiring greater storage space are models built on double the above scale, or 3 inches per Ångstrom. At least a few such models can be very useful. Not only are the atoms even easier to see, but one can use electrons and vacancies 1 inch in diameter, more easily visible through a large room. My own collection includes most of the atomic models of the major group elements, as well as a few molecules and ions.

For smaller group instruction and for special exercises such as those suggested for student laboratory periods in the preceding chapter, as well as for displays and teaching exhibits, a scale one-fifth the first, or 0.3 inch per Ångstrom, is very satisfactory. A hydrogen atom is then about one-fourth inch in diameter, and carbon, nitrogen, and oxygen atoms about one-half inch in diameter; the largest atoms and ions are about 1.5 inches in diameter.

Materials

From the viewpoint of availability, cost, and ease of construction the foamed polystyrene plastic known as "styrofoam" is excellent. Other possible materials are wood, cork, clay, bakelite, asbestos, and paper or cellulose in other forms. No doubt other materials might also be used.

Styrofoam may be purchased in the form of spheres over a range in diameters from ½ or ¾ to 10 inches or more. Intermediate sizes can usually be made by grinding down larger spheres with sandpaper or a power sander, or a power-driven wire brush. The latter is especially effective in reducing the size of large spheres, such as from 10 to 8½ inches in diameter. Considerable skill is needed to preserve sphericity during such grinding operations. Fortunately, a simpler method is available by which diameters may be reduced by up to ½ inch, easily by ¼ inch, while maintaining a satisfactory degree of sphericity. The ball is rolled in all directions between two smooth, level surfaces, its foamy structure being compressed toward the center by carefully controlled pressure on the rolling surface. If you use a small piece of plate glass for rolling the sphere on a table top, you can see what is happening to the sphere before it becomes uncontrollably misshapen. This rolling process not only decreases the diameter but also compacts and hardens the surface, making it easier to paint and more resistant toward denting and wear in general.

One can place the ball on a smooth table top, and, holding a short, smooth board, or even a hard-covered book, with both hands so that it rests on the ball, cause the ball to roll in all directions by careful manipulation of the board. Frequent inspection of the results is necessary to be sure that deviations from sphericity are caught in time for correction and that the correct diameter is reached. If you have cut down a larger sphere to a smaller one of approximate sphericity, you can accomplish a surprising amount of smoothing of what may initially have been an extremely rough surface.

For making the smaller scale models, ¾ inch, 1 inch, and 1¼ inches diameters fill most requirements. One can roll a 1-inch diameter ball, for example, down nearly to ½-inch diameter, which is approximately the lower limit. For hydrogen atoms on this scale, one must start with spheres not over ½-inch diameter (better, smaller), which can be made by sandpapering ¾-inch diameter balls. Alternatively, they can be made by cutting small cubes of styrofoam, carefully slicing off the corners, and then compressing the foam between thumb and finger to approximate sphericity before rolling to obtain the final smoothing. In fact, you may find it easier to perform the initial compacting of all these smaller spheres between thumb and forefinger, or between the palms, before carrying out the final rolling on a table.

For a guide to size, when making the small-scale models by rolling down larger styrofoam spheres, you will find a circle template invaluable. Such a device is simply a piece of plastic with holes of a large variety of diameters cut in it so it may be used for stencilling. It can be purchased in stationery or drafting supply stores. A series of holes differing each from the next by $\frac{1}{64}$ inch in diameter is very satisfactory. Lacking such a device, you can use a good set of drills to bore holes of appropriate diameters in a wooden board or heavy plastic sheet—or even a sharp set of cork borers may do the job. You may wish to make some cardboard guides of similar nature for larger model construction.

Incidentally, I have noticed that rolling 1-inch diameter balls to crush them to smaller diameter builds up a very considerable static charge when done on a plate glass surface. Even on a damp day, this charge is only very slowly lost, much remaining after several hours. Interesting demonstrations of electrostatic fields can be made by dropping such charged balls one by one on to the center of a surface of quiet water, as in a basin. The balls repel one another and move to more symmetrical arrangements.

Styrofoam spheres are easily cut with a knife (better with a serrated or sawlike blade), as is necessary when closer than tangential contact between two spheres is desired.

Dr. Richard Campbell of the University of Iowa has found an electrically heated wire to be excellent for making smooth cuts. A piece of nichrome wire, adequately supported and connected to the current source through a variable resistance such as a Variac, is all that is required; the temperature should be kept at the minimum needed for effective melting of the foam.

The chief disadvantage of styrofoam, though it is not too serious a disadvantage, is its mechanical weakness. It does not break easily but dents too easily. A sphere large enough to have appreciable weight—2 inches in diameter or larger—is likely to acquire a flat area if dropped on the floor, and can be dented by pressing between thumb and finger. Compacting by rolling to decrease the diameter helps strengthen the surface, and even without compacting, the spheres will stand ordinarily careful handling indefinitely long. There is little need to treat them roughly. Repairs can be made by gluing an extra piece of styrofoam in the dent and smoothing with pressure or sandpaper, or by filling with asbestos cement. Large models are heavy enough to place too much strain on the individual joints and they may break at the joint if the model is roughly treated, but again rough treatment can normally be avoided. It has been suggested that the weight of the larger spheres, in the range 6 to 12 inches in diameter, can be reduced if desired by carefully sawing a sphere in half, carving out most of the inside as one might hollow out a pumpkin, and gluing the two hollowed halves back together again.

Various suppliers of styrofoam spheres in assorted sizes are listed in Table 10-1. These are by no means the only suppliers. Styrofoam has become a widely used material for Christmas decorations, and many small local manufacturers of such decorations can supply the spheres. In the holiday season you will find a few sizes on sale at local department stores and other places; you will possibly not wish to pay the retail prices if you need very many of the spheres, but you can probably persuade the store manager to tell you the name of his supplier, who will usually sell by the dozen or the gross at much lower rates. You can also cut your own crudely from chunks of styrofoam plank, such as used by florists or in packing, and these can be rolled quite smooth with a little practice.

Various other materials can be used for inexpensive spheres. Some can be purchased already in ball form, including certain sizes of wood, cork, and bakelite or other plastic such as lucite. Others can easily be made into spheres. Art supply stores often have special powdered modelling clay that can be mixed with water, molded or shaped, and then baked to a fair strength and water resistance. Such clay can be used for small scale models, the shaping being done by rolling a little of the moistened clay between the palms. Ordinary asbestos cement (powdered asbestos), obtainable from paint or hardware stores or plumbing supply houses, can similarly be mixed with water and rolled easily into small spheres. When these have dried in the air, they can then be soaked in sodium silicate solution (commercial "water glass," diluted with one or two volumes of water) for several hours. Your druggist will probably be able to supply you. (If you mix the asbestos with sodium silicate solution in the first place, instead of with water, you will find it difficult to roll smooth balls from it.) When allowed to dry in the air, spheres so treated have much greater strength than the plain asbestos and are satisfactory for model building.

Mr. Harry F. Stubbs, of Milton Academy, has made some excellent small scale crystal models using macerated newspaper or alpha-cellulose, and rolling spheres from the wet pulp by hand. These he shellacs and then paints and assembles.

A disadvantage of materials such as clay, asbestos, and plastic (of the unfoamed variety) lies in the difficulty of making permanent connections at the correct bond angles, and with the spheres cut for the proper bond lengths. As will be discussed below, styrofoam spheres are easily fastened together.

Painting

Pigment. A cheap and satisfactory pigment for producing the desired colors is dry tempera. Recommended for the color scales described in Chapters 1 and 2 are the following: black, red, orange, yellow, green, and blue. White may also prove useful. You need not be much of an artist to know that red and yellow mix to give orange, and yellow and blue give green. However, I recommend purchasing orange and green, because our experience was that pleasing oranges and greens did not result from the primary red, yellow, and blue we were able to obtain. Be sure that these purchased colors all look bright and clean. You will then be able to mix very satisfactory intermediate hues, using red and orange for red-oranges, orange and yellow for yellow-oranges, yellow and green for yellow-greens, and green and blue for blue-greens.

We have found not only that different brands of tempera differ in hue of the same color name, but also that a color of the same brand is not always constant from container to container. Therefore the information of Table 10-3 is given only as an approximate guide. Your problem is to prepare five different red-oranges that are clearly distinguishable from red, from orange, and from one another. Similarly, you will need five different yellow-oranges, five different yellow-greens, and five different blue-greens. With your five basic colors you will have 25 hues. You will want these to be as evenly spaced as possible, but this will happen automatically if you make each as distinct from its neighbors as possible. Be sure to measure and record the relative volumes of pigments in each mixture so that you can reproduce the hue when the supply runs low.

Dry tempera can be mixed very easily merely by shaking in a closed container. About 2-4 ounces of each hue will suffice for a large number of models unless the scale is very large. An initial purchase of 1 pound each of black, red, and blue, and 2 pounds each of green, yellow, and orange should keep you supplied for some time, and at a cost, at time of writing, under one dollar per pound for the pigment.

Color-Blindness. If you have difficulty distinguishing colors or are worried about the fact that a small percentage of your students are likely to be so handicapped, you may wish a different color scale. Blues and grays are said to offer less difficulty than any other colors. You may then decide to adopt a black–white–blue scheme. For electronegativity, the range from very low to very high would be from blue through lighter blues, white, and increasingly darker grays to black. The same range would represent partial charge from high positive (blue) through neutral (white) to high negative (black).

Vehicle. Most commercial paints contain solvents that at least soften polystyrene and often dissolve it. Initially, paint for these models was made by mixing tempera with water. This presented the difficulty that water does not wet polystyrene well. A small amount of household dishwashing detergent solved this problem, although brushing rather than dipping was essential because of the rough surface, with crevices still not readily wetted. Increasing the concentration of sizing (glue) in the tempera might have helped improve the adherence of the paint, but as it was, the paint served satisfactorily but not really well. It tended to rub off slightly, and easily came off under abrasive conditions. However, when the models were separately wrapped in tissue and packed together in a trunk, they endured the handling of the nation's railways for thousands of miles without damage either to paint or model.

The Reverend Maurice Blackburn, of Edmonton, Alberta, reported that shellac made a good protective coating, which was superior to the plastic spray I had been using very lightly and recommending (with caution, because the spray is an excellent solvent for polystyrene). This suggested that white shellac might be a satisfactory medium instead of water in the first place. Indeed it is. It wets better, dries faster, gives brighter colors and a surface more resistant to abrasion. The tempera cuts the natural gloss of the shellac, giving a clean, velvety appearance that is very appealing. The durability of the color cannot yet be vouched for, but at least no change is noticeable after several months.

Where dipping is convenient, it appears to be as satisfactory as brushing, especially when shellac is the medium, or vehicle. This is notably true when the spheres have been rolled and thus have a smoother surface. It is a very effective and rapid method especially for the small-scale models. You merely drop the ball into a jar of paint and when you have fished it out, it is painted. This is a real timesaver in eliminating the need of cleaning brushes. The freshly painted sphere can be placed to dry on a piece of newspaper, avoiding the headlines which tend to come off on the model slightly. If the sphere is then rolled to a fresh position after it has dried for about 10 to 15 minutes, it will not become seriously stuck to the paper in completing the drying, which will take from 15 minutes to an hour longer.

Connectors and Glue

Any glue that does not dissolve styrofoam should be all right. The preparations of brand names "Duratite" and "Elmer's Glueall" are among those that are satisfactory. Glue alone can serve to connect styrofoam spheres, and in some more complex models where it is nearly impossible to put connectors in place, glue is the only means of holding the model together. Where possible, however, connectors are strongly recommended, to be used with the glue. These have both temporary and permanent value. Temporarily, until the glue can harden, they can serve to hold atoms together at the correct locations and angles—especially when single-bond covalence is indicated by tangential contact of the spheres. The permanent value of connectors is derived from the strength they supply. The glue may be unbreakably strong but the styrofoam is not.

A glued spot holding two styrofoam spheres together can easily break out a chunk of foam from one of the spheres. For large models, the larger the connector the better, for the more area the firmer the glued contact. My personal preference is for diamond-shaped wooden connectors about $\frac{1}{16}$ inch thick, $\frac{1}{2}$ inch at the greatest width, and 1 to 4 inches long depending on diameters of spheres to be connected. These can be cut from strips of hardwood by making a series of parallel angular cuts.

When two spheres are pushed together from opposite ends of a connector, it may not penetrate the two spheres evenly, but, encountering a tougher region in one sphere, may penetrate the other almost exclusively. This is the chief reason for the diamond shape—the resistance to penetration increases with depth, and an even placement of the connector is ordinarily assured.

Styrofoam is easily penetrated. You can hold between thumb and forefinger a connector such as described above and thrust it into a sphere readily without making a preliminary slot or hole. A simple procedure is to place a generous drop of glue on the sphere at the bond location and thrust the connector straight through the middle of the glue into the sphere until it reaches the widest part of the diamond. Then spread the glue generously over the protruding surface of the connector and thrust the connector into the second atom.

For the small scale models pipe cleaners work very well as connectors. Cut the pipe cleaner into appropriate lengths, using a wire cutter. At the point to be connected, thrust a sharp pencil point into the sphere about $\frac{1}{4}$ inch. Place a drop of glue over the hole and thrust the connector in, to the desired depth. Repeat, preparing the other atom for connection, and then push the atoms together until they make satisfactory contact and the pipe cleaner section is completely concealed. When the glue is partly but not entirely dry, the bond angles can be given final adjustment if necessary.

Electrons and Vacancies

The choice of materials to be used to represent the electrons and vacancies of the outer shell, both in the atomic models and in the molecular models where desired, depends on the scale of the models. For the large scale, 1-inch diameter styrofoam spheres fastened to the atomic surface like other atoms by glue and connector are satisfactory. For the medium scale, the electron and vacancy balls cannot be more than about $\frac{1}{4}$ to $\frac{3}{8}$ inch in diameter. Plastic balls of this size range are very inexpensive (e.g., bakelite or lucite). If not purchased in the needed color they may be painted and glued to the atoms in the desired locations. Wooden or plastic beads can similarly be painted and fastened to the atomic sphere by a combination of glue and nail. From the viewpoint of strength this is better as small balls merely glued are easily broken loose from the styrofoam simply by a tearing of the styrofoam. For the small-scale models, white and black glass-headed pins, which are cut the right length with wire cutters, are ideal. If these cannot be obtained, one can purchase in a hobby shop, black and white beads about $\frac{1}{16}$ to $\frac{1}{8}$ inch in diameter, such as are used in "beadcraft"—making beaded belts and other designs on leather goods. These are very inexpensive. Short common pins, about $\frac{1}{2}$ inch long, and glue are suitable for fastening these beads to the atoms. For either the glass-headed pin or the bead-and-pin, one first places a small spot of glue on the atomic surface, then thrusts the pin into the atom at that point. When common pins and beads are used, the pinheads can easily be touched up later with white or black paint—tempera plus shellac.

Locating Bond Positions

You may wish to improvise some type of jig for locating the positions on the atomic spheres for attaching other atoms at the proper bond angles. For suggestions see references 13 and 19 in the bibliography, page 129. However, a good eye for symmetry and a few simpler aids can make such a jig unnecessary, especially with styrofoam which lends itself well to minor corrections. The most common angles to locate are those of a regular tetrahedron, 109°28′. If you have a number of spheres of the same size, you may wish to prepare a simple guide for locating these positions. Such a guide is based on the fact that the diameter of a circle which would circumscribe any three corners of a tetrahedron is 0.93 times the diameter of the sphere which exactly encloses the entire tetrahedron. Draw on a piece of stiff cardboard or plastic sheet a circle 0.93 times the diameter of the spheres you intend to use as tetrahedral atoms. Inscribe an equilateral triangle in this circle and mark the points where its corners touch the circle. Cut out the circle, leaving a hole with the three points marked on its edge. Now, if you hold a sphere firmly in this hole, with a sharp pencil you can make on it the three points. These are three of the four corners of the inscribed tetrahedron. The fourth corner can be located visually as equidistant from the other three.

Ordinarily, a simple drawing on paper, consisting of a series of concentric circles of the approximate sizes of the atomic spheres you will use, with straight lines from its center indicating a variety of common angles, such as 90°, 100°, 109°28′, 120°, etc., can serve as a guide for most purposes. Simply hold the sphere over such a drawing so that it is properly centered to fit the appropriate circle, and mark the positions on its surface. When, for example, you have thus marked two positions making a bond angle of 109°28′ (toothpicks serving well as markers), you may find the other two corners of the terathedron in either of the following ways. You can select visually a point that makes an equilateral triangle with the first two, on one side of them, and then select another point that makes an equilateral triangle with the first two, on the other side of them. Alternatively, you can locate a point midway between the first two points and then another point exactly opposite this one on the other side of the sphere. Then locate two points equidistant from this last point, at the same distance as the first two points are distant from the point midway between them. These two new points form a straight line that is perpendicular to the line formed by the original two points. With a little practice you can thus assemble molecular tetrahedra visually, and the final test will be the symmetry of the completed structure. Even after the glue has dried, you can make minor alterations in bond angles by pressing the two "atoms" firmly together and applying a little extra pressure in the direction needed. New glue can then be added around this joint to tighten it again.

Construction Patterns

For all models which include multiple bonding, which means closer than tangential approach of bonded atoms, you will find it helpful to prepare a simple two-dimensional pattern. All you need is paper, compass, ruler, and protractor. First make a skeleton of the model, or portion of the model, consisting of straight lines forming the correct bond angles. The nucleus of one atom will be at the intersection of two or more such lines. Measure, to the correct scale, the exact internuclear distance to the next atom and mark a point there to represent its nucleus. Then, using these nuclei as centers, draw a circle of the correct radius for the atom in the compound, around each. Where these circles overlap, as they will if multiple bonding is involved, the correct line at which to cut off each sphere is indicated. Simply hold the sphere on a table resting directly over the circle that represents it, and cut off the segment as indicated. Be careful to make your cut straight down. Before attaching the spheres together, you can smooth out the two cut surfaces by pressing the two surfaces gently together and scrubbing them over one another. Such construction patterns are not only needed for help with multiple bonds, but they are also useful as guides in fastening the spheres at the correct bond angles.

Building Models

Complete details for building many atomic, molecular, and crystal models are given in the final section of this chapter. You certainly need not be limited to the models listed therein, for you can easily calculate all you need to know for the construction of many others, especially with the help of the tables provided.

The following procedure is typical:

1) From the chemical formula and the electronegativities of the component elements, calculate the electronegativity of the combination, as described on page 27 and with the help of the data of Table 10-2, page 136.

2) From the electronegativity of the combination, calculate the covalent radius of each atom in combination, as described on page 30 and with the help of the data of Table 2-2, page 132. This task should be greatly aided by the data of Table 10-2, from which all you need to do is interpolate if the radii you want are not already in the table. From these radii, and the appropriate factor for whatever scale you have chosen, you can determine what diameters are needed for each atomic sphere.

3) From the electronegativity of the combination, calculate the partial charge on each combined atom, as described on page 28 and with the help of the data of Table 2-1, page 131. This work, too, is greatly simplified by Table 10-2, which allows easy interpolation. Using Table 10-3, select the appropriate colors to paint the spheres.

4) Look up the structural data from some compilation of experimentally determined structures. You will find the book, *Interatomic Distances*, edited by L. E. Sutton and published by The Chemical Society, London, 1958, very useful. *Structural Inorganic Chemistry*, Second Ed., A. F. Wells, Oxford University Press, 1951, is an excellent reference. Structural data for many organic compounds have been summarized in an appendix of *Resonance in Organic Chemistry*, by G. W. Wheland, John Wiley and Sons, New York, 1953. If you have access to recent books on microwave spectroscopy, you may find needed structural information in one of these.

In such a source you should find bond lengths and bond angles. Certain of the bond lengths or angles may not be given, or, you may not find any information about the compound of which you would like to build a model. You may not even have access to any of the sources named above. This need not discourage your making a molecular model if you are reasonably sure from your general chemical knowledge which atoms are attached to which. You can then reason that the single bond lengths are not likely to differ substantially from the sum of the calculated radii, unless as suggested in Table 2-3. This table also suggests factors for determining the multiple bond lengths from the single bond lengths, which are the sums of the calculated atomic radii. You can predict the bond angles from the principles described on page 6.

5) Obtain the desired number and size of spheres, reducing larger

spheres if necessary to exact dimensions, as described on page 98. Also obtain the necessary number and size of connectors. Paint the spheres and let dry.

6) Draw full-scale patterns to guide your cutting segments from the spheres if necessary to make the bond length correct. Remember that no one knows for certain how far one atom extends, and where the other begins, along the line of a bond. What is known definitely, and often with much greater accuracy than will be significant in your models, is the distance between the two nuclei. If this distance is correct and the bond angles are correct in your model, the model shows all that is definitely known from experiment, whatever may be the relative sizes of the component atoms.

In most molecules you will find the reported bond length to be equal to or less than the sum of the calculated single covalent bond radii. However, occasionally, and especially in "ionic" crystals, you will find the internuclear distance to be greater than this. This means that the individual spheres chosen as the atoms will not come in contact. At least three ways out of this dilemma are possible. (1) Increase the diameter of the more negative atom by the necessary amount to permit contact at the correct internuclear distance. The justification for this is that a negatively charged atom is much more easily deformed (polarized) than is a positively charged atom, and in the crystal the negative ion is ordinarily completely surrounded by positive ions which exert a highly polarizing influence and might logically be thought of as causing expansion of the electron sphere of the negative atom. (2) If justified by the type of compound, use ionic instead of calculated covalent radii. This is the most conventional, although not necessarily the most accurate, method. Some ionic radii are listed in Table 10-4. These are "Goldschmidt" radii—empirical radii assigned from observations of many crystalline compounds. Such radii have the merit that their sums do usually give correct or nearly correct internuclear distances in many crystalline compounds. (3) Use the atomic spheres in sizes calculated for covalent radii-in-combination, but use extended connectors so that the spheres are connected with the correct internuclear distance, even though the spheres themselves are not in contact in the model.

7) Cut each sphere as necessary for connecting.

8) Using glue and connectors, assemble the model. If the model is intricate, you may wish to assemble only part at a time, waiting for the glue to harden before proceeding to the next part. A disadvantage of this is that small irregularities in size and angle have a disgusting habit of multiplying instead of cancelling one another. In fact, this seems to be one of the chief laws of model construction: Errors never cancel, always

add or multiply. You will probably discover the inexorable validity of this law the first time you try to assemble an intricate crystal model, or even a benzene ring. If you can discover, while all joints are still wet, that certain atoms fail to meet where they should, or the model is lopsided, or the spaces that ought to be identical are actually quite different, you can sometimes make corrections more easily. On the other hand, some corrections cannot readily be made until a certain amount of rigidity is present, or you will introduce new and worse errors while correcting the old.

If major reorientation becomes necessary, you need not abandon the model, for holes left by changing the position of joints can easily be plugged. For example, you can cut a scrap of styrofoam itself approximately to fit the hole, wet it with glue, shove it in place by brute force, and after smoothing the exterior, repaint the surface. Should this result in paint smears on adjacent atoms, simply use a knife to scrape them off when dry and repaint. No one will ever guess that your original effort was so miserable.

SPECIFIC INSTRUCTIONS

Atomic Models

Necessary data for construction of atomic models are listed in Table 10-5. The procedure is straightforward. Obtain or cut spheres to the correct size, paint the appropriate color, let dry, and fasten the electrons and vacancies at the correct positions on the surface.

Molecular Models: General

The construction of these is described under the categories: "elements," "binary compounds," "ternary compounds," and "four elements or more." For reference the compounds are numbered consecutively.

Models of the Elements

For most of the metallic elements, the usual states of aggregation can be represented by one or two of only three principal crystalline forms. Construction of these forms, (1) body-centered cubic, (2) face-centered cubic, and (3) hexagonal, is described on page 128. For photos see Figs. B-4, B-5, and B-7.

Models of the nonmetals may be constructed as described below, using the relative radius data given in Table 10-5, page 147. In keeping with the color-charge scheme used for models of compounds, all the component spheres should be painted yellow before assembling.

Hydrogen: (See Fig. B-1). Fasten two atoms together in tangential contact.

Helium: Just one atom suffices. Such a model may seem superfluous, but actually it serves to emphasize the extremely important fact that inert atoms do not form bonds, even with one another (see Fig. B-6).

Boron: In at least one crystalline form of the element, as well as in certain borides, boron atoms occur in icosahedral (20-faced) clusters of 12 atoms each. One of these clusters can be represented by fastening 12 spheres together as follows (see Fig. B-6): First, make a triangle, each sphere joined to the other two. Then make three more such triangles, and group the four triangles together in as spherical a form as possible, and attach them.

Carbon: Diamond: The model shown in Fig. B-2 (also B-6) contains 23 atoms. Assemble in tangential contact so that each interior carbon is connected to four other carbons at the corners of a regular tetrahedron surrounding it. When you have one layer of such interconnected tetrahedra resting on the table top, you may observe that two alternatives are possible for building the next layer. One would result in the wurtzite structure (Fig. B-11), the other in the diamond or sphalerite (zincblende) structure (Fig. B-10). Be sure you proceed correctly for the diamond structure, as the other form is not known in carbon.

Graphite: The model shown in Fig. B-2 contains 45 atoms. The bond length in graphite is 1.42Å. The bond angles in the planar layers are all 120°. The inter-layer distance is 3.35Å. Draw, as a pattern, a circle the size selected for a carbon atom, and at the correct intercenter distance to represent 1.42Å, draw a second circle. These circles will intersect at a line indicating where the spheres must be cut. Draw two more circles, thus forming an equilateral triangle around the central circle (bond angles 120°), and the pattern is complete. Hold each atomic sphere over the pattern and cut off the three segments. This will test your skill in cutting and your patience a little later when you begin to connect the atoms into hexagonal rings. Be sure the condensed rings are planar within a layer. Finally, the layers may be held at the proper separation by pieces of wood, which will be made relatively inconspicuous later by painting black or with camouflage paint.

One layer goes over another so that a carbon of one layer is centered over each hole in the other layer. You will observe two alternatives in the placement of a third layer. These lead to two different modifications of graphite. In the pictured model layer one exactly corresponds to layer three.

Nitrogen: The bond length is 1.10Å. Draw the pattern to scale and cut two spheres where needed, and join them together. (Fig. B-1).

Oxygen: Same as nitrogen, except that the bond length is 1.21Å.

Halogens: Connect two atoms in tangential contact. (Fig. B-1).

Silicon: Like diamond.

Phosphorus, P_4: (Fig. B-3). Connect three atoms in tangential contact to form a triangle, and place the fourth atom on the center of the triangle so it is connected to each of the other three. Alternatively, make two pairs of atoms and then join them together into the tetrahedron.

Sulfur, S_8: (Fig. B-3). Bond angles are 105°. Attach in tangential contact two sulfur atoms to one, making an angle of 105°. Prepare another group of three just like the first. Hold the two trios so that their terminal atoms form a planar square, and attach them together by two more atoms so that the two new atoms form another planar square with the central atoms of the first two trios. This square will be parallel to the first square and oriented with its corners nears the middle of each side of the first square.

Binary Compounds

As far as practical, most of the data for construction are tabulated. The tables, in order, are, 10-6 Binary Oxygen Compounds, 10-8 Binary Hydrogen Compounds, 10-9 Binary Fluorine Compounds, 10-10 Binary Chlorine Compounds, 10-11 Binary Bromine Compounds, 10-12 Binary Iodine Compounds, and 10-13 Binary Sulfur Compounds. Within these tables the order is that of major groups of the periodic table, then subgroups, then any miscellaneous related compounds. For each compound, the following information is given: reference number, formula, electronegativity, radii of the two atoms in Å, the diameter in inches for each atom on each of the three suggested scales, 100 times the partial charge, the colors, the type, and, where needed, the bond angle. The type is indicated by letter, for which the following instructions apply:

A. These are compounds containing only one single bond per gas molecule. The spheres should be attached in only slightly more than tangential contact.

B. These are molecules whose two single bonds are linear. Tangential contact is made at opposite sides of the central sphere.

C. These molecules are planar triangles with the same tangential contact for each bond and 120° angles between the bonds.

D. These are molecules in which the central atom is surrounded tetrahedrally by four pairs of electrons—which may or may not be involved in the bonds. When the bond angle is known to deviate significantly from the 109°28′ tetrahedral angle, it is listed in the last column. This only occurs when at least one of the four electron pairs is not used in the bonding. The individual bonds are formed just as in types A, B, and C.

E. These compounds are either giant molecules held together in all directions by covalent bonds, or "ionic" crystals having no individual molecules. For these, crystal models would be useful, but an "atom-pair" model will at least show the calculated radii and the charges on the two kinds of atoms. The painted spheres, one of each kind of element, are not attached directly but at opposite ends of a connecting rod which holds them a clearly visible distance apart. The purpose of such a model must be carefully explained as limited to representing (1) the condition of the component atoms, and (2) if outer electrons and vacancies are included, as they should be, the number of each and thus the tendency to condense.

F. These are compounds for which special instructions on model construction would be helpful. Such instructions are given under the appropriate reference number on page 124. Usually these models require drawing a simple full-scale diagram to be used as a pattern.

Binary Compounds, Specific Instructions

4) H_2O_2. Attach one H to each O. Connect the two O's together so each OOH angle is about 100°, and, when viewed along the O—O axis, the two OH bonds make an angle of about 90°.

23) CO. Make a pattern, showing where to cut the two spheres so that the bond length corresponds to 1.13Å. The two atoms are taken to be of equal radius because apparently the arrangement of electrons to form a triple bond counteracts the expected polarity effect. This also is why yellow is suggested as the color; the calculated colors would be 5P for C and 5N for O. Connect the two spheres through the cut areas.

24) CO_2. (Figs. C-7, C-14; also C-4.) This molecule is linear, with bond length 1.15Å and carbon in the middle. Draw a pattern on paper and cut segments from the carbon and oxygen spheres to give the proper bond length. Assemble.

25) $CO_3^{=}$. (Fig. C-6.) This ion is planar, with bond lengths 1.31Å, and 120° angles. A pattern is needed. Cut the atoms as required and assemble, attaching the three oxygens to the central carbon.

32) N_2O. Linear, NNO, with N—N 1.13Å and N—O 1.19Å. Draw a pattern and cut off segments of spheres to give the proper bond length, and connect.

33) NO. Bond length 1.15Å. Draw a pattern and cut spheres for the correct bond length, and connect.

34) N_2O_3. Assume ONONO structure, which is speculative but reasonable. Bond lengths are 1.13Å for the terminal oxygen to nitrogen, and 1.17Å for the middle oxygen to nitrogen. NON angle is 105°, and ONO

angle is 120°. Assume a planar structure and construct a pattern for cutting the atoms and connecting.

35) NO_2. The two oxygens are attached to the nitrogen at an angle of 132° and a distance of 1.19Å. Draw a pattern, cut off segments, and attach.

36) N_2O_5. (Fig. C-7.) Assemble a NO_3 group similar to that of HNO_3 (number 391). Assemble an NO_2 group similar to the italicized part of the *O_2N*OH, and then attach its nitrogen to the singly bonded oxygen of the first group so that the NON angle is about 105°, and with the two NO_2 groups at right angles to one another.

37) NO_3^-. (Fig. C-6.) Draw a pattern with three oxygens forming an equilateral triangle around nitrogen, with 120° bond angles and bond lengths about 1.24Å. Cut spheres and attach.

38) P_4O_6. (Fig. C-7.) This molecule can be considered to be derived from a tetrahedron of phosphorus atoms, only instead of their being in direct contact, they are held together by oxygen bridges. To one atom of phosphorus, attach three oxygens making 99° angles. Next, attach a phosphorus atom to each of these oxygens so that the POP angle is 128° *and* this P atom is directed toward the midpoint between the other two oxygens. Finally, attach the remaining three oxygens as bridges of these last three phosphorus atoms. All six oxygen bridges should be symmetrically directed *away* from the edge of the P_4 tetrahedron.

39) P_4O_{10}. (Fig. C-7.) Assemble a P_4O_6 group like No. 38. Then cut a segment off each P atom at opposite side from the tetrahedron and from each of the four new oxygens so that they can be connected, one oxygen to each phosphorus, at the corners of the tetrahedron and at bond lengths of 1.39Å.

40) $PO_4^{\equiv}$. (Fig. C-6.) The oxygens and phosphorus must be cut to permit attachment of four oxygens to phosphorus at corners of a regular tetrahedron with bond lengths of 1.54Å.

41) As_4O_6. This molecule resembles No. 38. The bond angles are OAsO 100° and AsOAs 128°.

43) Sb_4O_6. Like 38 and 41.

47) SO_2. (Fig. C-7.) Cut off segments of sulfur and two oxygens to represent bond lengths of 1.43Å, with OSO bond angle of 120°, and connect.

48) SO_3. (Fig. C-7.) Like SO_2, 47, except complete the triangle of oxygen atoms in a plane surrounding the sulfur. Same bond length and angles.

49) SeO_2. (Fig. C-13.) In this compound are continuous O—Se—O— chains with another oxygen joined to each selenium at a slightly shorter distance. SeOSe angles are 125° and OSeO angles 90°. The

O(bridge)SeO(nonbridge) angle is 98°. Some of the nonbridging oxygens are hidden from view in the photo. The selenium atoms of a chain are all in the same plane, and in a plane parallel to this are all the nonbridging oxygen atoms.

53) $SO_4^{=}$. (Fig. C-6.) In this ion, the oxygens surround the sulfur in a regular tetrahedral manner, with bond lengths of 1.44Å, which requires drawing a pattern and cutting the spheres accordingly.

55) ClO_2. This is a bent molecule, with angle 116° and bond length 149Å. Draw a pattern and cut the atoms, and connect, chlorine in the center.

56) Cl_2O_7. (Fig. C-7.) Structure not known. Suggest $(ClO_3)_2O$, as shown in photo. Cut off three segments from each chlorine, at corners of a tetrahedron, and one from each of six oxygens to prepare for multiple bond connections. Connect three oxygens to each chlorine, flat to flat area. Then attach the seventh oxygen to the fourth tetrahedral corner of each chlorine, making the bond angle about 110°.

57) ClO_4^-. (Fig. C-6.) Four oxygen atoms are double-bonded to the chlorine at the corners of a regular tetrahedron. Cut off the atoms as required and assemble.

74) B_2H_6. (Fig. C-9.) First attach two hydrogens to each boron at an angle of 120°. Then join the two BH_2 groups by two hydrogens as follows. Use two hydrogens about 20 per cent larger than the other four, in order for the boron-boron distance to be correct. Place the two BH_2 groups B to B so the hydrogens are as far apart as possible, and the groups, parallel to the table top, are all in the same plane. Have the borons separated by sufficient space that the B—B length corresponds to 1.77Å. Attach one bridging hydrogen on top between the two borons, and the other just opposite it, so that the plane of the bridging hydrogens and the borons is perpendicular to the plane of the original two BH_2 groups.

75) B_4H_{10}. (Fig. C-10.) Attach two borons barely in tangential contact. Attach a third boron to each of these two by means of two bridging hydrogens, the three borons and two hydrogens being in the same plane. The third boron should be 1.85Å from each of the first two. Then attach a fourth boron similarly to form a second hydrogen-bridged triangle like the first, with the first two borons forming a common side. The angle between the two triangles is 118°. Finally, attach two hydrogens to each apical boron and one to each base boron, making the molecule as symmetrical as possible. This means that the two terminal hydrogens on each boron come as close as possible to forming a regular tetrahedron with the two bridging hydrogens, and the single hydrogen on each of the central boron pair is as far from all the other bonds to that boron as possible.

76) B_5H_9. (Fig. C-10.) Attach two borons tangentially. Then attach

three other borons to one of the first two so that they are about 0.3″ apart (medium scale) and form the base of a square pyramid on top of which rests the fifth boron. Take four bridging hydrogens, each 20 per cent larger than the regular size hydrogens, and bridge the four 0.3 inch gaps at a position directly opposite the apical boron. Now connect the five regular size hydrogens, one to each boron, as far from all other bonds as possible.

77) $B_{10}H_{14}$. Connect two borons tangentially. On each side of this pair, at the junction, attach one more boron, so it is connected to each of the pair. The four borons thus assembled are not quite planar, one of the last borons being about 0.5 inch (medium scale) out of the plane of the triangle formed by the other three. Now, to each of these last two borons, attach one boron so that it forms an angle of about 100° with the near-plane of the first four. The idea is to construct a basketlike model. The last pair of borons will be separated from one another by a distance about 0.5 inch greater than the separation of the second pair of borons to be added. Now attach four more borons, two to each of the last connected borons, so that each also attaches to one of the initial pair of borons and nearly attaches to one of the second pair of borons. You will thus have formed a basket. The last borons added leave about 0.5 inch gap at each side of the basket rim. The basket bottom closely resembles the B_{12} cluster of elementary boron.

Now you will need four bridging hydrogens each about 20 per cent larger than the ten other hydrogens. Attach these four at the top rim of the basket, so that they connect all but the two 0.5 inch gaps previously mentioned. Taken alone, these four bridging hydrogens form a square. Now connect one regular size hydrogen to each of the ten borons at the point farthest from all other bonds. Look at Fig. C-10 while doing this construction—it may help.

81) Ga_2H_6. (Fig. C-9.) Like B_2H_6, 74.

86) C_2H_6. (Fig. C-14.) Mark four tetrahedral positions on each carbon. Attach three hydrogens to each carbon, and then the two methyl groups together. The most stable configuration would be the "staggered" position for the hydrogens, looking along the carbon-carbon axis, so all six hydrogens are uniformly distributed in the field of vision.

86a) C_2H_2 (or C_6H_6). (Fig. C-14.) Acetylene: Cut segments from the two carbons so their bond length will represent 1.20Å. Connect them, and at opposite sides attach one hydrogen to each carbon, making the whole molecule linear.

Benzene: Cut segments from the carbons to permit 1.39Å bond lengths and 120° angles. Connect the carbon atoms in threes, and then attach the two trios together, forming the planar ring of six. Finally, attach one hydrogen to each carbon in the same plane as the ring, evenly spaced so the HCC angles are 120°.

86b) C_2H_4. (Fig. C-14.) Cut two carbon atoms so their bond length will be 1.34Å. Connect them. Attach two hydrogens to each carbon so all atoms are in the same plane and all bond angles are 120°.

87) See benzene, 86a.

88) C_7H_{16}. (Fig. C-14.) n-Heptane: Attach all seven carbons in "straight" (zigzag) chain, with 109° bond angles. Completely fill the remaining tetrahedral positions with hydrogen atoms. "Triptane," 2,2,3-trimethylbutane: Attach four carbons in a "straight" chain (109° angles). Prepare three CH_3 groups and attach two to carbon (2) and one to carbon (3). Completely fill the remaining tetrahedral positions with hydrogens.

89) C_8H_{18}. (Fig. C-14.) "Isooctane," 2,2,4-trimethylpentane: Connect five carbons in "straight" chain. Prepare three methyl groups, and attach two of them to carbon (2) and one to carbon (4). Fill the remaining tetrahedral positions with hydrogens.

98) N_2H_4. (Fig. C-13.) Attach two hydrogens to each nitrogen at an angle of 109°. Attach the nitrogens together making the same angle with NH bonds, but the molecule is not symmetrical. The exact orientation is unknown, but probably resembles that of H_2O_2 (4).

100) P_2H_4. Probably like hydrazine, 98.

129) B_2F_4. Attach two fluorines to each boron at 120°. Then connect the two boron atoms so the two BF_2 planes are mutually perpendicular.

136) C_2F_6. Like C_2H_6 (86).

139) Si_2F_6. Similar.

146) N_2F_4. Probably resembles hydrazine (98).

148) PF_5. Attach three fluorines to phosphorus in the same plane, forming an equilateral triangle with the phosphorus at the center. Directly above this plane attach a fourth fluorine to the phosphorus. On the opposite side of the phosphorus, attach the fifth fluorine. Thus formed: a trigonal bipyramid.

153) SF_4. Possibly like PF_5 above with the fifth fluorine missing.

154) SF_6. (Fig. C-11.) Attach four fluorines to the sulfur in tangential contact, forming a planar square with sulfur at the center. Then attach a fifth fluorine directly over the sulfur perpendicular to the square, and a sixth fluorine exactly opposite this fifth. Result: six equally placed fluorines forming a regular octahedron around the sulfur.

155) S_2F_{10}. (Fig. C-11.) Attach five fluorines to each sulfur exactly as in SF_6 (154). Then connect the two sulfurs so that each fills the sixth

coordination space of the other, and the fluorine atoms are staggered when viewed along the FSSF axis (i.e., all 8 equatorial sulfurs are viewed as evenly spaced).

156) SeF_6. Like SF_6, 154.

157) Se_2F_{10}. Like S_2F_{10}.

158) TeF_6. Like SF_6.

159) Te_2F_{10}. Like 155.

161) ClF_3. Attach one fluorine to chlorine, bond length 1.60Å. Then attach each of the remaining two fluorines to the chlorine, at bond length 1.70Å, to make bond angles of 87°—all four atoms in the same plane.

162) BrF_3. Probably like 161.

163) BrF_5. Probably tetragonal pyramid with bromine on same side of plane of base as is the fifth fluorine, but closer.

164) IF_5. Probably same.

165) IF_7. Possibly pentagonal bipyramid.

181) B_2Cl_4. (Fig. C-12.) Like B_2F_4, 129.

182) B_4Cl_4. (Fig. C-12.) Connect the four borons in a tetrahedral cluster. Then attach one chlorine to each boron at the farthest possible distance from the other bonds.

183) Al_2Cl_6. (Fig. C-11.) Attach two chlorines to each aluminum, in tangential contact and forming a bond angle of 109°. Then place the two $AlCl_2$ groups on a table with the aluminums near and the chlorines opposite. Arrange so the aluminum surfaces are $1\frac{1}{4}$ inch apart (for the medium scale model). Then bridge them with a chlorine fastened to both, directly above the table. Invert and connect a second bridging chlorine. The bridging chlorines are thus about 1 inch apart and form a plane with the two aluminums that is perpendicular to the plane of the other four chlorine and the aluminums.

184) Ga_2Cl_6. Like 183.

185) In_2Cl_6. Like 183.

190) Si_2Cl_6. Like C_2H_6 (86).

198) PCl_5. (Fig. C-11.) Attach three chlorines tangentially to phosphorus, at corners of an equilateral triangle around the phosphorus, with 120° bond angles. Then attach *just barely* tangentially, the other two chlorines, one directly above the triangle, the other directly below, forming a trigonal bipyramid. The bond lengths for the last two chlorines (apical) are slightly greater than the others (equatorial).

203) S_2Cl_2. (Fig. C-11.) Connect tangentially one chlorine to each sulfur. Then connect the two sulfurs so that the SSCl bond angles are 104° and the plane of the two sulfurs and one chlorine makes an angle of 98° with the plane of the two sulfurs and the second chlorine.

205) Se_2Cl_2. Like 203.

206) $SeCl_4$. Probably like 207.

207) $TeCl_4$. Like PF_5, [illegible], but with one equatorial position vacant.

212) ICl_3. Probably like 161.

213) $ZnCl_2$ crystal. (Fig. C-12.) Attach six chlorines to one zinc with 90° angles, forming thus a regular octahedron. Do this by first attaching two chlorines, one at each side of a zinc, so the three atoms form a straight line. Then, at right angle to this line, attach two more chlorines at opposite positions on the zinc. You now have a square of chlorine atoms with zinc at the center. Now attach one chlorine directly above the square, another directly below. This is the regular octahedron. Now, allow the octahedron to rest on three of its chlorines. The other three chlorines will be held in the air. The zinc chloride crystal lattice consists of layers—each layer a sandwich, a plane of chlorine atoms on the table, a parallel plane of zinc atoms just above, and a parallel plane of chlorine atoms just above the zinc plane. Build on to the original $ZnCl_6$ group by attaching zinc atoms and other chlorine atoms until you have a layer large enough to suit. A reasonably large section contains about 11 zinc atoms and 22 chlorine atoms.

229) Al_2Br_6. Like 183.

230) Ga_2Br_6. Like 183.

241) PBr_5. Like 148.

245) S_2Br_2. Like 203.

246) Se_2Br_2. Like 203.

247) $TeBr_4$. Probably like 207.

266) Al_2I_6. Like 183.

281) TeI_4. Probably like 207.

313) S_4N_4. Possibly like As_4S_4, 315.

314) P_4S_{10}. Like 39.

315) As_4S_4. (Fig. C-13.) Attach the arsenic atoms together to form two pairs. To one arsenic of one pair attach two sulfurs so that the SAsS angle is 93° and the SAsAs angle is 100°. To each of the arsenics of the second pair, attach one sulfur so that SAsAs is 100° *and* the two sulfurs and two arsenics are planar. Now fit the two sections together so that each arsenic is attached to two sulfurs and each sulfur to two arsenics.

316) As_4S_6. Like 38.

317) Sb_2S_3. Probably like 38.

319) ZnS. (Figs. B-10 and B-11.) See later, instructions on zinc blende and wurtzite.

Ternary Compounds

These compounds are considered in alphabetical order of empirical formulas. Only the scale of 1.5″/Å is used here. One may easily convert to the other scales.

322) AgH_6N_2—$Ag(NH_3)_2^+$. (Fig. C-13.) Ag 3.8″d, 11P; N 2.3″d, 4N;

H $\frac{7}{8}$″d, 4P. Connect three hydrogens to each nitrogen at the corners of a regular tetrahedron. Fill the fourth corner of each nitrogen by the silver, so that the NAgN bond angle is 180°. There is no certain basis for deciding the relative orientations of the NH_3 groups; probably they should be staggered so that a view along the NAgN axis would show all six hydrogens symmetrically arranged.

323) AlB_3H_{12}. (Fig. C-10.) Al 3″d, 10P; B 2.3″d, 4P; H 1″d, 2N. Attach two hydrogens to each boron at 120° angle. Attach two other hydrogens to each boron to make as symmetrical as possible a tetrahedron, considering that one angle is already 120°. The angle between the last two hydrogens is approximately 109°. Then attach the three BH_4 groups to the aluminum, with the borons in a plane with the aluminum, at the corners of an equilateral triangle, by attaching the two 120° hydrogen atoms to the aluminum as a bridge from the boron. These hydrogen bridges are thus perpendicular to the boron—aluminum plane, placing the nonbridging hydrogens in that plane.

324) $AlH_{11}O_6$—$Al(H_2O)_5OH^{++}$. Like 325 except that one of the water molecules is replaced by OH. Al 2.7″d, 12P; H 0.8″d, 6P; O 2.3″d, 5N.

325) $AlH_{12}O_6$—$Al(H_2O)_6^{+++}$. (Fig. C-13.) Al 2.7″d, 12P; H $\frac{3}{4}$″d, 6P; O 2.3″d, 4N. Assemble 6 H_2O molecules (1). It is uncertain whether the waters should be attached to the aluminum through an electron pair of each oxygen or by dipole-ion interaction. The partial charges are calculated assuming equalization of electronegativity throughout the ion, but perhaps attachment as a dipole would be better. This means attaching the six oxygens to the aluminum at the point directly opposite the two hydrogens instead of with AlOH angle of 109°. The positions on the Al are symmetrically located, with 90° angles, the structure being octahedral. Make a square around the aluminum and then attach one water directly above and one below.

326) $B_3H_6N_3$—$B_3N_3H_6$. (Fig. C-10.) B 2.5″d, 6P; N 2.5″d, 6N; H 1″d, O. Prepare a ring like that of benzene, only having alternate boron and nitrogen atoms, and attach one hydrogen to each ring atom just as in benzene (86a).

327) BeH_8O_4—$Be(H_2O)_4^{++}$. Be 2.0″d, 12P; H 0.8″, 6P; O 2.3″d, 5N. Assemble four water molecules and attach them to the beryllium at corners of a regular tetrahedron. The BeOH angles should be 109°.

328) $BrCH_3$—CH_3Br. C 2.3″d, O; H 1″d, 2P; Br 3.6″d, 5N. Attach the three hydrogens and the bromine to the carbon, with tangential contact and all bond angles 109°.

329) BrH_3Si—SiH_3Br. Si 3″d, 7P; H 1″d, O; Br 3.7″d, 6N. Same as 328.

330) Br_2CH_2—CH_2Br_2. C 2.3″d, 2P; H 1″d, 4P; Br 3.6″d, 4N. Attach all other atoms tangentially to the carbon at 109° angles.

331) Br_2OS—$SOBr_2$. S 3″d, 4P; O 2.3″d, 4N; Br 3.4″d, O. Cut off S and

O atoms to make the bond lengths representative of 1.45A. Connect. Making 109° angles with the SO bond and with each other, attach the two bromines tangentially to the sulfur.

332) Br_3CH—$CHBr_3$. C 2.2″d, 3P; H 0.9″d, 5P; Br 3.5″d, 3N. Like 330.

333) Br_3OP—$POBr_3$. P 2.9″d, 7P; O 2.4″d, 5N, Br 3.4″d, 1N. Cut off the oxygen and phosphorus atoms to represent a bond length of 1.41Å. Connect. Attach the three bromine atoms tangentially to the phosphorus so that it is surrounded by four atoms tetrahedrally.

334) Br_3PS—$PSBr_3$. P 2.9″d, 6P; S 3″d, 1P; Br 3.5″d, 3N. Like 333. P—S bond length, 1.89Å.

335) $CaCO_3$. (Fig. C-8.) Ca ion, 3″d, 12P. CO_3 ion, see 25.

336) $CClH_3$—CH_3Cl. C 2.3°d, O; H 1″d, 3P; Cl 3.2″d, 6N. Like 328.

337) CCl_2F_2. C 2.3″d, 7P; Cl 3″d, O; F 2.5″d, 5N. Surround carbon with the other atoms tetrahedrally.

338) CCl_2H_2—CH_2Cl_2. C 2.3″d, 3P; H 1″d, 4P; Cl 3.2″d, 5N. Like 330.

339) CCl_3H—$CHCl_3$. (Fig. C-14.) C 2.3″d, 4P; H 0.8″d, 6P; Cl 3″d, 4N. Like 332.

340) CFH_3—CH_3F. C 2.3″d, 2P; H 1″d, 4P; F 2.5″d, 8N. Like 328.

341) CF_2H_2—CH_2F_2. C 2.2″d, 4P; H 0.8″d, 6P; F 2.4″d, 7N. Like 330.

342) CF_3H—CHF_3. C 2.1″d, 7P; H 0.8″d, 8P; F 2.3″d, 5N. Like 332.

343) CHI_3. C 2.3″d, O; H 1″d, 2P; I 4″d, 1N. Like 332.

344) CHO_3^-—HCO_3^-.

Prepare two cuts on carbon and one on each of two oxygens as in $CO_3^=$ (25). Connect. At the third corner of an equilateral triangle around the carbon, attach the OH tangentially, HOC angle about 105°, and the hydrogen coplanar with the rest of the ion.

345) CHN—HCN. C 2.3″d, 1P; H 1″d, 4P; N 2.4″d, 4N. Cut the carbon and nitrogen atoms to represent a bond length of 1.16Å, and connect. Then attach the hydrogen to the carbon exactly opposite the nitrogen, so the molecule is linear.

346) CH_2O—HCHO. C 2.3″d, 2P; H 1″d, 4P; O 2.4″d, 7N. Cut the carbon and oxygen to represent a bond length of 1.21Å, and connect. Attach the two hydrogens tangentially to the carbon to make an equilateral triangle of two hydrogens and one oxygen around the carbon, with bond angles 120°.

347) CH_2O_2—HCOOH. (Fig. C-14.) C 2.3″d, 4P; O 2.4″d, 6N; H 0.8″d, 5P. Cut segments from the carbon and oxygen for a double bond between them. Attach, and then attach the second oxygen at somewhat closer than tangential contact, to the carbon, making the OCO angle 123°. Attach the hydrogen atoms one to the second oxygen, toward the first oxygen, and one to the carbon and symmetrically opposite the two oxygens.

348) CH_3I. C 2.3″d, 1N; H 1.1″d, 1P; I 4.1″d, 2N. Like 328.

349) CH_4O—CH_3OH. (Fig. C-14.) C 2.2″d, O; H 1″d, 3P; O 2.4″d, 7N. Attach the three hydrogens and the oxygen to the corners of a regular tetrahedron around the carbon. Then attach the hydrogen to the oxygen at a bond angle of about 109°. All tangential contact, except that the oxygen and carbon are in slightly closer contact.

350) CH_4S—CH_3SH. C 2.3″d, 1N; H 1.1″d, 1P; S 3.2″d, 4N. Like 349.

351) CH_5N—CH_3NH_2. C 2.3″d, 1N; H 1″d, 2P; N 2.4″d, 5N. Like NH_3 and CH_4 except, attach the NH_2 to the carbon in place of the fourth hydrogen.

352) CH_5N_3—NH_2CNHNH_2 (guanidine). C 2.3″d, 1P; H 1″d, 3P; N 2.4″d, 4N. Prepare two NH_2 groups like NH_3. Cut a third nitrogen and the carbon to represent bond length of 1.26Å. Connect. Attach a hydrogen to the cut nitrogen so that the HNC angle is 109°. Attach both NH_2 groups tangentially to the carbon so that the three nitrogens form a triangle around the carbon, with 120° angles.

353) COS. C 2.2″d, 4P; O 2.3″d, 5N; S 3″d, 2P. Cut carbon, oxygen, and sulfur to represent bond lengths of 1.16Å for C—O and 1.56Å for CS, and to make a linear molecule. Connect.

354) $C_2F_3O_2$—CF_3COO^-. (Fig. C-6.) C 2.3″d, 4P; F 2.5″d, 7N; O 2.5″d, 5N. Cut one carbon and two oxygens to represent bond lengths of 1.24Å and 120° bond angle. Attach three fluorines to the second carbon at 109° angles. Then connect this carbon tangentially to the first, in the same plane with, and symmetrically opposite from the two oxygens.

355) C_2F_6O—$(CF_3)_2O$. C 2.1″d, 8P; F 2.2″d, 4N; O 2.2″d, O. Attach three fluorines to each carbon at tetrahedral corners, and then each carbon, at the fourth corner, to the oxygen so that the COC angle is about 125°. Orient CF_3 groups to give minimum interference.

356) C_2H_3N—CH_3CN. C 2.3″d, O; H 1″d, 2P; N 2.4″d, 5N. Like methane and HCN. Methyl carbon should be attached tangentially to the CN carbon, directly opposite from the nitrogen.

357) $C_2H_3O_2$—CH_3COO^-. (Fig. C-6.) C 2.4″d, 3N; H 1″d, 1N; O 2.5″d, 9N. Like 354.

358) $C_2H_4O_2$—CH_3COOH. (Fig. C-6.) C 2.3″d, 2P; H 0.8″d, 4P; O 2.4″d, 7N. Attach a methyl group, a double-bonded oxygen, and an OH group to a carbon atom forming a planar triangle with bond angles 120°.

359) C_2H_6O—CH_3CH_2OH. (Fig. C-14.) C 2.3″d, O; H 1″d, 2P; O 2.4″d, 8N. Attach three hydrogens tetrahedrally to one carbon and two hydrogens and an OH group similarly to the other carbon. Then join the two carbons at their fourth tetrahedral corners. HOC angle should be about 105°.

360) $(CH_3)_2O$. (Fig. C-14.) Same atoms as 359. Form two methyl groups and then attach them to the oxygen with the COC angle 111°.

Orient the two methyl groups to give minimum interference of hydrogens.

361) C_2H_6S—CH_3CH_2SH. C 2.3″d, 1N; H 1.1″d, 1P; S 3.2″d, 4N. Like 359.

362) $(CH_3)_2S$. Like 360.

363) C_2H_7N—$C_2H_5NH_2$. C 2.3″d, 1N; H 1.1″d, 1P; N 2.4″d, 5N. Like 359, only NH_2 in place of OH. Angles of bonds to nitrogen, about 107°.

364) C_3F_9N—$(CF_3)_3N$. C 2.1″d, 8P; N 2.4″d, 4P; F 2.3″d, 4N. Attach three fluorines to each carbon at tetrahedral corners. At the fourth corner of each carbon, attach to nitrogen, so that the CNC angle is 114°.

365) C_3H_9N—$(CH_3)_3N$. C 2.3″d, 1N; H 1.1″d, 1P; N 2.4″d, 5N. Attach three hydrogens to each carbon at tetrahedral corners, and each methyl group at the fourth corner of carbon to the nitrogen, making CNC angles of 109°.

366) C_5H_5N. C 2.5″d, O; H 1″d, 2P; N 2.5″d, 5N. Attach the five carbons and the nitrogen just like the benzene ring, and similarly attach one hydrogen to each carbon.

367) $C_6H_5O^-$. C 2.4″d, 3N; H 1″d, 1N; O 2.6″, 9N. Construct like benzene (86a) and attach O in place of one hydrogen, at somewhat greater than tangential contact.

368) C_6H_7N—$C_6H_5NH_2$. C 2.3″d, 1N; H 1″d, 2P; N 2.4″d, 5N. Like benzene and ammonia, only attach third position on the nitrogen to the carbon lacking hydrogen, keeping the nitrogen in the plane of the ring.

369) $C_9H_8O_4$-aspirin. (Fig. C-16.) C 2.5″d, 1P; H 1″d, 3P; O 2.5″d, 7N. Form a benzene ring with six carbons and add hydrogen to each of four adjacent carbons. To one of the remaining two ring carbons, attach an acetyl group, through oxygen (see CH_3COOH). To the other, attach the COOH group (as in formic acid). This should be oriented so the acid hydrogen is nearest an oxygen of the acetyl group.

370) $C_{12}H_{22}O_{11}$-sucrose-cane sugar. (Fig. C-15.) C 2.5″d, 2P; H 0.8″d, 4P; O 2.5″d, 7N. This molecule contains two rings, one of four carbon and one oxygen atoms, one of five carbons and one oxygen. The bonds are single. Construct Ring A of four carbons and one oxygen, keeping the bond angles 109° to carbon and about 105° to oxygen. Construct Ring B of 5 carbons and one oxygen, bond angles as before. Ring A will be nearly planar, Ring B not. Join the two rings through an outside oxygen atom, as a bridge, attached to a ring carbon next to ring oxygen, on each ring. Then prepare three CH_2OH groups separately. Attach one to Ring A at the same ring carbon that is attached to the bridge oxygen. Attach another, to Ring A at the ring carbon which is separated from the above mentioned ring carbon by the ring oxygen. Attach the third CH_2OH group to Ring B on the ring carbon analogous to the last mentioned Ring A carbon. Now prepare five OH groups and, with HOC

angle of 105°, attach one to each ring carbon, of both rings, that does not already have a CH_2OH group or a bridge oxygen attached to it. This will be two OH's on Ring A and three on Ring B. Finally, complete the valence of all carbon atoms where necessary, by attaching hydrogen atoms.

371) $C_{14}H_9Cl_5$-DDT (poorly named, *d*ichloro*d*iphenyl*t*richloroethane). (Fig. C-15.) C 2.5″d, 1P; H 1″d, 3P; Cl 3″d, 6N. In this molecule, two chlorophenyl groups and one trichloromethyl group, and one hydrogen, are attached tetrahedrally to one carbon. Prepare two C_6 rings, like benzene, with a chlorine attached to each, in the same plane, and hydrogen attached to each other carbon except to the carbon opposite the chlorine. Attach three chlorines tetrahedrally to another carbon. Attach hydrogen to still another carbon, and complete its tetrahedron by attaching also the two chlorophenyl groups and the CCl_3 group.

372) $C_{20}H_{30}O$-vitamin A. (Fig. C-15.) C 2.3″d, 1N; H 1.1″d, 1 P; O 2.3″d, 1N. Attach five pairs of carbons separately by double bonds, like C_2H_4. Each carbon of these pairs will now form two more bonds at 120° with double bond and each other. To one pair, attach a chain of four carbons so that they form a 6-membered ring having one double bond. This will be close to planar. Attach the remaining four double bonded pairs so they form a planar zigzag chain of 8 carbons attached to one of the double-bonded carbons of the ring. To the single-bonded ring carbon next to this one, attach two methyl groups. Attach a methyl group to the other double-bonded ring carbon (this methyl is missing from the model in Fig. C-15). To the other ring carbons attach hydrogens to fill in the vacancies. Now, to the third chain carbon away from the ring, and to the seventh, attach one methyl group each. To the end carbon of this chain, opposite the ring, attach an OH group. Fill any remaining chain vacancies with hydrogen.

373) $C_{21}H_{28}O_5$-cortisone. (Fig. C-16.) C 2.5″d, O; H 1″d, 2P; O 2.5″d, 8N. Better consult a book of biochemistry giving this structure before trying this one—which is not too difficult to construct but quite difficult to describe in words.

374) ClHO—HOCl. H 0.8″d, 6P; O 2.5″d, 4N; Cl 3″d, 3N. Attach both hydrogen and chlorine to the oxygen in tangential contact, making a bond angle of 109°. (Fig. C-6).

375) $ClHO_2$—HOClO. H 0.8″d, 7P; Cl 3″d, 2N; O 2.5″d, 4N. (Fig. C-6.) Cut off segments of chlorine and one oxygen to form a double bond, and connect. Attach a second oxygen in tangential contact, to the chlorine at 109° angle from the first oxygen. Connect hydrogen to this oxygen at 109° angle with the chlorine bond and nearest to the first oxygen.

376) $ClHO_3$—$HOClO_2$. (Fig. C-6.) H 0.8″d, 8P; Cl 3″d, 1N; O 2.5″d,

3N. Cut off two segments at tetrahedral corners of chlorine, as sufficient for two double bonds to oxygen. Cut off similar segments from the two oxygens. Then to a third tetrahedral corner of the chlorine, attach the third oxygen, in tangential contact. To it, attach hydrogen at 109° and either over one other oxygen or midway between the two other oxygens.

377) $ClHO_4$—$HOClO_3$. (Fig. C-6.) H 0.7″d, 8P; Cl 3″d, O; O 2.5″d, 3N. Cut off three segments from three tetrahedral corners around the chlorine. Cut off corresponding segments from each of three oxygens, and connect. Attach the fourth oxygen to the fourth corner of the chlorine, in tangential contact, and to it, one hydrogen, over one of the other oxygens or midway between two of them.

378) ClH_2N—NH_2Cl. N 2.3″d, 3N; H 1″d, 4P; Cl 3.2″d, 5N. Attach the two hydrogens and the chlorine to the nitrogen, making bond angles of 109°.

379) ClH_3Si—SiH_3Cl. (Fig. C-10.) Si 3″d, 7P; H 1.2″d, O; Cl 3.3″d, 7N. Like CH_3Cl.

380) Cl_2OS—$SOCl_2$. (Fig. C-13.) O 2.3″d, 3N; S 3″d, 5P; Cl 3″d, 1N. Cut the sulfur and oxygen atoms to represent a bond length of 1.45Å. Connect, and then attach the two chlorines to the sulfur so that the ClSCl angle is 114° and the OSCl angle is 106°.

381) Cl_2O_2S—SO_2Cl_2. S 3″d, 5P; O 2.3″d, 3N; Cl 3″d, O. Cut the sulfur and oxygen atoms for an SO bond length of 1.43Å and an OSO angle of 120°. Then attach the two chlorines to the sulfur so that their plane is perpendicular to the OSO plane and the ClSCl angle is 112°.

382) Cl_3HSI—$SiHCl_3$. Si 3″d, 7P; H 1.2″d, O; Cl 3.3″d, 8N. Attach hydrogen and chlorines tetrahedrally to the silicon.

383) Cl_3OP—$POCl_3$. (Fig. C-13.) P 3″d, 8P; O 2.5″d, 4N; Cl 3″d, 2N. Cut the phosphorus and oxygen atoms for a bond length of 1.45Å and connect. Then attach the three chlorines to the phosphorus with ClPCl angle of 104°.

384) Cl_3PS—$PSCl_3$. P 2.9″d, 7P; S 3.1″d, 3P; Cl 3.1″d, 4N. Like 383, except cut phosphorus and sulfur for a bond length about 1.9Å.

385) FH_3Si—SiH_3F. Si 3″d, 8P; H 1″d, 1P; F 2.5″d, 9N. Attach the hydrogens and fluorine tetrahedrally around the silicon.

386) FNO—NOF. N 2.2″d, 4P; O 2.3″d, 1N; F 2.3″d, 4N. Cut the nitrogen and oxygen atoms for a bond length of 1.13Å, and connect. Attach the fluorine to the nitrogen so that the FNO angle is 110°.

387) F_2OS—SOF_2. S 3″d, 6P; O 2.3″d, O; F 2.3″d, 4N. Like $SOCl_2$.

388) F_2O_2S—SO_2F_2. S 3″d, 7P; O 2.3″d, O; F 2.3″d, 4N. Cut the sulfur and oxygens for a bond length of 1.4Å, and an OSO angle of 130°, and connect. Attach the two fluorines to the sulfur in a plane perpendicular to the OSO plane, with an FSF angle of 93°.

389) F_3OP—POF_3. P 2.7″d, 10P; O 2.3″d, 1N; F 2.3″d, 4N. Like 383.

390) $F_3PS—PSF_3$. P 2.8″d, 9P; S 2.9″d, 5P; F 2.3″d, 5N. Like 384.

391) HNO_3. (Fig. C-6.) H 0.8″d, 7P; N 2.2″d, 2P; O 2.3″d, 4N. Cut the nitrogen and two of the oxygens for bond lengths of 1.22Å, and 130° bond angle, and connect. Connect the third oxygen so the O—N length represents 1.41Å, directly opposite the other oxygens and in the same plane with the NO_2. Attach hydrogen to the third oxygen in the same plane and with an HON angle of 105°.

392) H_2SO_4. (Figs. C-5, C-6.) Prepare two OH groups, and attach them and two double-bonded oxygens to four corners of a tetrahedron around the sulfur, cutting the sulfur and double-bonded oxygens in preparation. H 0.8″d, 6P; S 3″d, 3P; O 2.3″d, 4N.

393) $Zn(NH_3)_4^{++}$ (Fig. C-13.) Zn 3.5″d, 9P; N 2.3″d, 3N; H 0.8″d, 5P. Construct four ammonia molecules and attach them tetrahedrally around the zinc.

Miscellaneous Compounds Containing Four or More Elements

394) CF_3COOH. (Fig. C-6.) C 2.3″d, 6P; F 2.5″d, 5N; O 2.5″d, 3N; H 0.8″d, 8P. Attach three fluorines to a carbon at three corners of a regular tetrahedron. Cut the second carbon as in acetic acid, and continue as described.

395) $BF_3 \cdot O(CH_3)_2$. (Fig. C-11.) B 2.2″d, 8P; F 2.4″d, 8N; C 2.3″d, 2P; H 0.8″d, 4P; O 2.4″d, 6N. Attach tangentially three fluorines and an oxygen around the corners of a regular tetrahedron surrounding boron. Attach three hydrogens at the tetrahedral corners around each carbon, and then at the fourth corner of each carbon, attach to the two tetrahedron corners of oxygen (boron is at the third corner).

396) $C_3H_5N_3O_9$-nitroglycerin. (Fig. C-15.) C 2.3″d, 5P; H 0.8″d, 6P; N 2.3″d, O; O 2.3″d, 5N. Prepare three nitrate groups just like HNO_3 without the hydrogen. Attach the three carbons together with two hydrogens on each terminal carbon and one hydrogen on the central carbon. All carbon bond angles should be 109°. Then to the fourth position of each carbon, attach the single-bonded oxygen of the nitrate group.

397) $C_6H_8O_2N_2S$-sulfanilamide. (Fig. C-16.) C 2.5″d, 1P; H 1″d, 3P; O 2.5″d, 7N; N 2.5″d, 4N; S 3″d, 2N. Make a benzene ring, and at 120° angles attach nitrogen to one carbon, sulfur to the opposite carbon, and hydrogen to each of the other four carbons in the ring. Add two hydrogens at 109° to the nitrogen, a similar NH_2 group to the sulfur, and two oxygens also to the sulfur so it is tetrahedrally surrounded, with the oxygens double-bonded.

398) $C_7H_5N_3O_6$-TNT-trinitrotoluene. (Fig. C-15.) C 2.5″d, 3P; H 0.8″d, 5P; N 2.3″d, 2N; O 2.5″d, 6N. Prepare a benzene ring with one methyl group attached to one carbon. Prepare three NO_2 multiple-bonded

groups and attach to the carbons on each side of the methyl and opposite it, so that they are in the plane with the carbon ring. To each of the other two ring carbons, add one hydrogen.

Rock Salt (NaCl) Structure

Herein (Figs. B-7, C-12) each atom has a coordination number of 6, all neighbors being of opposite kind. To make the model shown in the photo, make three separate checkerboard pattern layers of nine atoms each, two squares with black corners and one with white. Then assemble the layers with the white cornered layer in the middle, forming a black-cornered cube. Some compounds having this type of structure are listed in Table 10-14.

Cesium Chloride Structure

In this crystal, as shown in Fig. B-8, each kind of atom is at the center of a cube of 8 atoms of the other kind—8:8 coordination. The structure thus resembles a fluorite structure but with no holes. Enclose one black by 8 whites at the corners of a cube. The bond angle is 70°32′ between nearest bond pairs. Then complete a black cube surrounding one of the corner atoms of the white cube. Extend this procedure as far as you like. The pictured model contains 12 atoms of each kind. Some compounds having this type of structure are listed in Table 10-15.

Nickel Arsenide: NiAs

In this crystal, shown in Fig. B-9, each nonmetal atom is at the center of a triangular prism of six metal atoms of the other kind, instead of the usual octahedron, in 6:6 coordination. Each metal atom is surrounded by a distorted octahedron of nonmetal atoms. The pictured model contains 21 whites and 12 blacks. First there is a layer of 7 whites, a separated hexagon with one at the center. Next layer is a triangle of 6 blacks. Next is a layer of whites just like the first. Next is a triangle of 6 blacks just like the second only inverted. Next is another hexagonal layer of whites.

First construct a triangular prism of six whites around a black, so that all closest neighbor whites are equally spaced. The spacing is about 0.5 radius between white sphere surfaces. Then construct a second prism with one edge in common with the first, so that six whites are in the same rectangular plane. Using the reverse side of this plane as a base, construct two more such prisms opposite to the first two. You now have the first three layers mentioned above, save for a few blacks. Now build four new prisms above the first four, using their tops for a common base. However, stagger the centers, so they are not one directly above another.

Finally, add three blacks to each black layer, to make triangle points protruding from the hexagonal prism model. Some compounds having this structure are listed in Table 10-16.

Zinc Blende (Sphalerite) and Wurtzite Structures

These, illustrated in Fig. B-10 and B-11, are very similar, except in the positions, relatively, of the layers of tetrahedra. The coordination is 4:4, each atom being surrounded tetrahedrally by four of the other kind. Examples of compounds having these structures are given in Tables 10-17 and 10-18.

Corundum Structure: M_2X_3

This structure, typical of alpha alumina and ferric oxide, is shown in Fig. B-12. It is actually identical with the simple cubic lattice of NaCl, except that every third cation location is vacant. As will be seen in the figure, this changes the appearance remarkably, especially from certain angles. The model pictured contains four parallel planes that run diagonally through an ordinary cubic structure. These are alternately of black and of white atoms. The total is 32 blacks and 16 whites.

One of many possible ways to construct such a model is to begin by forming a square of blacks around a white. Using one edge of this square as a common edge of an adjacent square in the same plane, attach another white to this edge and complete the square. You now should have 8 balls in a rectangular plane—two black squares with a side in common using 6 blacks, and one white at the center of each square. Make two such assemblies at first.

Now prepare four squares, each of four blacks around a white. Attach two of these squares parallel to one of the initial planar assemblies, as follows. Let the corner of one square cover the central atom of one of the two squares in the first assembly, and the center of this new square cover the corner of the square of the first assembly. You will now have two parallel planes, one of joined squares, the next of two separate squares. This pattern of alternate layers is repeated throughout the crystal.

Fluorite and Antifluorite Structures: MX_2 or M_2X

The model shown in Fig. B-13 consists of 14 white balls and 13 black balls, and is actually antifluorite if the white are metal. First construct a cube of whites around one black. The bond angle between two nearest neighbor bonds is 70.5°. Be sure the cube is symmetrical. Then assemble a similar cube, all but one edge. Attach this incomplete cube to the first cube so that an edge of the latter completes the former. In other words, an edge (two whites) is shared in common, and the two cubes should be aligned like stairs. The final structure, if extended far enough, becomes a regular assembly of such white cubes, sharing all six faces at the interior of the crystal, and having a black ball at the center of every other cube. Keeping this in mind, attach black balls to the two assembled cubes in such positions that they would occupy the centers of every other adjacent cube. Thus the more abundant element shows a coordination number of 8, the other, 4. Each atom is at the center of a cube of the other kind of atom, but half the cubes of the more abundant element surround a hole instead of an atom. See Table 10-19 for examples.

Rutile (TiO_2) Structure

The model shown in Fig. B-14 contains 13 white balls and 20 black balls. In this crystal the coordination numbers of white and black are 6 and 3. You may begin by assembling two regular octahedra of black surrounding white, having one edge in common. Holding these so you see a plane of 6 blacks, in a verticle rectangle, attach one white to each of these six blacks to extend that rectangle to left and right. You now have a horizontal rectangle bordered on left and right edges by three white balls each. Now, perpendicular to this plane, connect two blacks to the three whites at each edge so as to bridge them. Turn the rectangle upside down and connect four more blacks just opposite the last four mentioned. To each of these, attach one white so that the white-black pair is perpendicular to the plane of the rectangle. Also bridge the two uppermost blacks of the original two octahedra by attaching one white. Looking down on the rectangle plane, you will now see five whites in a plane parallel to the rectangle and nearest to your eye: two at the left, two at the right, and one in the middle. You can now connect these whites together by a black at the center of each white triangle. The near plane will then consist of five whites and two blacks. The model as illustrated is now complete. For examples of compounds having the rutile structure, see Table 10-20.

Layer Lattice: MX_2

The type of crystal model shown in Fig. B-15 consists of 6 white and 13 black spheres, all the same size. Begin by connecting 6 blacks octahedrally to one white. Make a planar square of blacks around a white, and then attach the fifth and sixth black above and below the square. Let this assembly rest on a level surface so that it is stably supported on three blacks. The other three blacks will then form a triangle parallel to the base triangle but inverted in orientation. Then connect two whites to two of the base blacks so that each is also connected to a vertex black of the top triangle, and continue to extend the layer as far as desired. The entire layer is simply a combination of octahedra, all similarly oriented and sharing blacks in common. Each white ball, representing a metal atom, has 6 black balls, representing halogen atoms, coordinated to it. Each black ball is part of three octahedra in the layer and thus has a coordination number of 6. By different relative positions of such layers, modifications of layer lattices are produced. Examples of compounds having such structures are given in Table 10-21.

Body-Centered Cubic Structure

Metals having this structure are listed in Table 3-1. Some of these have other forms also. In a model, an atom has 8 closest neighbors at the corners of a cube surrounding it. At the centers of the six surrounding cubes are six more neighbors to the first, but these are about 15 per cent farther away.

Face-Centered Cubic Structure

This is also called "cubic close packing." Metals having this structure are listed in Table 3-2. To make a model in which one atom has 12 closest neighbors, attach four spheres around one, at the corners of a square. Then imagine two cubes to be constructed, one from each side of the plane of this square. Four faces of each cube are thus based on the original square and perpendicular to it. At the center of each of these eight faces is a sphere that touches the original central sphere. Thus are the 12 closest neighbors arranged.

Hexagonal Close Packing

Here again each atom has 12 closest neighbors, but the arrangement is slightly different. In one plane, attach a ring of six spheres to one. Then make two triangles of three spheres in mutual contact. Attach, to the central atom, one triangle above, the other below, both parallel to the plane of its hexagon. The triangles should be oriented alike. (Opposite orientation gives cubic close packing.) Table 3-3 lists metals having this structure.

BIBLIOGRAPHY

The following list of publications on models is not comprehensive, but includes only some of the more pertinent and interesting papers that have been published in the *Journal of Chemical Education*. References to similar papers appearing in other journals will be found in these.

1) Anker, R. M., *36*, 138 (1959), "Construction of Molecular Models." Describes models made of sponge rubber balls cemented together.
2) Ashley, R. H., *7*, 2904 (1930), "The Making and Use of Tetrahedral Models."
3) Barnett, E. D., *35*, 186 (1958), "The Face-Centered Cube and Cubical Close-Packing."
4) Blackwell, R. Q., *34*, 500 (1957), "Schematic Models of Biochemical Polymers." Use of "Pop-it" beads in polypeptide models.
5) Brode, W. R., and Boord, C. E., *9*, 1774 (1932), "Molecular Models in the Elementary Organic Laboratory."
6) Campbell, J. A., *25*, 200 (1948), "Structural Molecular Models."
7) Campbell, J. A., *34*, 210 (1957), "Some Simple Solid State Models."
8) Davidson, N., *29*, 249 (1952), "Cork-Ball Experiments on Crystalline and Molecular Structure."
9) Dore, W. H., *3*, 319 (1926), "A Device for Constructing Models of Carbon Compounds."
10) Entriken, J. B., *9*, 2091 (1932), "A New Type of Atomic Model for Organic Chemistry."
11) Fowles, G. W. A., *32*, 260 (1955), "Orbital Models."
12) French, S. F., *7*, 2687 (1930), "The Use of Models in Teaching Polarity."
13) Gibb, T. R. P., Jr., and Bassow, H., *34*, 99 (1957), "Construction of Crystal Models from Styrofoam Spheres." Describes jig for drilling holes at proper bond angles.
14) Godfrey, J. C., *36*, 140 (1959), "Accurate Molecular Models."
15) Hazelhurst, T. H., Jr., and Neville, H. A., *12*, 128, 228 (1935), "New Models of Old Molecules. Their Construction and Use in Chemical Education."
16) James, F. L., *33*, 408 (1956), "A Molecular Model Examination in Organic Chemistry."
17) Kauffman, G. B., *36*, 82 (1959), "Simplified Models of Inorganic Stereoisomers."
18) Kenney, M. E., *35*, 513 (1958), "Permanent Packing Type Crystal Models." Styrofoam spheres in transparent plastic boxes.
19) Lambert, F. L., *30*, 503, (1953), "Molecular Models for Lecture Demonstrations in Organic Chemistry." Describes jigs, etc., and mentions earlier use of styrofoam for models by L. R. Brantley in 1952.

20) Lambert, F. L., *34,* 217 (1957), "Atomic and Molecular Orbital Models."
21) Minné, N., *6,* 1984 (1929), "Molecular Models in Organic Chemistry."
22) Myers, R. T., *35,* 152 (1958), "Models of Metal Coordination Compounds."
23) Noyce, W. K., *28,* 29 (1951), "Molecular Models of Silicates for Lecture Demonstration."
24) Pierce, J. B., *36,* 595 (1959), "Molecular Models: A General Chemistry Exercise."
25) Pouleur, A. L., *9,* 301 (1932), "Models as a Visual Aid in the Teaching of Chemistry. Atomic and Molecular Structure."
26) Robey, R. F., *12,* 378 (1935), "Molecular Models in Inorganic Chemistry."
27) Sanderson, R. T., *36,* 507 (1959), "Models for Demonstrating Electronegativity and 'Partial Charge'."
28) Sanderson, R. T., *37,* 307 (1960), "Atomic Models in Teaching Chemistry."
29) Shine, H. J., *34,* 355 (1957),
30) Slabaugh, W. H., *36,* 288 (1959), "Crystal Models." Solid crystal forms, of Plexiglas.
31) Subluskey, L. A., *35,* 26 (1958), "Molecular Models with Variable Bond Angles."
32) Tanaka, J., *34,* 603 (1957), "Inexpensive Molecular Models for Use in the Laboratory." Wax ball models.
33) Wade, I. W., *5,* 193 (1928), "Construction and Use of Models in Chemistry."
34) Wendlandt, W. W., *34,* 223 (1957), "A Magnetic Model for Complex Ions and Molecules."
35) Westbrook, J. H., and Devries, R. C., *34,* 220 (1957), "A New Type of Crystal Model." Electrically lighted spheres.
36) Whalen, T. A., *34,* 136 (1957), "Model of the Alpha Helix Configuration in Polypeptides." Paper models.
37) J. Chem. Educ., *38,* 477 (1961) gives information on film strips by J. A. Campbell.

The following three films are lecture-demonstrations by R. T. Sanderson, each about 45 minutes, sound-color. They can be rented or purchased from the Bureau of Audio-Visual Instruction, Extension Division, University of Iowa, Iowa City, Iowa.

U-5113. "Atomic Models, Valence, and the Periodic Table."
U-5114. "New Models of Molecules, Ions, and Crystals: Their Construction and General Use in Teaching Chemistry."
U-5115. "A Special Set of Models for Introducing Chemistry."

Supplied with each film rental or purchase is a booklet entitled, "Principles and Construction of New Chemistry Teaching Aids."

Table 2-1

DATA FOR CALCULATING MOLECULAR ELECTRONEGATIVITY AND PARTIAL CHARGE

	S	log S	change in S/unit charge		S	log S	change in S/unit charge
H	3.55	0.5502	3.919	As	3.91	0.5922	4.112
Li	0.74	-0.1308	1.789	Se	4.25	0.6284	4.289
Be	1.91	0.2810	2.875	Br	4.53	0.6561	4.426
B	2.84	0.4533	3.505	Rb	0.53	-0.2757	1.514
C	3.79	0.5786	4.050	Sr	1.10	0.0414	2.267
N	4.49	0.6522	4.408	Y	1.75	0.2430	2.752
O	5.21	0.7168	4.749	Zr	2.26	0.3541	3.126
F	5.75	0.7597	4.988	Ag	2.30	0.3617	3.155
Na	0.70	-0.1549	1.741	Cd	2.59	0.4133	3.347
Mg	1.56	0.1931	2.661	In	2.86	0.4564	3.517
Al	1.94	0.2878	2.968	Sn	3.10	0.4914	3.663
Si	2.62	0.4183	3.418	Sb	3.37	0.5276	3.819
P	3.34	0.5237	3.802	Te	3.62	0.5587	3.958
S	4.11	0.6138	4.216	I	3.84	0.5843	4.077
Cl	4.93	0.6928	4.618	Cs	0.49	-0.3098	1.456
K	0.56	-0.2518	1.556	Ba	1.02	0.0086	2.189
Ca	1.22	0.0864	2.376	La	1.96	0.2923	2.912
Sc	1.88	0.2742	2.852	Au	2.88	0.4594	3.535
Ti	2.27	0.3560	3.272	Hg	2.93	0.4669	3.585
Cu	2.43	0.3856	3.243	Tl	3.02	0.4800	3.653
Zn	2.84	0.4533	3.529	Pb	3.08	0.4886	3.693
Ga	3.23	0.5092	3.772	Bi	3.16	0.4997	3.740
Ge	3.59	0.5551	3.942				

Table 2-2

DATA FOR CALCULATION OF RADIUS-IN-COMBINATION

(See also Table 10-2)

Z	r_i^3	Z	r_i^3	Z	r_i^3	Z	r_i^3
2	0.81	13	3.20	30	6.39	47	8.25
3	1.10	14	3.56	31	6.46	48	8.40
4	1.36	15	3.94	32	6.53	49	8.54
5	1.57	16	4.34	33	4.34	50	8.65
6	1.75	17	4.78	34	6.65	51	8.76
7	1.90	18	5.27	35	6.71	52	8.90
8	2.03	19	5.36	36	6.75	53	9.04
9	2.13	20	5.48	37	6.89	54	9.13
10	2.25	21	5.60	38	7.05	55	9.25
11	2.56	22	5.71	39	7.20	56	9.36
12	2.86	29	6.32	40	7.35		

Table 2-3

SOME BOND LENGTH FACTORS

To estimate bond lengths when experimental measurements are not available, calculate the single bond lengths as the sum of the radii-in-combination (as estimated from Table 2-2). Multiply this sum by the appropriate factor from the list below:

factor	description
1.0000	Single covalent bonds, except as listed below.
0.962	Single bonds to double-bonded atoms.
	Single bonds of F, O, Cl, or N to highly electronegative atoms (F, O, Cl, or N bearing low negative charge, or positive charge).
0.923	Most single bonds to N, O, or F.
	Single bonds between two olefinic double bonds.
	Single bonds to triple-bonded atoms.
0.885	Carbon-carbon bonds in aromatic rings.
	Carbon to sulfur double bonds.
	Single bonds between two triple-bonded atoms.
0.845	Olefinic double bonds.
	Sulfur and selenium bonds to oxygen in oxides and oxyhalides.
0.808	Sulfur to oxygen in sulfones, sulfoxides.
	Nitrogen to oxygen in ≡N=O compounds.
0.770	All carbon to carbon and carbon to nitrogen triple bonds.
	All carbonyl bonds, including carbon oxides and derivatives, and organic and inorganic carbonyl compounds.
	Nitrogen to oxygen in -N=O compounds.

(When both atoms bear partial positive charge, the bond length is usually greater than estimated by use of the above factors.)

Table 3-1

METALS HAVING BODY-CENTERED CUBIC STRUCTURE

Li	Ba	Ti	V	Cr	Fe
Na		Zr	Nb	Mo	
K		Hf	Ta	W	
Rb					
Cs					

Table 3-2

METALS HAVING CUBIC CLOSE PACKING (FACE-CENTERED CUBIC)

Ca	Sc	Fe	Co	Ni	Cu	Al	Pb
Sr	La		Rh	Pd	Ag	In	
			Ir	Pt	Au		

Table 3-3

METALS HAVING HEXAGONAL CLOSE PACKING

Be	Sc	Ti	Mo	Tc	Ru	Co	Ni	Zn
Mg	Y	Zr		Re	Os			Cd
	La	Hf						

Table 10-1

Some Suppliers of Styrofoam

Frostee Sno Co., Depot St., Antioch, Illinois

Craft House Products, Dorothy Flicek Industries, 5680 Northwest highway, Chicago 30, Illinois

Star Band Co., Broad and Commerce Sts., Portsmouth, Virginia

Snow Foam Products Inc., 1615 W. Gidley, El Monte, California

Table 10-2

ELECTRONEGATIVITY, CHARGE, AND RADIUS OF ELEMENTS IN COMPOUNDS

H			Li			Be			B		
S	ch	r	S	ch	r	S	ch	r	S	ch	r
1.0	-65		0.74	0	114	2.1	7	87	2.4	-12	87
1.2	-60		0.79	3	112	2.2	10	85	2.5	-10	86
1.4	-55		0.84	6	109	2.3	14	84	2.6	-7	84
1.6	-50		0.89	8	107	2.4	17	83	2.7	-4	83
1.8	-45		0.94	11	105	2.5	21	81	2.8	-1	82
2.0	-40		0.99	14	104	2.6	24	80	2.9	2	81
2.2	-34		1.04	17	102	2.7	28	79	3.0	5	80
2.4	-29		1.09	20	100	2.8	31	79	3.1	7	80
2.6	-24		1.14	22	99	2.9	35	78	3.2	10	79
2.8	-19		1.19	25	97	3.0	38	77	3.3	13	78
3.0	-14		1.24	28	96	3.1	42	76	3.4	16	77
3.2	-9		1.29	31	95	3.2	45	75	3.5	19	77
3.4	-4		1.34	34	94	3.3	49	74	3.6	21	76
3.6	1		1.39	36	93	3.4	52	73	3.7	24	75
3.8	6		1.44	39	91	3.5	56	73	3.8	27	74
4.0	11		1.49	42	90	3.6	59	72	3.9	30	74
4.2	17		1.54	45	89	3.7	63	72	4.0	33	73
4.4	22		1.59	48	89	3.8	66	71	4.1	36	72
4.6	27		1.64	50	88	3.9	70	70	4.2	38	72
4.8	32		1.69	53	87	4.0	73	70	4.3	41	72
5.0	37		1.74	56	86	4.1	77	69	4.4	44	71
5.2	42		1.79	59	85	4.2	80	69	4.5	47	70
5.4	47		1.84	61	84	4.3	83	69	4.6	50	70
5.6	52		1.89	64	83	4.4	87	68	4.7	52	69
									4.8	55	69

Note: charge, in electrons, and radius, in Å, above are multiplied by 100. For radii of H, see Table 10-7.

Table 10-2 (continued)

C			N			O			F		
S	ch	r	S	ch	r	S	ch	r	S	ch	r
2.9	-22	84	3.0	-34	86	1.0	-89	127	1.6	-83	110
3.0	-20	83	3.1	-32	85	1.2	-84	119	1.7	-81	108
3.1	-17	82	3.2	-29	84	1.4	-80	113	1.8	-79	106
3.2	-15	82	3.3	-27	83	1.6	-76	108	1.9	-77	104
3.3	-12	81	3.4	-25	82	1.8	-72	104	2.0	-75	103
3.4	-10	80	3.5	-22	81	2.0	-68	101	2.1	-73	101
3.5	-7	79	3.6	-20	81	2.2	-63	97	2.2	-71	99
3.6	-5	79	3.7	-18	80	2.4	-59	95	2.3	-69	98
3.7	-2	78	3.8	-16	79	2.6	-55	92	2.4	-67	97
3.8	0	77	3.9	-13	79	2.8	-51	90	2.6	-63	94
3.9	3	77	4.0	-11	78	3.0	-47	88	2.8	-59	92
4.0	5	76	4.1	-9	77	3.2	-42	86	3.0	-55	90
4.1	8	75	4.2	-7	77	3.4	-38	84	3.2	-51	87
4.2	10	75	4.3	-4	76	3.6	-34	82	3.4	-47	86
4.3	13	74	4.4	-2	75	3.8	-30	81	3.6	-43	84
4.4	15	74	4.5	0	75	4.0	-25	80	3.8	-39	83
4.5	18	73	4.6	2	74	4.2	-21	78	4.0	-35	81
4.6	20	72	4.7	5	74	4.4	-17	77	4.2	-31	80
4.7	22	72	4.8	7	74	4.6	-13	76	4.4	-27	79
4.8	25	71	4.9	9	73	4.8	-9	75	4.6	-23	78
4.9	27	71	5.0	12	72	5.0	-4	74	4.8	-19	77
5.0	30	70	5.1	14	72	5.2	0	73	5.0	-15	76
5.1	32	70	5.2	16	72	5.4	4	72	5.2	-11	74
5.2	35	70	5.3	18	71	5.6	8	71	5.4	-7	74
5.3	37	69	5.4	21	70				5.6	-3	73

Table 10-2 (continued, 2)

Na			Mg			Al			Si		
S	ch	r	S	ch	r	S	ch	r	S	ch	r
1.40	40	122	2.0	17	113	2.5	19	109	1.8	-24	126
1.45	43	121	2.1	20	111	2.6	22	107	1.9	-21	123
1.50	46	119	2.2	24	109	2.7	26	106	2.0	-18	121
1.55	49	118	2.3	28	107	2.8	29	104	2.1	-15	119
1.60	52	117	2.4	32	106	2.9	32	103	2.2	-12	117
1.65	55	116	2.5	35	104	3.0	36	102	2.3	-9	116
1.70	57	115	2.6	39	103	3.1	39	101	2.4	-6	114
1.75	60	113	2.7	43	102	3.2	42	100	2.5	-3	112
1.80	63	112	2.8	47	101	3.3	46	99	2.6	0	111
1.85	66	111	2.9	50	100	3.4	49	98	2.8	5	108
1.90	69	110	3.0	54	98	3.5	53	97	3.0	11	106
1.95	72	109	3.1	58	97	3.6	56	96	3.2	17	104
2.00	75	109	3.2	62	96	3.7	59	95	3.4	23	102
2.05	78	108	3.3	65	95	3.8	63	94	3.6	29	100
2.10	80	107	3.4	69	94	3.9	66	94	3.8	35	98
2.15	83	106	3.5	73	94	4.0	69	93	4.0	40	96
2.20	86	105	3.6	77	93	4.1	73	92	4.2	46	95
2.25	89	104	3.7	80	92	4.2	76	91	4.4	52	93
2.30	92	104	3.8	84	91	4.3	80	90	4.6	58	92
2.35	95	103	3.9	88	90	4.4	83	90	4.8	64	90
2.40	98	102	4.0	92	90	4.5	86	89	5.0	70	89

Table 10-2 (continued, 3)

P			S			Cl			K		
S	ch	r	S	ch	r	S	ch	r	S	ch	r
1.8	-41	130	1.0	-74	163	1.1	-83	154	1.05	31	172
1.9	-38	127	1.2	-69	154	1.3	-79	163	1.10	35	170
2.0	-35	125	1.4	-64	146	1.5	-74	147	1.15	38	167
2.1	-33	123	1.6	-60	139	1.7	-70	141	1.20	41	165
2.2	-30	121	1.8	-55	134	1.9	-66	136	1.25	44	162
2.3	-27	119	2.0	-50	129	2.1	-61	132	1.30	48	160
2.4	-25	118	2.2	-45	125	2.3	-57	128	1.35	51	158
2.5	-22	116	2.4	-41	122	2.5	-53	124	1.40	54	156
2.6	-19	115	2.6	-36	119	2.7	-48	121	1.45	57	155
2.7	-17	113	2.8	-31	116	2.9	-44	118	1.50	60	153
2.8	-14	112	3.0	-26	113	3.1	-40	115	1.55	64	151
2.9	-12	111	3.2	-22	111	3.3	-35	113	1.60	67	150
3.0	-9	109	3.4	-17	109	3.5	-31	111	1.65	70	148
3.2	-4	107	3.6	-12	107	3.7	-27	109	1.70	73	147
3.4	2	105	3.8	-7	104	3.9	-22	107	1.75	76	145
3.6	7	103	4.0	-3	103	4.1	-18	105	1.80	80	144
3.8	12	101	4.2	2	101	4.3	-14	104	1.85	83	143
4.0	17	100	4.4	7	100	4.5	-9	102	1.90	86	141
4.2	23	98	4.6	12	98	4.7	-5	101	1.95	89	140
4.4	28	97	4.8	16	97	4.9	0	99	2.00	93	139
4.6	33	95	5.0	21	95	5.1	4	98	2.05	96	138
4.8	38	94	5.2	26	94	5.3	8	97	2.10	99	137
5.0	44	93	5.4	31	93	5.5	12	96			
5.2	49	91	5.6	35	92	5.7	17	94			

Table 10-2 (continued, 4)

Ca			Zn			Ga			Ge		
S	ch	r	S	ch	r	S	ch	r	S	ch	r
2.40	50	132	2.8	-1	132	2.8	-11	132	3.0	-15	130
2.45	52	131	2.9	2	130	2.9	-9	131	3.1	-12	128
2.50	54	130	3.0	5	129	3.0	-6	129	3.2	-10	127
2.55	56	129	3.1	7	127	3.1	-3	128	3.3	-7	126
2.60	58	128	3.2	10	126	3.2	0	126	3.4	-5	124
2.65	60	127	3.3	13	125	3.3	2	125	3.5	-2	123
2.70	62	127	3.4	16	123	3.4	5	124	3.6	0	122
2.75	64	126	3.5	19	122	3.5	7	123	3.7	3	121
2.80	67	125	3.6	22	121	3.6	10	121	3.8	5	120
2.85	69	124	3.7	24	120	3.7	12	120	3.9	8	119
2.90	71	124	3.8	27	119	3.8	15	119	4.0	10	118
2.95	73	123	3.9	30	118	3.9	18	118	4.1	13	117
3.00	75	122	4.0	33	117	4.0	20	117	4.2	15	116
3.05	77	122	4.1	36	116	4.1	23	116	4.3	18	115
3.10	79	121	4.2	39	115	4.2	26	115	4.4	21	114
3.15	81	120	4.3	41	114	4.3	28	114	4.5	23	113
3.20	83	119	4.4	44	113	4.4	31	114	4.6	26	112
3.25	85	119	4.5	47	112	4.5	34	113	4.7	28	112
3.30	88	118	4.6	50	112	4.6	36	112	4.8	31	111
3.35	90	118	4.7	53	111	4.7	39	111	4.9	33	110
3.40	92	117	4.8	56	110	4.8	42	111	5.0	36	109
3.45	94	117	4.9	58	109	4.9	44	110	5.1	38	109
3.50	96	116	5.0	61	109	5.0	47	109	5.2	41	108

Table 10-2 (continued, 5)

As			Se			Br			Rb		
S	ch	r	S	ch	r	S	ch	r	S	ch	r
3.5	-10	123	3.5	-17	124	1.4	-71	169	0.95	28	194
3.6	-8	122	3.6	-15	123	1.6	-66	161	1.00	31	190
3.7	-5	121	3.7	-13	122	1.8	-62	155	1.05	34	187
3.8	-3	120	3.8	-10	121	2.0	-57	150	1.10	38	184
3.9	0	119	3.9	-8	120	2.2	-53	145	1.15	41	182
4.0	3	118	4.0	-6	118	2.4	-48	141	1.20	44	179
4.1	5	117	4.1	-3	117	2.6	-44	137	1.25	48	177
4.2	8	116	4.2	-1	117	2.8	-39	134	1.30	51	174
4.3	10	115	4.3	1	116	3.0	-35	131	1.35	54	172
4.4	12	114	4.4	3	115	3.2	-30	128	1.40	57	170
4.5	15	113	4.5	6	114	3.4	-26	125	1.45	61	168
4.6	17	112	4.6	8	113	3.6	-21	123	1.50	64	166
4.7	20	111	4.7	10	112	3.8	-16	121	1.55	67	165
4.8	22	110	4.8	13	112	4.0	-12	119	1.60	71	163
4.9	25	110	4.9	15	111	4.2	-7	117	1.65	74	161
5.0	27	109	5.0	17	110	4.4	-3	115	1.70	77	159
5.1	29	108	5.1	20	109	4.6	2	113	1.75	81	158
5.2	32	108	5.2	22	109	4.8	6	112	1.80	84	157
5.3	34	107	5.3	24	108	5.0	11	110	1.85	87	155
5.4	37	107	5.4	27	107	5.2	15	109	1.90	90	154
5.5	39	106	5.5	29	107	5.4	20	107	1.95	94	152
5.6	42	106	5.6	31	106	5.6	24	106	2.00	97	151

Table 10-2 (continued, 6)

Sr			Cd			In			Sn		
S	ch	r	S	ch	r	S	ch	r	S	ch	r
1.6	22	164	2.6	0	148	2.8	-2	145	3.1	0	141
1.7	26	161	2.7	3	146	2.9	1	143	3.2	3	139
1.8	31	158	2.8	6	144	3.0	4	142	3.3	5	138
1.9	35	155	2.9	9	143	3.1	7	140	3.4	8	136
2.0	40	152	3.0	12	141	3.2	10	139	3.5	11	135
2.1	44	150	3.1	15	139	3.3	13	137	3.6	14	134
2.2	49	147	3.2	18	138	3.4	15	136	3.7	16	133
2.3	53	145	3.3	21	137	3.5	18	135	3.8	19	132
2.4	57	143	3.4	24	135	3.6	21	133	3.9	22	130
2.5	62	141	3.5	27	134	3.7	24	132	4.0	25	129
2.6	66	139	3.6	30	133	3.8	27	131	4.1	27	128
2.7	71	138	3.7	33	131	3.9	30	130	4.2	30	127
2.8	75	136	3.8	36	130	4.0	32	129	4.3	33	126
2.9	79	134	3.9	39	129	4.1	35	128	4.4	35	125
3.0	84	133	4.0	42	128	4.2	38	127	4.5	38	124
3.1	88	131	4.2	45	126	4.4	44	125	4.6	41	123
3.2	93	130	4.4	48	124	4.6	49	123	4.7	44	123
3.3	97	129	4.6	51	122	4.8	55	121	4.8	46	122
3.4	101	127	4.8	54	121	5.0	61	120	4.9	49	121
3.5	106	126	5.0	57	119	5.2	67	118	5.0	52	120
3.6	110	125	5.2	60	117	5.4	72	116	5.1	55	119

Table 10-2 (continued, 7)

Sb			Te			I			Cs		
S	ch	r	S	ch	r	S	ch	r	S	ch	r
2.4	-25	154	1.0	-66	207	1.2	-65	196	0.80	21	226
2.6	-20	150	1.2	-61	195	1.4	-60	186	0.85	25	222
2.8	-15	146	1.4	-56	185	1.6	-55	178	0.90	28	217
3.0	-10	143	1.6	-51	177	1.8	-50	171	0.95	32	214
3.2	-4	140	1.8	-46	170	2.0	-45	165	1.00	35	210
3.4	0	137	2.0	-41	165	2.2	-40	160	1.05	38	206
3.5	3	136	2.2	-36	160	2.4	-35	156	1.10	42	203
3.6	6	134	2.4	-31	155	2.6	-30	152	1.15	45	200
3.7	9	133	2.6	-26	151	2.8	-26	148	1.20	49	197
3.8	11	132	2.8	-21	147	3.0	-21	144	1.25	52	195
3.9	14	131	3.0	-16	144	3.2	-16	141	1.30	56	192
4.0	16	130	3.2	-11	141	3.4	-11	139	1.35	59	190
4.1	19	129	3.4	-6	138	3.6	-6	136	1.40	62	188
4.2	22	128	3.6	0	135	3.8	0	134	1.45	66	185
4.3	24	127	3.8	5	133	4.0	4	131	1.50	69	183
4.4	27	126	4.0	10	131	4.2	9	129	1.55	73	181
4.5	30	125	4.2	15	129	4.4	14	127	1.60	76	179
4.6	32	124	4.4	20	126	4.6	19	125	1.65	80	178
4.7	35	123	4.6	25	125	4.8	24	123	1.70	83	176
4.8	37	122	4.8	30	123	5.0	28	122	1.75	87	174
4.9	40	121	5.0	35	121	5.2	33	120	1.80	90	173
5.0	43	121	5.2	40	120	5.4	38	119	1.85	93	171
5.1	45	120	5.4	45	118	5.6	43	117	1.90	97	170
5.2	48	119	5.6	50	117				1.95	100	168

Table 10-2 (continued, 8)

Ba			Hg			Tl			Pb			Bi		
S	ch	r	S	ch	r	S	ch	r	S	ch	r	S	ch	r
1.0	0	211	3.0	2	148	3.0	0	148	3.1	1	146	3.2	1	145
1.1	4	204	3.1	5	146	3.1	2	146	3.2	3	145	3.3	4	143
1.2	8	198	3.2	8	145	3.2	5	145	3.3	6	143	3.4	6	142
1.3	13	193	3.3	10	143	3.3	8	143	3.4	9	142	3.5	9	141
1.4	17	188	3.4	13	142	3.4	10	142	3.5	11	141	3.6	12	139
1.5	22	184	3.5	16	141	3.5	13	141	3.6	14	139	3.7	14	138
1.6	26	180	3.6	19	139	3.6	16	139	3.7	17	138	3.8	17	137
1.7	31	177	3.7	21	138	3.7	19	138	3.8	19	137	3.9	20	136
1.8	36	173	3.8	24	137	3.8	21	137	3.9	22	136	4.0	22	135
1.9	40	170	3.9	27	136	3.9	24	136	4.0	25	135	4.1	25	134
2.0	45	167	4.0	30	135	4.0	27	135	4.1	28	134	4.2	28	132
2.1	49	165	4.1	33	134	4.1	30	134	4.2	30	132	4.3	30	131
2.2	54	162	4.2	35	132	4.2	32	132	4.3	33	131	4.4	33	130
2.3	58	160	4.3	38	131	4.3	35	131	4.4	36	130	4.5	36	129
2.4	63	157	4.4	41	130	4.4	38	130	4.5	38	129	4.6	39	128
2.5	68	155	4.5	44	129	4.5	41	129	4.6	41	128	4.7	41	128
2.6	72	153	4.6	47	128	4.6	43	128	4.7	44	128	4.8	44	127
2.7	77	151	4.7	49	128	4.7	46	128	4.8	47	127	4.9	47	126
2.8	81	149	4.8	52	127	4.8	49	127	4.9	49	126	5.0	49	125
2.9	86	148	4.9	55	126	4.9	51	126	5.0	52	125	5.1	52	124
3.0	90	146	5.0	58	125	5.0	54	125	5.1	55	124	5.2	55	123
3.1	95	144	5.1	61	124	5.1	57	124	5.2	57	123			
3.2	100	143	5.2	63	123	5.2	60	123						

Table 10-3

COLORS FOR REPRESENTING ELECTRONEGATIVITY AND PARTIAL CHARGE

Electronegativity	Partial Charge	Color No.	Color	Approximate Mix, Dry Tempera, by Volume
0.49 - 0.69	0.60 or higher	12P	red	R (red)
0.70 - 0.90	0.50 - 0.59	11P	orange-red	2-0/5R
0.91 - 1.11	0.43 - 0.49	10P		3-0/4R
1.12 - 1.32	0.36 - 0.42	9P	red-orange	2-0/1R
1.33 - 1.53	0.30 - 0.359	8P		6-0/1R
1.54 - 1.74	0.25 - 0.299	7P	orange	0 (orange)
1.75 - 1.95	0.20 - 0.249	6P		1Y/5-0
1.96 - 2.16	0.15 - 0.199	5P	yellow-orange	1Y/1-0
2.17 - 2.37	0.10 - 0.149	4P		2Y/1-0
2.38 - 2.58	0.07 - 0.099	3P	orange-yellow	4Y/1-0
2.59 - 2.79	0.04 - 0.069	2P		6Y/1-0
2.80 - 3.00	0.02 - 0.039	1P		24Y/1-0
3.01 - 3.21	0 to ± 0.019	0	yellow	Y (yellow)
3.22 - 3.42	-0.02 to -0.039	1N	greenish yellow	24Y/1G
3.43 - 3.63	-0.04 to -0.069	2N		13Y/1G
3.64 - 3.84	-0.07 to -0.099	3N		6Y/1G
3.85 - 4.05	-0.10 to -0.149	4N	yellow-green	5Y/2G
4.06 - 4.26	-0.15 to -0.199	5N		4Y/3G
4.27 - 4.47	-0.20 to -0.249	6N		3Y/4G
4.48 - 4.68	-0.25 to -0.299	7N	green	G (green)
4.69 - 4.89	-0.30 to -0.359	8N		5G/1B
4.90 - 5.10	-0.36 to -0.429	9N	blue-green	5G/2B
5.11 - 5.31	-0.43 to -0.499	10N		4G/3B
5.32 - 5.52	-0.50 to -0.599	11N		3G/5B
5.53 - 5.75	-0.60 or higher	12N	blue	B (blue)

Table 10-4

EMPIRICAL (GOLDSCHMIDT) IONIC RADII
(Angstrom units)

Li^{+} 0.78	Al^{+++} 0.57	Fe^{++} 0.83	Sr^{++} 1.27	Cs^{+} 1.65
Be^{++} 0.34	$S^{=}$ 1.74	Fe^{+++} 0.67	Ag^{+} 1.13	Ba^{++} 1.43
$O^{=}$ (1.4)	Cl^{-} 1.81	Zn^{++} 0.83	Cd^{++} 1.03	Hg^{++} 1.12
F^{-} (1.4)	K^{+} 1.33	$Se^{=}$ 1.91	In^{+++} 0.92	Tl^{+} 1.49
Na^{+} 0.98	Ca^{++} 1.06	Br^{-} 1.96		Pb^{++} 1.32
Mg^{++} 0.78	Sc^{+++} 0.83	Rb^{+} 1.49		

Table 10-5

DATA FOR CONSTRUCTION OF ATOMIC MODELS

No.	Element	r,Å	S	diameter, inches: small	medium	large	color	electrons	vacancies	d electrons
1	H	0.37	3.55	0.22	1.11	2.2	2N	1	1	
2	He	0.93		0.56	2.79	5.6	black	2	0	
3	Li	1.34	0.74	0.80	4.02	8.0	11P	1	7	
4	Be	0.90	1.91	0.54	2.70	5.4	6P	2	6	
5	B	0.82	2.84	0.50	2.46	5.0	1P	3	5	
6	C	0.77	3.79	0.46	2.31	4.6	3N	4	4	
7	N	0.75	4.49	0.45	2.25	4.5	7N	5	3	
8	O	0.73	5.21	0.44	2.19	4.4	10N	6	2	
9	F	0.72	5.75	0.43	2.16	4.3	12N	7	1	
10	Ne	1.31		0.79	3.93	7.9	black	8	0	
11	Na	1.54	0.70	0.92	4.62	9.2	12P	1	7	
12	Mg	1.30	1.56	0.78	3.90	7.8	7-8P	2	6	
13	Al	1.18	1.94	0.71	3.54	7.1	6P	3	5	
14	Si	1.11	2.62	0.67	3.33	6.7	2P	4	4	
15	P	1.06	3.34	0.64	3.18	6.4	1N	5	3	
16	S	1.02	4.11	0.61	3.06	6.1	5N	6	2	
17	Cl	0.99	4.93	0.60	2.97	6.0	9N	7	1	
18	Ar	1.74		1.04	5.22	10.4	black	8	0	
19	K	1.96	0.56	1.19	5.88	11.9	12P	1	7	
20	Ca	1.74	1.22	1.04	5.22	10.4	9P	2	6	
21	Sc	1.44	1.88	0.86	4.32	8.6	6P	2	6	1
22	Ti	1.36	2.27	0.82	4.08	8.2	4P	2	6	2
23	V							2	6	3
24	Cr							1	7	5
25	Mn							2	6	5
26	Fe							2	6	6
27	Co							2	6	7
28	Ni							2	6	8
29	Cu	1.38	2.43	0.83	4.14	8.3	3P	1	7	10
30	Zn	1.31	2.84	0.79	3.93	7.9	1P	2	6	
31	Ga	1.26	3.23	0.76	3.78	7.6	0-1N	3	5	
32	Ge	1.22	3.59	0.73	3.66	7.3	2N	4	4	

Table 10-5 (continued)

No.	Element	r,Å	S	diameter, inches: small	medium	large	color	electrons	vacancies	d electrons
33	As	1.19	3.91	0.72	3.57	7.2	4N	5	3	
34	Se	1.16	4.25	0.70	3.48	7.0	5-6N	6	2	
35	Br	1.14	4.53	0.68	3.42	6.8	7N	7	1	
36	Kr	1.89		1.13	5.67	11.3	black	8	0	
37	Rb	2.11	0.53	1.27	6.33	12.7	12P	1	7	
38	Sr	1.92	1.10	1.15	5.76	11.5	10P	2	6	
39	Y	1.62	1.75	0.97	4.86	9.7	6-7P	2	6	1
40	Zr	1.48	2.26	0.88	4.44	8.8	4P	2	6	2
41	Nb							2	6	3
42	Mo							1	7	5
43	Tc							2	6	5
44	Ru							1	7	7
45	Rh							1	7	8
46	Pd							0	8	10
47	Ag	1.53	2.30	0.92	4.59	9.2	4P	1	7	10
48	Cd	1.48	2.59	0.89	4.44	8.9	2-3P	2	6	
49	In	1.44	2.86	0.86	4.32	8.6	1P	3	5	
50	Sn	1.41	3.10	0.85	4.23	8.5	0	4	4	
51	Sb	1.38	3.37	0.83	4.14	8.3	1N	5	3	
52	Te	1.35	3.62	0.81	4.05	8.1	2-3N	6	2	
53	I	1.33	3.84	0.80	3.99	8.0	3-4N	7	1	
54	Xe	2.09		1.25	6.27	12.5	black	8	0	
55	Cs	2.25	0.49	1.35	6.75	13.5	12P	1	7	
56	Ba	1.98	1.02	1.19	5.94	11.9	10P	2	6	
57	La	1.69	1.92	1.01	5.07	10.1	6P	2	6	1
58	Ce						(6P)	2	6	
59	Pr						(6P)	2	6	
60	Nd						(6P)	2	6	
61	Pm						(6P)	2	6	
62	Sm						(5P)	2	6	
63	Eu						(5P)	2	6	
64	Gd						(5P)	2	6	1
65	Tb						(5P)	2	6	
66	Dy						(5P)	2	6	
67	Ho						(5P)	2	6	

Table 10-5 (continued, 2)

No.	Element	r,Å	S	diameter, inches: small	medium	large	color	electrons	vacancies	d electrons
68	Er						(4P)	2	6	
69	Tm						(4P)	2	6	
70	Yb						(4P)	2	6	
71	Lu						(4P)	2	6	1
72	Hf						(4P)	2	6	2
73	Ta						(3P)	2	6	3
74	W						(3P)	2	6	4
75	Re						(3P)	2	6	5
76	Os						(2P)	2	6	6
77	Ir						(2P)	2	6	7
78	Pt						(2P)	1	7	9
79	Au	1.50	2.88	0.90	4.50	9.0	1P	1	7	10
80	Hg	1.49	2.93	0.89	4.47	8.9	1P	2	6	
81	Tl	1.48	3.02	0.89	4.44	8.9	0	3	5	
82	Pb	1.47	3.08	0.88	4.41	8.8	0	4	4	
83	Bi	1.46	3.16	0.88	4.38	8.8	0	5	3	
84	Po			(0.87)	(4.3)	(8.7)	(0)	6	2	
85	At			(0.87)	(4.3)	(8.7)	(1N)	7	1	
86	Rn	2.14		1.28	6.4	12.8	black	8	0	
87	Fr							1	7	
88	Ra							2	6	
89	Ac							2	6	1
90	Th							2	6	2
91	Pa							2	6	1
92	U							2	6	1
93	Np							2	6	1
94	Pu							2	6	1
95	Am							2	6	0
96	Cm							2	6	1
97	Bk							2	6	1
98	Cf							2	6	1
99	Es							2	6	1
100	Fm							2	6	1
101	Mv							2	6	1
102	No							2	6	1

Table 10-6

BINARY OXYGEN COMPOUNDS: DATA FOR MODEL CONSTRUCTION

	formula	S	radius, Å		diameter, inches small		medium		large		100x charge		color		type	angle
			E	X	E	X	E	X	E	X	E	X	E	X		
1	H_2O	4.034		0.80	0.20	0.48	1.0	2.4	2.0	4.8	12	-25	4P	6N	D	105
2	H_3O^+	4.925		0.74	0.15	0.44	0.75	2.2	1.5	4.4	35	-6	8P	2N	D	109
3	OH^-	2.157	0.98		0.59	0.30	2.9	1.5	5.9	3.0	-64	-36	12N	8N	A	
4	H_2O_2	4.300		0.78	0.18	0.50	0.9	2.4	1.8	4.8	19	-19	5P	5N	F	
5	Li_2O	1.418	0.97	1.15	0.58	0.68	2.9	3.4	5.8	6.8	38	-76	9P	12N	E	
6	Na_2O	1.367	1.23	1.15	0.74	0.69	3.7	3.4	7.4	6.8	38	-77	9P	12N	E	
7	Na_2O_2	1.910	1.45	1.02	0.87	0.61	4.4	3.1	8.7	6.1	70	-70	12P	12N	E	
8	K_2O	1.178	1.66	1.18	0.98	0.71	4.9	3.6	9.8	7.1	40	-80	10P	12N	E	
9	KO_2	2.477	1.29	0.93	0.78	0.56	3.9	2.8	7.8	5.6	100	-50	12P	11N	E	
10	Rb_2O	1.135	1.81	1.21	1.09	0.72	5.5	3.6	10.9	7.2	40	-80	10P	12N	E	
11	Cs_2O	1.077	2.05	1.23	1.24	0.74	6.2	3.7	12.4	7.4	40	-80	10P	12N	E	
12	BeO	3.154	0.76	0.86	0.45	0.52	2.3	2.6	4.5	5.2	43	-43	10P	10N	E	
13	MgO	2.851	1.00	0.89	0.60	0.53	3.0	2.7	6.0	5.3	50	-50	11P	11N	E	
14	CaO	2.521	1.29	0.93	0.77	0.56	3.9	2.8	7.7	5.6	57	-57	11P	11N	E	
15	SrO	2.394	1.43	0.95	0.86	0.57	4.3	2.9	8.6	5.7	59	-59	11P	11N	E	
16	BaO	2.306	1.60	0.96	0.96	0.58	4.8	2.9	9.6	5.8	61	-61	12P	12N	E	
17	B_2O_3	4.086	0.72	0.80	0.43	0.48	2.2	2.4	4.3	4.8	36	-24	9P	6N	E	
18	Al_2O_3	3.509	0.97	0.83	0.58	0.50	2.9	2.5	5.8	5.0	54	-36	11P	9N	E	
19	Ga_2O_3	4.303	1.15	0.78	0.69	0.47	3.5	2.3	6.9	4.7	29	-19	7P	5N	E	
20	In_2O_3	4.098	1.28	0.79	0.77	0.47	3.8	2.4	7.7	4.7	35	-23	8P	6N	E	
21	Tl_2O	3.622	1.39	0.82	0.81	0.49	4.2	2.5	8.1	4.9	17	-33	5P	8N	E	
22	Tl_2O_3	4.189	1.32	0.78	0.79	0.47	4.0	2.3	7.9	4.7	32	-21	8P	6N	E	
23	CO	4.443	0.73	0.77	0.48	0.48	2.4	2.4	4.8	4.8	16	-16	0	0	F	
24	CO_2	4.685	0.72	0.76	0.43	0.46	2.2	2.3	4.3	4.6	22	-11	6P	4N	F	
25	$CO_3^=$	2.546	0.88	0.93	0.53	0.56	2.6	2.8	5.3	5.6	-31	-56	8N	11N	F	
26	SiO_2	4.143	0.95	0.79	0.57	0.47	2.9	2.4	5.7	4.7	45	-23	10P	6N	E	
27	GeO_2	4.601	1.12	0.76	0.67	0.46	3.4	2.3	6.7	4.6	26	-13	7P	4N	E	
28	SnO	4.019	1.29	0.80	0.78	0.48	3.9	2.4	7.8	4.8	25	-25	7P	7N	E	
29	SnO_2	4.382	1.25	0.77	0.75	0.46	3.8	2.3	7.5	4.6	35	-17	8P	5N	E	
30	PbO	4.007	1.35	0.80	0.81	0.48	4.1	2.4	8.1	4.8	25	-25	7P	7N	E	
31	PbO_2	4.372	1.30	0.77	0.78	0.46	3.9	2.3	7.8	4.6	35	-18	8P	5N	E	

Table 10-6 (continued)

formula	S	radius, Å		diameter, inches small		medium		large		100x charge		color		type	angle
		E	X	E	X	E	X	E	X	E	X	E	X		
32 N_2O	4.717	0.74	0.76	0.44	0.46	2.2	2.3	4.4	4.6	5	-10	2P	4N	F	
33 NO	4.837	0.73	0.75	0.44	0.45	2.2	2.3	4.4	4.5	8	-8	3P	3N	F	
34 N_2O_3	4.911	0.73	0.74	0.44	0.44	2.2	2.2	4.4	4.4	10	-6	4P	2N	F	
35 NO_2	4.958	0.73	0.74	0.44	0.44	2.2	2.2	4.4	4.4	11	-5	4P	2N	F	
36 N_2O_5	4.992	0.75	0.73	0.45	0.44	2.2	2.2	4.5	4.4	11	-5	4P	2N	F	
37 NO_3^-	3.871	0.79	0.81	0.47	0.49	2.4	2.4	4.8	4.8	-14	-29	4N	7N	F	
38 P_4O_6	4.361	0.97	0.77	0.58	0.46	2.9	2.3	5.8	4.6	27	-18	7P	5N	F	
39 P_4O_{10}	4.587	0.95	0.76	0.57	0.46	2.9	2.3	5.7	4.6	33	-13	8P	4N	F	
40 $PO_4^{\equiv}$	2.058	1.24	0.99	0.74	0.60	3.7	3.0	7.4	6.0	-34	-67	8N	12N	F	
41 As_4O_6	4.645	1.12	0.76	0.68	0.48	3.4	2.3	6.8	4.8	18	-12	5P	4N	F	
42 As_2O_5	4.800	1.11	0.75	0.67	0.45	3.3	2.3	6.7	4.5	22	-9	6P	3N	E	
43 Sb_4O_6	4.376	1.26	0.77	0.76	0.46	3.8	2.3	7.6	4.6	26	-18	7P	5N	F	
44 Sb_2O_5	4.599	1.24	0.76	0.74	0.46	3.7	2.3	7.4	4.6	32	-13	8P	4N	E	
45 Bi_2O_3	4.266	1.31	0.78	0.79	0.47	3.9	2.3	7.9	4.7	29	-20	5P	6N	E	
46 Bi_2O_5	4.516	1.28	0.76	0.77	0.46	3.8	2.3	7.7	4.6	37	-15	9P	5N	E	
47 SO_2	4.814	0.97	0.75	0.60	0.46	2.9	2.3	6.0	4.6	17	-8	5P	3N	F	
48 SO_3	4.910	0.96	0.74	0.60	0.44	2.9	2.2	6.0	4.4	19	-6	5P	2N	F	
49 SeO_2	4.868	1.11	0.75	0.65	0.46	3.3	2.3	6.5	4.6	14	-7	4P	3N	F	
50 SeO_3	4.951	1.10	0.74	0.65	0.44	3.3	2.2	6.5	4.4	16	-6	5P	2N	E	
51 TeO_2	4.614	1.25	0.76	0.76	0.46	3.8	2.3	7.6	4.6	25	-13	7P	4N	F	
52 TeO_3	4.757	1.23	0.75	0.74	0.45	3.7	2.3	7.4	4.5	29	-10	7P	3N	E	
53 $SO_4^{=}$	3.130	1.11	0.87	0.67	0.52	3.3	2.6	6.7	5.2	-23	-44	6N	10N	F	
54 Cl_2O	5.021	0.98	0.74	0.60	0.44	3.0	2.2	6.0	4.4	2	-4	1P	2N	D	111
55 ClO_2	5.114	0.98	0.73	0.59	0.44	2.9	2.2	5.9	4.4	4	-2	2P	1N	F	
56 Cl_2O_7	5.146	0.98	0.73	0.58	0.44	2.9	2.2	5.8	4.4	5	-1	2P	0	F	
57 ClO_4^-	4.224	1.04	0.78	0.62	0.47	3.1	2.3	6.2	4.7	-15	-21	5N	6N	F	
58 OF_2	5.564	0.71	0.73	0.43	0.44	2.1	2.2	4.3	4.4	7	-4	3P	1N	D	111
59 I_2O_5	4.774	1.24	0.75	0.74	0.44	3.7	2.2	7.4	4.4	23	-9	6P	3N	E	
60 ZnO	3.847	1.18	0.81	0.71	0.49	3.5	2.4	7.1	4.9	29	-29	7P	7N	E	
61 CdO	3.673	1.32	0.82	0.79	0.49	4.0	2.5	8.0	4.9	32	-32	8P	8N	E	
62 HgO	3.908	1.36	0.80	0.82	0.48	4.1	2.4	8.2	4.8	27	-27	7P	7N	E	
63 TiO_2	3.949	1.13	0.80	0.68	0.48	3.4	2.4	6.8	4.8	54	-27	11P	7N	E	

Table 10-7

SUGGESTED DIAMETERS FOR HYDROGEN

charge	diameter, inches small	medium	large
more than 0.25	0.15	0.8	1.5
0.20 thru 0.24	0.17	0.8	1.7
0.15 thru 0.19	0.18	0.9	1.8
0.10 thru 0.14	0.20	1.0	2.0
0.05 thru 0.09	0.21	1.0	2.1
0 thru ± 0.04	0.22	1.1	2.2
-0.05 thru -0.09	0.23	1.2	2.3
-0.10 thru -0.14	0.24	1.2	2.4
-0.15 thru -0.19	0.25	1.3	2.5
-0.20 thru -0.24	0.26	1.3	2.6
-0.25 thru -0.29	0.27	1.4	2.7
-0.30 thru -0.34	0.28	1.4	2.8
-0.35 thru -0.39	0.30	1.5	3.0
-0.40 thru -0.44	0.32	1.6	3.2
-0.45 thru -0.49	0.34	1.7	3.4
-0.50 or higher	0.35	1.8	3.5

Table 10-8

BINARY HYDROGEN COMPOUNDS: DATA FOR MODEL CONSTRUCTION

formula	S	radius, Å		diameter, inches small		medium		large		100x charge		color		type	angle
		E	X	E	X	E	X	E	X	E	X	E	X		
64 LiH	1.621	0.88		0.53	0.34	2.7	1.7	5.3	3.4	49	-49	10P	10N	A	
65 NaH	1.576	1.13		0.68	0.35	3.4	1.8	6.8	3.6	50	-50	11P	11N	A	
66 KH	1.410	1.58		0.96	0.35	4.7	1.8	9.6	3.6	55	-55	11P	11N	A	
67 RbH	1.372	1.70		1.02	0.35	5.1	1.8	10.2	3.6	56	-56	11P	11N	A	
68 CsH	1.319	1.91		1.15	0.35	5.7	1.8	11.5	3.6	57	-57	11P	11N	A	
69 BeH_2	2.887	0.78		0.47	0.25	2.4	1.3	4.7	2.6	34	-17	8P	5N	B	
70 MgH_2	2.699	1.02		0.61	0.26	3.1	1.3	6.1	2.6	43	-22	10P	6N	B	
71 CaH_2	2.486	1.30		0.78	0.27	3.9	1.4	7.8	2.7	54	-27	11P	7N	B	
72 SrH_2	2.402	1.42		0.85	0.27	4.3	1.4	8.5	2.7	58	-29	11P	7N	B	
73 BaH_2	2.343	1.58		0.95	0.28	4.7	1.4	9.5	2.8	61	-31	12P	8N	B	
74 B_2H_6	3.358	0.78		0.46	0.23	2.3	1.2	4.6	2.3	15	-5	4P	2N	F	
75 B_4H_{10}	3.331	0.78		0.46	0.23	2.3	1.2	4.6	2.3	14	-6	4P	2N	F	
76 B_5H_9	3.278	0.78		0.46	0.23	2.3	1.2	4.6	2.3	12	-7	4P	2N	F	
77 $B_{10}H_{14}$	3.234	0.79		0.48	0.23	2.4	1.2	4.8	2.3	11	-8	4P	3N	F	
78 BH_4^-	2.633	0.84		0.50	0.26	2.5	1.3	5.0	2.6	-6	-23	2N	6N	D	
79 AlH_3	3.052	1.02		0.61	0.24	3.1	1.2	6.1	2.4	38	-13	9P	4N	C	
80 AlH_4^-	2.404	1.10		0.66	0.27	3.3	1.4	6.6	2.7	16	-29	5P	7N	D	
81 Ga_2H_6	3.467	1.23		0.74	0.22	3.7	1.1	7.4	2.2	6	-2	2P	1N	F	
82 InH_3	3.364	1.37		0.82	0.23	4.1	1.2	8.2	2.3	14	-5	4P	2N	C	
83 CH_4	3.597	0.79		0.47	0.22	2.4	1.1	4.7	2.2	-5	1	2N	0	D	
84 CH_3^+	4.592	0.72		0.48	0.15	2.4	0.8	4.8	1.5	20	27	5P	7P	C	
85 CH_3^-	2.628	0.87		0.52	0.21	2.6	1.1	5.2	2.2	-29	-24	7N	6N	D	
86 C_2H_6	3.608	0.78		0.50	0.22	2.5	1.1	5.0	2.2	-5	2	2N	0	F	
86a C_2H_2	3.668	0.78		0.47	0.22	2.3	1.1	4.7	2.2	-3	3	1N	1P	F	
86b C_2H_4	3.628	0.78		0.47	0.22	2.3	1.1	4.7	2.2	-4	2	2N	1P	F	
87 C_6H_6	3.668	0.78		0.47	0.22	2.3	1.1	4.7	2.2	-3	3	1N	1P	F	
88 C_7H_{16}		0.78		0.47	0.22	2.3	1.1	4.7	2.2	-4	2	2N	0	F	
89 C_8H_{18}		0.78		0.47	0.22	2.3	1.1	4.7	2.2	-4	2	2N	0	F	
90 SiH_4	3.341	1.02		0.61	0.23	3.1	1.2	6.1	2.3	21	-5	6P	2N	D	
91 Si_2H_6	3.290	1.03		0.62	0.23	3.1	1.2	6.2	2.3	20	-7	6P	3N	F	

Table 10-8 (continued)

formula	S	radius, Å		diameter, inches small		medium		large		100x charge		color		type	angle
		E	X	E	X	E	X	E	X	E	X	E	X		
92 GeH_4	3.558	1.23		0.74	0.22	3.7	1.1	7.4	2.2	-1	0	0	0	D	
93 SnH_4	3.455	1.36		0.82	0.22	4.1	1.1	8.2	2.2	10	-2	4P	1N	D	
94 PbH_4	3.450	1.41		0.84	0.22	4.2	1.1	8.4	2.2	10	-3	4P	1N	D	
95 NH_3	3.764	0.80		0.48	0.21	2.4	1.0	4.8	2.1	-17	6	5N	2P	D	107
96 NH_4^+	4.516	0.75		0.45	0.15	2.3	0.8	4.5	1.5	1	25	0	6P	D	
97 NH_2^-	2.490	0.91		0.54	0.27	2.7	1.4	5.4	2.7	-45	-27	10N	7N	D	
98 N_2H_4	3.839	0.74		0.50	0.20	2.5	1.0	5.0	2.0	-15	7	4N	3P	F	
99 PH_3	3.496	1.04		0.62	0.22	3.1	1.1	6.2	2.2	4	-1	2P	0	D	
100 P_2H_4	3.479	1.04		0.62	0.22	3.1	1.1	6.2	2.2	4	-2	2P	1N	F	
101 AsH_3	3.637	1.22		0.73	0.22	3.7	1.1	7.3	2.2	-7	2	3N	1P	D	102
102 SbH_3	3.504	1.36		0.82	0.22	4.1	1.1	8.2	2.2	4	-1	2P	0	D	
103 BiH_3	3.448	1.42		0.85	0.22	4.3	1.1	8.5	2.2	7	-3	3P	1N	D	
104 H_2O	4.034		0.80	0.20	0.48	1.0	2.4	2.0	4.8	12	-25	4P	7N	D	105
105 H_2S	3.728		1.05	0.21	0.63	1.0	3.2	2.1	6.3	5	-9	2P	3N	D	92
106 H_2Se	3.770		1.21	0.21	0.73	1.0	3.6	2.1	7.3	6	-11	2P	4N	D	91
107 H_2Te	3.573		1.36	0.22	0.82	1.1	4.1	2.2	8.2	1	-1	0	0	D	
108 HF	4.519		0.78	0.17	0.50	0.8	2.5	1.6	5.0	25	-25	6P	6N	A	
109 FHF^-	3.378		0.86	0.22	0.52	1.1	2.6	2.2	5.2	-48	-4	10N	2N	B	
110 HCl	4.183		1.05	0.18	0.63	0.9	3.2	1.8	6.3	16	-16	5P	5N	A	
111 HBr	4.010		1.19	0.18	0.72	0.9	3.6	1.8	7.2	12	-12	4P	4N	A	
112 HI	3.692		1.35	0.20	0.81	1.0	4.1	2.0	8.1	4	-4	1P	1N	A	
113 ZnH_2	3.295	1.25		0.75	0.21	3.8	1.0	7.6	2.1	13	-6	4P	2N	B	
114 CdH_2	3.196	1.38		0.83	0.23	4.1	1.2	8.2	2.3	18	-9	5P	3N	B	
115 HgH_2	3.330	1.43		0.86	0.21	4.3	1.0	8.6	2.1	11	-6	4P	2N	B	

Table 10-9

BINARY FLUORINE COMPOUNDS: DATA FOR MODEL CONSTRUCTION

formula	S	radius, Å		diameter, inches small		medium		large		100x charge		color		type	angle
		E	X	E	X	E	X	E	X	E	X	E	X		
116 HF	4.519		0.79	0.15	0.47	0.8	2.4	1.5	4.7	25	-25	7P	7N	A	
117 LiF	2.063	0.73	1.03	0.44	0.62	2.2	3.1	4.4	6.2	74	-74	12P	12N	A	
118 NaF	2.007	1.04	1.04	0.62	0.62	3.1	3.1	6.2	6.2	75	-75	12P	12N	A	
119 KF	1.795	1.43	1.08	0.86	0.65	4.3	3.2	8.6	6.5	79	-79	12P	12N	A	
120 RbF	1.746	1.57	1.09	0.94	0.65	4.7	3.3	9.4	6.5	80	-80	12P	12N	A	
121 CsF	1.679	1.76	1.10	1.06	0.66	5.3	3.3	10.6	6.6	82	-82	12P	12N	A	
122 BeF_2	3.982	0.70	0.81	0.42	0.48	2.1	2.4	4.2	4.8	71	-35	12P	8N	B	
123 MgF_2	3.723	0.92	0.83	0.55	0.50	2.8	2.5	5.5	5.0	81	-41	12P	9N	B	
124 CaF_2	3.430	1.16	0.86	0.70	0.52	3.5	2.6	7.0	5.2	93	-47	12P	10N	B	
125 SrF_2	3.314	1.29	0.87	0.78	0.52	3.9	2.6	7.8	5.2	98	-49	12P	10N	B	
126 BaF_2	3.231	1.42	0.87	0.85	0.52	4.3	2.6	8.5	5.2	101	-51	12P	11N	B	
127 BF_3	4.821	0.69	0.76	0.42	0.46	2.1	2.3	4.2	4.6	56	-19	11P	5N	C	
128 BF_4^-	4.079	0.73	0.81	0.44	0.49	2.2	2.4	4.4	4.9	35	-34	8P	8N	D	
129 B_2F_4	4.545	0.70	0.78	0.42	0.47	2.1	2.3	4.2	4.7	48	-24	10P	6N	F	
130 AlF_3	4.382	0.87	0.79	0.52	0.47	2.6	2.4	5.2	4.7	82	-27	12P	7N	E	
131 GaF_3	4.979	1.09	0.76	0.65	0.46	3.3	2.3	6.5	4.6	47	-16	10P	5N	E	
132 InF_3	4.830	1.21	0.77	0.73	0.46	3.6	2.3	7.3	4.6	55	-18	11P	5N	E	
133 TlF	4.168	1.32	0.80	0.79	0.47	4.0	2.4	7.9	4.7	32	-32	8P	8N	A	
134 TlF_3	4.895	1.26	0.76	0.76	0.46	3.8	2.3	7.6	4.6	51	-17	11P	5N	E	
135 CF_4	5.290	0.71	0.74	0.42	0.44	2.1	2.2	4.2	4.4	37	-9	9P	3N	D	
136 C_2F_6	5.181	0.72	0.74	0.43	0.44	2.2	2.2	4.3	4.4	34	-11	8P	4N	F	
137 SiF_4	4.913	0.90	0.76	0.60	0.46	3.0	2.3	6.0	4.6	68	-17	12P	5N	D	
139 Si_2F_6	4.725	0.91	0.77	0.54	0.46	2.7	2.3	5.4	4.6	62	-21	12P	6N	F	
140 GeF_4	5.235	1.08	0.74	0.65	0.44	3.2	2.2	6.5	4.4	40	-10	9P	4N	D	
141 SnF_2	4.681	1.23	0.77	0.74	0.46	3.7	2.3	7.4	4.6	43	-21	10P	6N	E	
142 SnF_4	5.081	1.19	0.75	0.72	0.45	3.6	2.3	7.2	4.5	52	-13	11P	4N	D	
143 PbF_2	4.670	1.28	0.78	0.77	0.46	3.8	2.3	7.7	4.6	43	-22	10P	6N	E	
144 PbF_4	5.076	1.24	0.75	0.74	0.45	3.7	2.3	7.4	4.5	54	-14	11P	4N	D	
145 NF_3	5.405	0.71	0.74	0.43	0.44	2.1	2.2	4.3	4.4	21	-7	6P	2N	D	102

Table 10-9 (continued)

formula	S	radius, Å		diameter, inches small		medium		large		100x charge		color		type	angle
		E	X	E	X	E	X	E	X	E	X	E	X		
146 N_2F_4	5.295	0.71	0.74	0.43	0.44	2.1	2.2	4.3	4.4	18	-9	5P	3N	F	
147 PF_3	5.020	0.92	0.75	0.55	0.45	2.8	2.3	5.5	4.5	44	-15	10P	5N	D	104
148 PF_5	5.252	0.91	0.74	0.55	0.44	2.7	2.2	5.5	4.4	50	-10	11P	4N	F	
149 AsF_3	5.221	1.08	0.74	0.65	0.44	3.2	2.2	6.5	4.4	32	-11	8P	4N	D	102
150 SbF_3	5.031	1.22	0.75	0.73	0.45	3.7	2.3	7.3	4.5	43	-14	10P	4N	D	
151 BiF_3	4.951	1.26	0.76	0.76	0.46	3.8	2.3	7.6	4.6	48	-16	10P	5N	E	
152 OF_2	5.564	0.71	0.73	0.43	0.44	2.1	2.2	4.3	4.4	7	-4	3P	2N	D	
153 SF_4	5.376	0.93	0.74	0.56	0.44	2.8	2.2	5.6	4.4	30	-8	8P	3N	F	
154 SF_6	5.481	0.93	0.73	0.60	0.44	3.0	2.2	6.0	4.4	32	-5	8P	2N	F	
155 S_2F_{10}	5.438	0.93	0.73	0.60	0.44	3.0	2.2	6.0	4.4	32	-6	8P	2N	F	
156 SeF_6	5.506	1.07	0.73	0.64	0.44	3.2	2.2	6.4	4.4	29	-5	7P	2N	F	
157 Se_2F_{10}	5.468	1.07	0.73	0.64	0.44	3.2	2.2	6.4	4.4	28	-6	7P	2N	F	
158 TeF_6	5.383	1.18	0.74	0.71	o.44	3.5	2.2	7.1	4.4	44	-7	10P	3N	F	
159 Te_2F_{10}	5.323	1.18	0.74	0.71	0.44	3.5	2.2	7.1	4.4	43	-9	10P	3N	F	
160 ClF	5.325	0.97	0.74	0.60	0.44	3.0	2.2	6.0	4.4	9	-9	3P	3N	A	
161 ClF_3	5.534	0.95	0.73	0.57	0.44	2.9	2.2	5.7	4.4	13	-4	4P	2N	F	
162 BrF_3	5.417	1.07	0.74	0.64	0.44	3.2	2.2	6.4	4.4	20	-7	6P	3N	F	
163 BrF_5	5.526	1.07	0.73	0.64	0.44	3.2	2.2	6.4	4.4	23	-5	6P	2N	F	
164 IF_5	5.376	1.19	0.74	0.71	0.44	3.6	2.2	7.1	4.4	38	-8	9P	3N	F	
165 IF_7	5.467	1.18	0.73	0.71	0.44	3.5	2.2	7.1	4.4	40	-6	9P	2N	F	
166 ZnF_2	4.545	1.12	0.78	0.67	0.47	3.4	2.3	6.7	4.7	48	-24	10P	6N	B	
167 CdF_2	4.407	1.24	0.79	0.74	0.48	3.7	2.4	7.4	4.8	54	-27	11P	7N	B	
168 HgF_2	4.593	1.28	0.78	0.77	0.47	3.8	2.3	7.7	4.7	46	-23	10P	6N	B	

Table 10-10

BINARY CHLORINE COMPOUNDS: DATA FOR MODEL CONSTRUCTION

formula	S	radius, Å		diameter, inches small		medium		large		100x charge		color		type	angle
		E	X	E	X	E	X	E	X	E	X	E	X		
169 HCl	4.183		1.05	0.18	0.63	0.9	3.2	1.8	6.3	16	-16	5P	5N	A	
170 LiCl	1.910	0.75	1.40	0.45	0.84	2.3	4.2	4.5	8.4	65	-65	12P	12N	A	
171 NaCl	1.858	1.07	1.42	0.64	0.86	3.2	4.3	6.4	8.6	67	-67	12P	12N	A	
172 KCl	1.662	1.47	1.47	0.88	0.88	4.4	4.4	8.8	8.8	71	-71	12P	12N	A	
173 RbCl	1.619	1.61	1.48	0.97	0.89	4.8	4.4	9.7	8.9	72	-72	12P	12N	A	
174 CsCl	1.554	1.80	1.50	1.08	0.90	5.4	4.5	10.8	9.0	73	-73	12P	12N	A	
175 $BeCl_2$	3.593	0.72	1.10	0.44	0.66	2.2	3.3	4.4	6.6	58	-29	11P	7N	B	
176 $MgCl_2$	3.359	0.95	1.12	0.58	0.68	2.9	3.4	5.8	6.8	68	-34	12P	8N	B	
177 $CaCl_2$	3.095	1.21	1.19	0.72	0.72	3.6	3.6	7.2	7.2	79	-40	12P	9N	B	
178 $SrCl_2$	2.990	1.32	1.17	0.79	0.71	4.0	3.5	7.9	7.1	84	-42	12P	9N	B	
179 $BaCl_2$	2.916	1.47	1.18	0.88	0.71	4.4	3.5	8.8	7.1	87	-44	12P	9N	B	
180 BCl_3	4.294	0.71	1.04	0.44	0.62	2.2	3.1	4.4	6.2	41	-14	9P	4N	C	
181 B_2Cl_4	4.102	0.73	1.05	0.44	0.63	2.2	3.2	4.4	6.3	36	-18	8P	5N	F	
182 B_4Cl_4	3.741	0.75	1.09	0.50	0.60	2.5	3.0	5.0	6.0	26	-26	7P	7N	F	
183 Al_2Cl_6	3.905	0.94	1.07	0.56	0.64	2.8	3.2	5.6	6.4	67	-22	12P	6N	F	
184 Ga_2Cl_6	4.435	1.13	1.03	0.68	0.62	3.4	3.1	6.8	6.2	32	-11	8P	4N	F	
185 In_2Cl_6	4.302	1.26	1.04	0.76	0.62	3.8	3.1	7.6	6.2	41	-14	9P	4N	F	
186 TlCl	3.858	1.36	1.07	0.82	0.64	4.1	3.2	8.2	6.4	23	-23	6P	6N	A	
187 $TlCl_3$	4.361	1.30	1.04	0.78	0.62	3.9	3.1	7.8	6.2	37	-12	9P	4N	C	
188 CCl_4	4.677	0.72	1.01	0.45	0.60	2.3	3.0	4.5	6.0	23	-6	6P	2N	D	
189 $SiCl_4$	4.344	0.94	1.03	0.56	0.62	2.8	3.1	5.6	6.2	51	-13	11P	4N	D	
190 Si_2Cl_6	4.209	0.95	1.05	0.57	0.63	2.9	3.2	5.7	6.3	47	-16	10P	5N	F	
191 $GeCl_4$	4.627	1.12	1.01	0.67	0.61	3.4	3.0	6.7	6.1	26	-7	7P	3N	D	
192 $SnCl_2$	4.224	1.27	1.04	0.71	0.62	3.5	3.1	7.1	6.2	31	-15	8P	5N	E	
193 $SnCl_4$	4.493	1.25	1.02	0.75	0.61	3.8	3.1	7.5	6.1	38	-10	9P	4N	D	
194 $PbCl_2$	4.214	1.32	1.04	0.79	0.62	4.0	3.1	7.9	6.2	31	-16	8P	5N	E	
195 $PbCl_4$	4.488	1.29	1.02	0.77	0.61	3.9	3.1	7.7	6.1	38	-10	9P	4N	D	
196 NCl_3	4.816	0.73	1.00	0.45	0.60	2.3	3.0	4.5	6.0	8	-3	3P	1N	D	106
197 PCl_3	4.472	0.96	1.02	0.58	0.62	2.9	3.1	5.8	6.2	30	-10	7P	3N	D	100
198 PCl_5	4.620	0.95	1.01	0.58	0.62	2.9	3.1	5.8	6.2	34	-7	8P	2N	F	

Table 10-10 (continued)

formula	S	radius, Å		diameter, inches small		medium		large		100x charge		color		type	angle
		E	X	E	X	E	X	E	X	E	X	E	X		
199 $AsCl_3$	4.651	1.12	1.01	0.67	0.61	3.4	3.0	6.7	6.1	18	-6	5P	2N	D	100
200 $SbCl_3$	4.482	1.25	1.02	0.75	0.61	3.8	3.1	7.5	6.1	29	-10	7P	4N	D	
201 $BiCl_3$	4.411	1.30	1.03	0.78	0.62	3.9	3.1	7.8	6.2	34	-11	8P	4N	D	100
202 Cl_2O	5.021	0.98	0.74	0.59	0.44	2.9	2.2	5.9	4.4	2	-4	1P	2N	D	
203 S_2Cl_2	4.501	0.99	1.02	0.60	0.60	3.0	3.0	6.0	6.0	9	-9	3P	3N	F	
204 SCl_2	4.640	0.98	1.01	0.60	0.60	3.0	3.0	6.0	6.0	13	-6	4P	2N	D	102
205 Se_2Cl_2	4.577	1.13	1.02	0.68	0.61	3.4	3.1	6.8	6.1	8	-8	3P	3N	F	
206 $SeCl_4$	4.785	1.12	1.00	0.67	0.60	3.4	3.0	6.7	6.0	13	-3	4P	1N	F	
207 $TeCl_4$	4.634	1.25	1.01	0.75	0.61	3.8	3.0	7.5	6.1	26	-7	7P	3N	F	
208 ClF	5.325	0.97	0.74	0.60	0.44	3.0	2.2	6.0	4.4	9	-9	3P	3N	A	
209 ClF_3	5.533	0.96	0.73	0.58	0.44	2.9	2.2	5.8	4.4	13	-4	4P	2N	F	
210 $BrCl$	4.727	1.12	1.01	0.67	0.61	3.4	3.0	6.7	6.1	4	-4	2P	2N	A	
211 ICl	4.351	1.27	1.03	0.76	0.62	3.8	3.1	7.6	6.2	13	-13	4P	4N	A	
212 ICl_3	4.631	1.25	1.01	0.75	0.61	3.8	3.0	7.5	6.1	19	-7	5P	3N	F	
213 $ZnCl_2$	4.10	1.16	1.05	0.70	0.64	3.5	3.2	7.0	6.4	36	-18	8P	5N	B	
214 $CdCl_2$	3.977	1.28	1.06	0.77	0.64	3.8	3.2	7.7	6.4	41	-21	9P	6N	B	
215 $HgCl_2$	4.145	1.33	1.03	0.80	0.60	4.0	3.0	8.0	6.0	34	-17	8P	5N	B	
216 Hg_2Cl_2	3.801	1.37	1.08	0.82	0.65	4.1	3.2	8.2	6.5	24	-24	6P	6N	B	

Table 10-11

BINARY BROMINE COMPOUNDS: DATA FOR MODEL CONSTRUCTION

formula	S	radius, Å		diameter, inches small		medium		large		100x charge		color		type	angle
		E	X	E	X	E	X	E	X	E	X	E	X		
217 HBr	4.010		1.19	0.20	0.72	1.0	3.6	2.0	7.2	12	-12	4P	4N	A	
218 LiBr	1.830	0.76	1.55	0.46	0.93	2.3	4.7	4.6	9.3	61	-61	12P	12N	A	
219 NaBr	1.781	1.08	1.56	0.65	0.94	3.2	4.7	6.5	9.4	62	-62	12P	12N	A	
220 KBr	1.593	1.49	1.62	0.89	0.97	4.5	4.9	8.9	9.7	66	-66	12P	12N	A	
221 RbBr	1.546	1.63	1.63	0.98	0.98	4.9	4.9	9.8	9.8	67	-67	12P	12N	A	
222 CsBr	1.489	1.83	1.65	1.10	0.99	5.5	5.0	11.0	10.0	69	-69	12P	12N	A	
223 $BeBr_2$	3.397	0.73	1.25	0.44	0.75	2.2	3.8	4.4	7.5	51	-26	11P	7N	B	
224 $MgBr_2$	3.175	0.96	1.29	0.58	0.76	2.9	3.8	5.8	7.6	61	-31	12P	8N	B	
225 $CaBr_2$	2.925	1.24	1.32	0.74	0.79	3.7	4.0	7.4	7.9	72	-36	12P	9N	B	
226 $SrBr_2$	2.826	1.36	1.34	0.82	0.80	4.1	4.0	8.2	8.0	76	-39	12P	9N	B	
227 $BaBr_2$	2.756	1.50	1.35	0.90	0.81	4.5	4.1	9.0	8.1	80	-40	12P	9N	B	
228 BBr_3	4.031	0.73	1.19	0.44	0.71	2.2	3.6	4.4	7.1	34	-11	8P	4N	C	
229 Al_2Br_6	3.664	0.95	1.23	0.57	0.74	2.9	3.7	5.7	7.4	59	-20	11P	6N	F	
230 Ga_2Br_6	4.163	1.15	1.17	0.69	0.70	3.5	3.5	6.9	7.0	25	-8	7P	3N	F	
231 $InBr_3$	4.038	1.29	1.19	0.77	0.71	3.9	3.6	7.7	7.1	33	-11	8P	4N	E	
232 TlBr	3.699	1.38	1.19	0.83	0.71	4.1	3.6	8.3	7.1	11	-11	4P	4N	A	
233 $TlBr_3$	4.094	1.34	1.17	0.80	0.70	4.0	3.5	8.0	7.0	18	-6	5P	2N	E	
234 CBr_4	4.371	0.74	1.15	0.44	0.69	2.2	3.5	4.4	6.9	14	-4	4P	2N	D	
235 $SiBr_4$	4.060	0.96	1.19	0.58	0.71	2.9	3.6	5.8	7.1	42	-11	9P	4N	D	
236 $GeBr_4$	4.324	1.15	1.16	0.69	0.70	3.5	3.5	6.9	7.0	19	-5	5P	2N	D	
237 $SnBr_2$	3.992	1.29	1.19	0.77	0.71	3.9	3.6	7.7	7.1	25	-12	6P	4N	E	
238 $SnBr_4$	4.200	1.27	1.17	0.76	0.70	3.8	3.5	7.6	7.0	30	-8	8P	3N	D	
239 $PbBr_2$	3.983	1.35	1.17	0.81	0.70	4.1	3.5	8.1	7.0	14	-7	4P	3N	E	
240 PBr_3	4.198	0.98	1.17	0.59	0.70	2.9	3.5	5.9	7.0	23	-8	6P	3N	D	101
241 PBr_5	4.305	0.97	1.16	0.58	0.70	2.9	3.5	5.8	7.0	25	-5	7P	2N	F	
242 $AsBr_3$	4.366	1.14	1.15	0.68	0.69	3.4	3.5	6.8	6.9	8	-3	3P	1N	D	101
243 $SbBr_3$	4.203	1.28	1.17	0.77	0.70	3.8	3.5	7.7	7.0	22	-7	6P	3N	D	

Table 10-11 (continued)

formula	S	radius, Å		diameter, inches small		medium		large		100x charge		color		type angle
		E	X	E	X	E	X	E	X	E	X	E	X	
244 $BiBr_3$	4.140	1.33	1.16	0.80	0.70	4.0	3.5	8.0	7.0	14	-5	4P	2N	D
245 S_2Br_2	4.314	1.00	1.16	0.60	0.70	3.0	3.5	6.0	7.0	5	-5	2P	2N	F
246 Se_2Br_2	4.387	1.15	1.15	0.69	0.69	3.5	3.5	6.9	6.9	3	-3	1P	1N	F
247 $TeBr_4$	4.331	1.27	1.16	0.76	0.70	3.8	3.5	7.6	7.0	18	-5	5P	2N	F
248 BrCl	4.727	1.12	1.01	0.67	0.60	3.4	3.0	6.7	6.0	4	-4	2P	2N	A
249 BrF_3	5.417	1.07	0.74	0.64	0.44	3.2	2.2	6.4	4.4	20	-7	6P	3N	F
250 BrF_5	5.526	1.07	0.73	0.64	0.44	3.2	2.2	6.4	4.4	23	-5	6P	2N	F
250a IBr	4.171	1.29	1.17	0.77	0.70	3.9	3.5	7.7	7.0	8	-8	3P	3N	A
251 $ZnBr_2$	3.877	1.18	1.20	0.71	0.72	3.5	3.6	7.1	7.2	30	-15	8P	5N	B
252 $CdBr_2$	3.760	1.30	1.21	0.78	0.73	3.9	3.6	7.8	7.3	35	-17	8P	5N	B
253 $HgBr_2$	3.917	1.36	1.20	0.82	0.72	4.1	3.6	8.2	7.2	27	-14	7P	4N	B

Table 10-12

BINARY IODINE COMPOUNDS: DATA FOR MODEL CONSTRUCTION

formula	S	radius, Å		diameter, inches small		medium		large		100x charge		color		type	angle
		E	X	E	X	E	X	E	X	E	X	E	X		
254 HI	3.692		1.35	0.22	0.61	1.1	3.1	2.2	6.1	4	-4	1P	1N	A	
255 LiI	1.685	0.78	1.76	0.47	1.06	2.3	5.3	4.7	10.6	53	-53	11P	11N	A	
256 NaI	1.639	1.11	1.77	0.67	1.06	3.3	5.3	6.7	10.6	54	-54	11P	11N	A	
257 KI	1.466	1.53	1.84	0.92	1.10	4.6	5.5	9.2	11.0	58	-58	11P	11N	A	
258 RbI	1.427	1.68	1.86	1.01	1.12	5.0	5.6	10.1	11.2	59	-59	11P	11N	A	
259 CsI	1.372	1.88	1.88	1.13	1.13	5.6	5.6	11.3	11.3	61	-61	12P	12N	A	
260 BeI_2	3.042	0.77	1.44	0.46	0.86	2.3	4.3	4.6	8.6	39	-19	9P	5N	B	
261 MgI_2	2.844	1.01	1.47	0.61	0.88	3.0	4.4	6.1	8.8	48	-24	10P	6N	B	
262 CaI_2	2.620	1.28	1.52	0.77	0.91	3.8	4.6	7.7	9.1	60	-30	12P	8N	B	
263 SrI_2	2.531	1.40	1.54	0.84	0.92	4.2	4.6	8.4	9.2	64	-32	12P	8N	B	
264 BaI_2	2.468	1.56	1.55	0.94	0.93	4.7	4.7	9.4	9.3	67	-34	12P	8N	B	
265 BI_3	3.562	0.76	1.36	0.46	0.82	2.3	4.1	4.6	8.2	20	-7	6P	3N	C	
266 Al_2I_6	3.237	1.00	1.41	0.60	0.85	3.0	4.2	6.0	8.5	44	-15	10P	5N	F	
267 GaI_3	3.677	1.20	1.35	0.72	0.81	3.6	4.1	7.2	8.1	12	-4	4P	2N	C	
268 InI_3	3.567	1.34	1.36	0.80	0.82	4.0	4.1	8.0	8.2	20	-7	6P	3N	C	
269 TlI	3.406	1.42	1.35	0.85	0.81	4.3	4.1	8.5	8.1	3	-3	1P	1N	A	
270 TlI_3	3.617	1.39	1.34	0.83	0.80	4.2	4.0	8.3	8.0	6	-2	2P	1N	E	
271 CI_4	3.830	0.77	1.34	0.46	0.80	2.3	4.0	4.6	8.0	1	0	0	0	D	
272 SiI_4	3.557	1.00	1.36	0.60	0.82	3.0	4.1	6.0	8.2	28	-7	7P	3N	D	
273 GeI_4	3.789	1.20	1.34	0.72	0.80	3.6	4.0	7.2	8.0	5	-1	2P	0	D	
274 SnI_2	3.576	1.34	1.36	0.40	0.82	4.0	4.1	8.0	8.2	13	-6	4P	2N	E	
275 SnI_4	3.678	1.33	1.35	0.40	0.81	4.0	4.1	8.0	8.1	16	-4	5P	2N	D	
276 PbI_2	3.567	1.40	1.36	0.84	0.82	4.2	4.1	8.4	8.2	13	-7	4P	3N	E	
277 PI_3	3.709	1.02	1.35	0.61	0.81	3.1	4.1	6.1	8.1	10	-3	4P	1N	D	100
278 AsI_3	3.857	1.19	1.33	0.71	0.80	3.6	4.0	7.1	8.0	-1	0	0	0	D	99
279 SbI_3	3.716	1.33	1.35	0.80	0.81	4.0	4.1	8.0	8.1	9	-3	3P	1N	D	
280 BiI_3	3.658	1.38	1.35	0.83	0.80	4.1	4.1	8.3	8.0	12	-4	4P	2N	D	

Table 10-12 (continued)

formula	S	radius, Å		diameter, inches small		medium		large		100x charge		color		type	angle
		E	X	E	X	E	X	E	X	E	X	E	X		
281 TeI_4	3.795	1.33	1.34	0.80	0.80	4.0	4.0	8.0	8.0	4	-1	2P	0	F	
282 IF_5	5.376	1.19	0.74	0.71	0.44	3.6	2.2	7.1	4.4	37	-7	9P	3N	F	
283 IF_7	5.467	1.18	0.73	0.71	0.44	3.5	2.2	7.1	4.4	40	-6	9P	2N	F	
284 ICl	4.351	1.27	1.04	0.76	0.62	3.8	3.1	7.6	6.2	13	-13	4P	4N	A	
285 ICl_3	4.631	1.25	1.01	0.75	0.61	3.8	3.0	7.5	6.1	20	-7	6P	3N	F	
286 IBr	4.171	1.29	1.17	0.77	0.70	3.9	3.5	7.7	7.0	8	-8	3P	3N	A	
287 ZnI_2	3.472	1.22	1.38	0.73	0.83	3.7	4.1	7.3	8.3	18	-9	5P	3N	B	
288 CdI_2	3.368	1.35	1.39	0.81	0.83	4.1	4.2	8.1	8.3	23	-12	6P	4N	B	
289 HgI_2	3.712	1.38	1.35	0.83	0.81	4.1	4.1	8.3	8.1	6	-3	2P	1N	B	

Table 10-13

BINARY SULFUR COMPOUNDS: DATA FOR MODEL CONSTRUCTION

formula	S	radius, Å		diameter, inches small		medium		large		100x charge		color		type	angle
		E	X	E	X	E	X	E	X	E	X	E	X		
290 H_2S	3.728		1.05	0.20	0.63	1.0	3.2	2.0	6.3	5	-9	2P	3N	D	
291 Li_2S	1.310	0.94	1.54	0.56	0.92	2.8	4.6	5.6	9.2	32	-66	8P	12N	E	
292 Na_2S	1.263	1.27	1.56	0.76	0.94	3.8	4.7	7.6	9.4	33	-66	8P	12N	E	
293 K_2S	1.088	1.70	1.64	1.02	0.98	5.1	4.9	10.2	9.8	35	-69	8P	12N	E	
294 Rb_2S	1.050	1.87	1.66	1.12	1.00	5.6	5.0	11.2	10.0	36	-71	9P	12N	E	
295 Cs_2S	0.996	2.10	1.63	1.26	0.98	6.3	4.9	12.6	9.8	36	-72	9P	12N	E	
296 BeS	2.801	0.79	1.16	0.47	0.70	2.4	3.5	4.7	7.0	31	-31	8P	8N	E	
297 MgS	2.533	1.04	1.20	0.62	0.72	3.1	3.6	6.2	7.2	37	-37	9P	9N	E	
298 CaS	2.240	1.35	1.24	0.82	0.74	4.1	3.7	8.2	7.4	44	-44	10P	10N	E	
299 SrS	2.126	1.49	1.26	0.90	0.76	4.5	3.8	9.0	7.6	46	-46	10P	10N	E	
300 BaS	2.046	1.66	1.28	1.00	0.77	5.0	3.8	10.0	7.7	48	-48	10P	10N	E	
301 B_2S_3	3.545	0.77	1.08	0.46	0.65	2.3	3.2	4.6	6.5	20	-13	6P	4N	E	
302 Al_2S_3	3.043	1.02	1.13	0.61	0.68	3.1	3.4	6.1	6.8	38	-25	9P	6N	E	
303 Ga_2S_3	3.733	1.20	1.05	0.72	0.63	3.6	3.2	7.2	6.3	13	-9	4P	3N	E	
304 In_2S_3	3.556	1.34	1.07	0.80	0.64	4.0	3.2	8.0	6.4	20	-13	6P	4N	E	
305 Tl_2S	3.347	1.43	1.10	0.86	0.66	4.3	3.3	8.6	6.6	9	-18	3P	5N	E	
306 Tl_2S_3	3.633	1.39	1.07	0.83	0.64	4.2	3.2	8.3	6.4	17	-11	5P	4N	E	
307 CS_2	4.000	0.76	1.03	0.44	0.62	2.2	3.1	4.4	6.2	5	-3	2P	1N	E	
308 SiS_2	3.536	1.01	1.08	0.60	0.65	3.0	3.2	6.0	6.5	27	-13	7P	4N	E	
309 GeS_2	3.928	1.19	1.03	0.71	0.62	3.6	3.1	7.1	6.2	9	-4	3P	2N	E	
310 SnS	3.569	1.34	1.07	0.80	0.64	4.0	3.2	8.0	6.4	13	-13	4P	4N	E	
311 SnS_2	3.741	1.33	1.05	0.80	0.63	4.0	3.2	8.0	6.3	18	-9	5P	3N	E	
312 PbS	3.558	1.40	1.06	0.84	0.64	4.2	3.2	8.4	6.4	13	-13	4P	4N	E	
313 S_4N_4	4.295	0.98	0.76	0.59	0.46	2.9	2.3	5.9	4.6	4	-4	2P	2N	F	
314 P_4S_{10}	3.875	1.00	1.04	0.60	0.62	3.0	3.1	6.0	6.2	14	-6	4P	2N	F	
315 As_4S_4	4.009	1.18	1.03	0.75	0.60	3.8	3.0	7.5	6.0	2	-2	1P	1N	F	
316 As_4S_6	4.029	1.18	1.03	0.71	0.62	3.5	3.1	7.1	6.2	3	-2	1P	1N	F	
317 Sb_2S_3	3.796	1.32	1.04	0.79	0.62	4.0	3.1	7.9	6.2	11	-7	4P	3N	F	
318 Bi_2S_3	3.700	1.38	1.06	0.83	0.50	4.1	2.5	8.3	5.0	14	-10	4P	4N	E	
319 ZnS	3.416	1.23	1.08	0.74	0.65	3.7	3.2	7.4	6.5	16	-16	5P	5N	E	
320 CdS	3.263	1.37	1.10	0.82	0.66	4.1	3.3	8.2	6.6	20	-20	6P	6N	E	
321 HgS	3.471	1.41	1.08	0.84	0.50	4.2	2.5	8.4	5.0	15	-15	5P	5N	E	

Table 10-14

SOME COMPOUNDS HAVING ROCK SALT (NaCl) STRUCTURE

LiF	LiCl	LiBr	LiI	LiH	MgO	MgS	MgSe	CaTe	NbC	NbN	KCN
NaF	NaCl	NaBr	NaI	NaH	CaO	CaS	CaSe	SrTe	TiC	CrN	SnSb
KF	KCl	KBr	KI	KH	SrO	SrS	SrSe	BaTe	VC	ScN	SnAs
RbF	RbCl	RbBr	RbI	RbH	BaO	BaS	BaSe	PbTe	ZrC	TiN	
CsF	AgCl	AgBr	NH_4I	CsH	FeO	MnS	PbSe	SnTe		VN	
AgF	NH_4Cl	NH_4Br			CoO	PbS	MnSe			ZrN	
					NiO						
					CdO						
					TiO						
					MnO						

Table 10-15

SOME COMPOUNDS HAVING CESIUM CHLORIDE STRUCTURE

NH_4Cl	NH_4Br	NH_4I	MgAg	CuPd	NiAl
CsCl	CsBr	CsI	CdAg	CuZn	TlSb
TlCl	TlBr	TlI	ZnAg		TlBi

Table 10-16

SOME COMPOUNDS HAVING THE NICKEL ARSENIDE (NiAs) STRUCTURE

AuSn	CrS	FeS	MnAs	NiSb	PdSb
CoS	CrSb	FeSb	MnSb	NiSe	PdTe
CoSb	CrSe	FeSe	MnTe	NiSn	PtSb
CoSe	CrTe	FeTe	NiAs	NiTe	PtSn
CoTe	CuSn	FeSn	NiS	NiBi	PtBi

Table 10-17

SOME COMPOUNDS HAVING ZINC BLENDE STRUCTURE

CuCl	BeO	AlP	GaP	InSb	ZnS	CdS	HgS
CuBr	BeS	AlAs	GaAs	SiC	ZnSe	CdSe	HgSe
CuI	BeSe	AlSb	GaSb		ZnTe	CdTe	HgTe
AgI	BeTe						

Table 10-18

SOME COMPOUNDS HAVING WURTZITE STRUCTURE

BeO	ZnO	CdS	LCuH	TaN
MgTe	ZnS	CdSe	AgI	MnS
NH_4F	ZnTe			

Table 10-19

SOME COMPOUNDS HAVING FLUORITE (CaF_2) OR ANTIFLUORITE STRUCTURE

Li_2O	CeO_2	CaF_2	Mg_2Si	Li_2S	Cu_2S	$SrCl_2$
Na_2O	ZrO_2	SrF_2	Mg_2Sn	Na_2S	Cu_2Se	
K_2O	HfO_2	BaF_2	Mg_2Pb			
Rb_2O	PrO_2	PbF_2				
	ThO_2	CdF_2				
	UO_2					
	NpO_2					
	PuO_2					
	AmO_2					

Table 10-20

SOME COMPOUNDS HAVING RUTILE (TiO_2) STRUCTURE

$CaCl_2$ (deformed)	TiO_2	
$SrCl_2$ (deformed)	NbO_2	
ZnF_2	IrO_2	
MgF_2	OsO_2	VO_2
MnF_2	SnO_2	WO_2
FeF_2	PbO_2	MnO_2
CoF_2	RuO_2	
NiF_2	TeO_2	

Table 10-21

SOME COMPOUNDS HAVING LAYER STRUCTURES

Ag_2F	$ZnCl_2$	$MgBr_2$	MnI_2	$Ca(OH)_2$	TiS_2	$TiSe_2$	$TiTe_2$
	$CdCl_2$	$CdBr_2$	FeI_2	$Co(OH)_2$	SnS_2	$ZrSe_2$	$PtTe_2$
	$FeCl_2$	$MnBr_2$	CdI_2	$Mn(OH)_2$	ZrS_2		$PdTe_2$
	$MnCl_2$	$FeBr_2$	PbI_2	$Ni(OH)_2$	PtS_2		
	$MgCl_2$			$\frac{1}{2}Cd(OH)_2$			

Table 10-22

LOGARITHMS

N	0	1	2	3	4	5	6	7	8	9
1.0	.0000	.0043	.0086	.0128	.0170	.0212	.0253	.0294	.0334	.0374
1.1	.0414	.0453	.0492	.0531	.0569	.0607	.0645	.0682	.0719	.0755
1.2	.0792	.0828	.0864	.0899	.0934	.0969	.1004	.1038	.1072	.1106
1.3	.1139	.1173	.1206	.1239	.1271	.1303	.1335	.1367	.1399	.1430
1.4	.1461	.1492	.1523	.1553	.1584	.1614	.1644	.1673	.1703	.1732
1.5	.1761	.1790	.1818	.1847	.1875	.1903	.1931	.1959	.1987	.2014
1.6	.2041	.2068	.2095	.2122	.2148	.2175	.2201	.2227	.2253	.2279
1.7	.2304	.2330	.2355	.2380	.2405	.2430	.2455	.2480	.2504	.2529
1.8	.2553	.2577	.2601	.2625	.2648	.2672	.2695	.2718	.2742	.2765
1.9	.2788	.2810	.2833	.2856	.2878	.2900	.2923	.2945	.2967	.2989
2.0	.3010	.3032	.3054	.3075	.3096	.3118	.3139	.3160	.3181	.3201
2.1	.3222	.3243	.3263	.3284	.3304	.3324	.3345	.3365	.3385	.3404
2.2	.3424	.3444	.3464	.3483	.3502	.3522	.3541	.3560	.3579	.3598
2.3	.3617	.3636	.3655	.3674	.3692	.3711	.3729	.3747	.3766	.3784
2.4	.3802	.3820	.3838	.3856	.3874	.3892	.3909	.3927	.3945	.3962
2.5	.3979	.3997	.4014	.4031	.4048	.4065	.4082	.4099	.4116	.4133
2.6	.4150	.4166	.4183	.4200	.4216	.4232	.4249	.4265	.4281	.4298
2.7	.4314	.4330	.4346	.4362	.4378	.4393	.4409	.4425	.4440	.4456
2.8	.4472	.4487	.4502	.4518	.4533	.4548	.4564	.4579	.4594	.4609
2.9	.4624	.4639	.4654	.4669	.4683	.4698	.4713	.4728	.4742	.4757
3.0	.4771	.4786	.4800	.4814	.4829	.4843	.4857	.4871	.4886	.4900
3.1	.4914	.4928	.4942	.4955	.4969	.4983	.4997	.5011	.5024	.5038
3.2	.5051	.5065	.5079	.5092	.5105	.5119	.5132	.5145	.5159	.5172
3.3	.5185	.5198	.5211	.5224	.5237	.5250	.5263	.5276	.5289	.5302
3.4	.5315	.5328	.5340	.5353	.5366	.5378	.5391	.5403	.5416	.5428
3.5	.5441	.5453	.5465	.5478	.5490	.5502	.5514	.5527	.5539	.5551
3.6	.5563	.5575	.5587	.5599	.5611	.5623	.5635	.5647	.5658	.5670
3.7	.5682	.5694	.5705	.5717	.5729	.5740	.5752	.5763	.5775	.5786
3.8	.5798	.5809	.5821	.5832	.5843	.5855	.5866	.5877	.5888	.5899
3.9	.5911	.5922	.5933	.5944	.5955	.5966	.5977	.5988	.5999	.6010
4.0	.6021	.6031	.6042	.6053	.6064	.6075	.6085	.6096	.6107	.6117
4.1	.6128	.6138	.6149	.6160	.6170	.6180	.6191	.6201	.6212	.6222
4.2	.6232	.6243	.6253	.6263	.6274	.6284	.6294	.6304	.6314	.6325
4.3	.6335	.6345	.6355	.6365	.6375	.6385	.6395	.6405	.6415	.6425
4.4	.6435	.6444	.6454	.6464	.6474	.6484	.6493	.6503	.6513	.6522
4.5	.6532	.6542	.6551	.6561	.6571	.6580	.6590	.6599	.6609	.6618
4.6	.6628	.6637	.6646	.6656	.6665	.6675	.6684	.6693	.6702	.6712
4.7	.6721	.6730	.6739	.6749	.6758	.6767	.6776	.6785	.6794	.6803
4.8	.6812	.6821	.6830	.6839	.6848	.6857	.6866	.6875	.6884	.6893
4.9	.6902	.6911	.6920	.6928	.6937	.6946	.6955	.6964	.6972	.6981
5.0	.6990	.6998	.7007	.7016	.7024	.7033	.7042	.7050	.7059	.7067
5.1	.7076	.7084	.7093	.7101	.7110	.7118	.7126	.7135	.7143	.7152
5.2	.7160	.7168	.7177	.7185	.7193	.7202	.7210	.7218	.7226	.7235
5.3	.7243	.7251	.7259	.7267	.7275	.7284	.7292	.7300	.7308	.7316
5.4	.7324	.7332	.7340	.7348	.7356	.7364	.7372	.7380	.7388	.7396
N	**0**	**1**	**2**	**3**	**4**	**5**	**6**	**7**	**8**	**9**

Table 10-22 (continued)

LOGARITHMS

N	0	1	2	3	4	5	6	7	8	9
5.5	.7404	.7412	.7419	.7427	.7435	.7443	.7451	.7459	.7466	.7474
5.6	.7482	.7490	.7497	.7505	.7513	.7520	.7528	.7536	.7543	.7551
5.7	.7559	.7566	.7574	.7582	.7589	.7597	.7604	.7612	.7619	.7627
5.8	.7634	.7642	.7649	.7657	.7664	.7672	.7679	.7686	.7694	.7701
5.9	.7709	.7716	.7723	.7731	.7738	.7745	.7752	.7760	.7767	.7774
6.0	.7782	.7789	.7796	.7803	.7810	.7818	.7825	.7832	.7839	.7846
6.1	.7853	.7860	.7868	.7875	.7882	.7889	.7896	.7903	.7910	.7917
6.2	.7924	.7931	.7938	.7945	.7952	.7959	.7966	.7973	.7980	.7987
6.3	.7993	.8000	.8007	.8014	.8021	.8028	.8035	.8041	.8048	.8055
6.4	.8062	.8069	.8075	.8082	.8089	.8096	.8102	.8109	.8116	.8122
6.5	.8129	.8136	.8142	.8149	.8156	.8162	.8169	.8176	.8182	.8189
6.6	.8195	.8202	.8209	.8215	.8222	.8228	.8235	.8241	.8248	.8254
6.7	.8261	.8267	.8274	.8280	.8287	.8293	.8299	.8306	.8312	.8319
6.8	.8325	.8331	.8338	.8344	.8351	.8357	.8363	.8370	.8376	.8382
6.9	.8388	.8395	.8401	.8407	.8414	.8420	.8426	.8432	.8439	.8445
7.0	.8451	.8457	.8463	.8470	.8476	.8482	.8488	.8494	.8500	.8506
7.1	.8513	.8519	.8525	.8531	.8537	.8543	.8549	.8555	.8561	.8567
7.2	.8573	.8579	.8585	.8591	.8597	.8603	.8609	.8615	.8621	.8627
7.3	.8633	.8639	.8645	.8651	.8657	.8663	.8669	.8675	.8681	.8686
7.4	.8692	.8698	.8704	.8710	.8716	.8722	.8727	.8733	.8739	.8745
7.5	.8751	.8756	.8762	.8768	.8774	.8779	.8785	.8791	.8797	.8802
7.6	.8808	.8814	.8820	.8825	.8831	.8837	.8842	.8848	.8854	.8859
7.7	.8865	.8871	.8876	.8882	.8887	.8893	.8899	.8904	.8910	.8915
7.8	.8921	.8927	.8932	.8938	.8943	.8949	.8954	.8960	.8965	.8971
7.9	.8976	.8982	.8987	.8993	.8998	.9004	.9009	.9015	.9020	.9025
8.0	.9031	.9036	.9042	.9047	.9053	.9058	.9063	.9069	.9074	.9079
8.1	.9085	.9090	.9096	.9101	.9106	.9112	.9117	.9122	.9128	.9133
8.2	.9138	.9143	.9149	.9154	.9159	.9165	.9170	.9175	.9180	.9186
8.3	.9191	.9196	.9201	.9206	.9212	.9217	.9222	.9227	.9232	.9238
8.4	.9243	.9248	.9253	.9258	.9263	.9269	.9274	.9279	.9284	.9289
8.5	.9294	.9299	.9304	.9309	.9315	.9320	.9325	.9330	.9335	.9340
8.6	.9345	.9350	.9355	.9360	.9365	.9370	.9375	.9380	.9385	.9390
8.7	.9395	.9400	.9405	.9410	.9415	.9420	.9425	.9430	.9435	.9440
8.8	.9445	.9450	.9455	.9460	.9465	.9469	.9474	.9479	.9484	.9489
8.9	.9494	.9499	.9504	.9509	.9513	.9518	.9523	.9528	.9533	.9538
9.0	.9542	.9547	.9552	.9557	.9562	.9566	.9571	.9576	.9581	.9586
9.1	.9590	.9595	.9600	.9605	.9609	.9614	.9619	.9624	.9628	.9633
9.2	.9638	.9643	.9647	.9652	.9657	.9661	.9666	.9671	.9675	.9680
9.3	.9685	.9689	.9694	.9699	.9703	.9708	.9713	.9717	.9722	.9727
9.4	.9731	.9736	.9741	.9745	.9750	.9754	.9759	.9763	.9768	.9773
9.5	.9777	.9782	.9786	.9791	.9795	.9800	.9805	.9809	.9814	.9818
9.6	.9823	.9827	.9832	.9836	.9841	.9845	.9850	.9854	.9859	.9863
9.7	.9868	.9872	.9877	.9881	.9886	.9890	.9894	.9899	.9903	.9908
9.8	.9912	.9917	.9921	.9926	.9930	.9934	.9939	.9943	.9948	.9952
9.9	.9956	.9961	.9965	.9969	.9974	.9978	.9983	.9987	.9991	.9996
N	0	1	2	3	4	5	6	7	8	9

INDEX

Note: References to photos of models are given as B- or C-numbers, corresponding to the photo section near the center of the book. Data for construction of models of many binary compounds *not* specifically indexed here are listed in the tables beginning on page 131. See indexed under "nonmetal" here: for example, "oxygen compounds, data for models." T indicates a table.